1668 – 2018
Sault Ste. Marie, Michigan's
350TH Anniversary

Explore the history of the Soo Locks and so much more!

Sault Ste Marie
PURE MICHIGAN®

1-800-647-2858
saultstemarie.com
#ilovethesoo

1

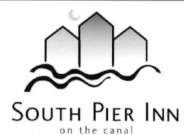

Contents

Marine Publishing Co. Inc.
317 S. Division St. #8
Ann Arbor, MI 48104
1-855-KYS-SHIP (855-597-7447)

knowyourships@gmail.com
KnowYourShips.com

Editor/Publisher: Roger LeLievre

Crew: Kathryn Lau, Nancy
Kuharevicz, Matt Miner, John
Philbin, Neil Schultheiss, William
Soleau, Wade P. Streeter, John
Vournakis, George Wharton
and Sam Hankinson

Founder: Tom Manse (1915-1994)

FRONT COVER: *The passenger ship Victory I on the St. Marys River.*
THIS PAGE: *Federal Margaree upbound for grain.* (Both photos, Roger LeLievre)

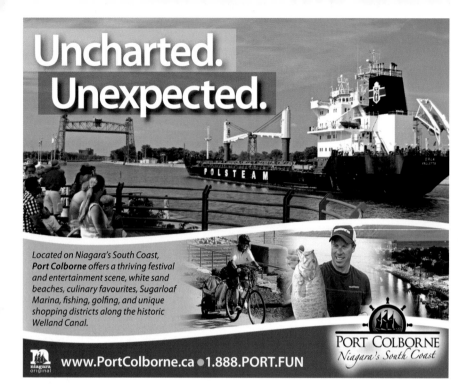

4

Passages

Changes in the shipping scene since our last edition

Pineglen, scrapped in 2017, heads under the Blue Water Bridge at Port Huron / Sarnia in 2016. (Marc Dease)

Out with the old, in with the new

The big news as 2018 began was the surprise sale, in the final days of 2017 by the American Steamship Co., of four vessels to the Algoma Central Corp. Involved were the *Buffalo* and *Adam E. Cornelius,* as well as the steamers *American Valor* and *American Victory*, which last sailed in 2008. New names are expected for the first two (*Algoma Buffalo* has been mentioned for *Buffalo*). However it is unknown what plans the company has for the old steamers. Algoma also welcomed two new vessels in 2017: *Algoma Strongfield* and *Algoma Niagara*. Arriving in 2018 are *Algoma Innovator, Algoma Sault* and *Algoma Conveyor*. With the good news comes some sad. *John B. Aird* was towed to Turkey for scrap in May 2017. During the course of 2018, Algoma may scrap or sideline the familiar *Algoway, Algorail, Algoma Olympic, Algosteel* and *Algolake*.

Algorail above the Blue Water Bridge. *(Marc Dease)*

Continued on Page 10

Algoma Niagara on her maiden arrival at Hamilton, Ont., in 2017. (Ted Willish)

Algoway at Lorain, Ohio, on one of her last trips ever, December 2017. (Scott Tish)

Algoma Strongfield loading grain at Sarnia, Ont., in 2017 (top). (Marc Dease)

Algolake (right) unloading at the 92nd Street Salt Dock in South Chicago, Ill. (Peter Groh)

Rust-rimmed Algosteel in the Welland Canal during December 2017 (below). (Jeff Cameron)

Buffalo (top) and
Adam E. Cornelius
(left) are two out of
four vessels added
in late 2017 to the
Algoma Central Corp.
fleet. *(Gordy Garris,
Roger LeLievre)*

Algoma Olympic
(below), unloading
at Hamilton, may be
sent for scrap in 2018.
(Ted Willish)

Groupe Desgagnés had a busy 12 months in 2017, adding *Acadia Desgagnés, Argentina Desgagnés, Nordica Desgagnés, Taiga Desgagnés* and the tankers *Damia Desgagnés, Mia Desgagnés* to its fleet. *Paul A. Desgagnés* is due in 2018. With that growth came some departures, as the fleet said goodbye to *Amelia Desgagnés* (launched as *Soodoc* in 1976), *Anna Desgagnés* and *Camilla Desgagnés*.

Lower Lakes Towing Co.'s 1952-built self-unloading barge *Lewis J. Kuber* (*Sparrows Point, Buckeye*) was renamed *Menominee* in May 2017. ...There are changes ahead in the Lake Ontario cement trade. *Stephen B. Roman* (built in 1965 as *Fort William*) and *English River* will be replaced by *McKeil Spirit* (ex-*Ardita*), *NACC Toronto* (ex-*Arklow Wave*) and *NACC Quebec* (ex-*Tenace*), saltwater vessels recently adapted for the cement trade.

Paul H. Townsend scrap tow on Lake Huron.
(Ben / Chanda McClain, Floyd Hepworth)

Barge Menominee / tug Olive L. Moore on the Saginaw River. *(Gordy Garris)*

Two familiar vessels were towed away for scrap in 2017. Canada Steamship Lines' bulk carrier *Pineglen* (built in 1985 as *Paterson*) was towed from Montreal on Sept. 18 for scrapping at Aliaga, Turkey. The cement carrier *Paul H. Townsend*, which had been inactive for several years, arrived Sept. 11 at Port Colborne, Ont., for scrapping.

Continued on Page 12

Tugs gather at Montreal to tow Pineglen to Turkey for demolition. (René Beauchamp)

Cement carrier Stephen B. Roman at full speed on Lake Ontario. She is scheduled to be replaced by a new vessel in 2018. (Ted Willish)

Argentia Desgagnés in the Welland Canal. (Jeff Cameron)

This and that

The former steamer *John G. Munson* reentered service May 5, 2017 under diesel power. ... The last load of iron ore was shipped from Escanaba, Mich., on April 18 aboard the steamer *Wilfred Sykes*, ending a 165-year tradition. ... Canada Steamship Lines' laid-up *CSL Tadoussac* will be back in service in 2018 thanks to a brisk trade in iron ore pellets from western Lake Superior ports down the seaway for reshipment overseas. In other good news, the 1949-vintage *Wilfred Sykes* was treated to extensive boiler repairs over the winter and will be back working the Lake Michigan stone trade in 2018. ... The former Canadian Coast Guard icebreaker *Alexander Henry* arrived at Thunder Bay, Ont., under tow on June 27, 2017. She had served as a marine museum in Kingston, Ont., since 1986 and will continue as such at the Canadian lakehead. ... Rand Logistics Inc., the corporate parent of Grand River Navigation Co. a Lower Lakes Transportation Co. affiliate, filed for voluntary Chapter 11 in January 2018. The firm's Canadian operations were not included in the bankruptcy and the U.S.-flagged vessels are expected to continue operation while Rand restructures.

Lay ups

Arthur M. Anderson, **long a boatwatcher favorite**, entered possible long-term lay-up at Duluth on Jan. 15, 2017. *Edward L. Ryerson* remained laid up at Superior, Wis., in 2017, where she has been since May 2009. *Manistee* and *Sarah Spencer* are still at Toledo, Ohio, with little hope of ever sailing again due to extensive repairs needed. *John Sherwin* continues her stay at DeTour, Mich., while *McKee Sons* is still idle at Muskegon, Mich. *Manitoba*, believed to have been headed for scrap in 2017, continued her slumber at Montreal as 2018 began. *American Courage* spent 2016 and 2017 laid up at Sturgeon Bay, Wis. *Adam E. Cornelius* spent 2015-17 idle at Huron, Ohio, but is expected to sail in 2018, likely under a new name, since she has been sold to the Algoma Central Corp. The futures of the long-idle *American Victory* (at Superior, Wis.), and *American Valor* (at Toledo) are still unknown since their sale to Algoma.

The inactive vessels American Victory (right) and Manistee (below) were moved to new lay-up berths in late 2017.
(Kent Rengo, Jim Hoffman)

Former icebreaker Alexander Henry was towed up the Welland Canal by the tug M.R. Kane in 2017 to become a marine museum at Thunder Bay, Ont. (Barry Andersen)

Manitoba at Montreal in 2017 awaiting scrapping. (Philip A. Clayton)

Shipping season on ice

As the 2017-2018 shipping season ground to a close, weeks of subzero temperatures led to heavy ice from Duluth, Minn., to Montreal, Que., with channels clogged and Coast Guard icebreakers and private tugs doing a herculean job of keeping the locks and other narrow waterways open. Here some stunning images from around the Great Lakes.

USCG Mackinaw with the tug North Dakota at Green Bay, Wis. (Jeff Rueckert)

James R. Barker in the grip of an icy Lake Erie. (Capt. Gary Kafcsak)

Ice-covered Walter J. McCarthy Jr. at the Soo Locks. *(Michelle Briggs)*

34
33
32

Mississagi at Mission Point in Sault Ste. Marie, Mich. *(Kari Eliason)*

MISSISSAGI

vessel index

Great Lakes Towing Co. tug Michigan with a barge on Lake Erie. (Paul C. LaMarre III)

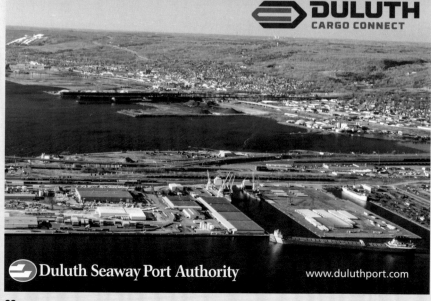

23

Michigan Lighthouse FESTIVAL

MICHIGAN LIGHTHOUSE FESTIVAL

August 3rd, 4th & 5th, 2018
Paradise, Michigan

SPONSORS:

Paradise Area Tourism Council
Bay Mills Resort & Casinos
Mackinaw Pastie and
Cookie Company
Radio Eagle
Sault Ste. Marie Convention &
Visitors Bureau
Newberry Chamber of Commerce

FEATURING:

- Whitefish Point Lighthouse
- Crisp Point Lighthouse
- Point Iroquois

michiganlighthousefestival.com

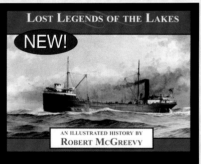

Great Lakes Fleet
TRANSPORTERS OF BULK CARGOES

The Art of Logistics.

Your business and today's supply chains expect more than haphazard dependability, cryptic scheduling, and a sea of broken promises. Avoid the runaround. Our accomplished staff and premier vessels are at the ready to deliver, backed by more than 2 billion tons worth of cargo experience. Bulk may be our business, but unsurpassed service is what we sell. Leave the art of logistics to the industry leader - Great Lakes Fleet.

cn.ca/greatlakesfleet

Fleet Listings

Michipicoten follows CSL St-Laurent downbound at the Rock Cut. (Roger LeLievre)

LAKES / SEAWAY FLEETS

Listed after each vessel in order are Type of Vessel, Year Built, Type of Engine, Maximum Cargo Capacity (at midsummer draft in long tons) or Gross Tonnage*, Overall Length, Breadth and Depth (from the top of the keel to the top of the upper deck beam) or Draft*. Only vessels over 30 feet long are included. The figures given are as accurate as possible and are for informational purposes only. Vessels and owners are listed alphabetically as per American Bureau of Shipping and Lloyd's Register of Shipping format. Builder yard and location, as well as other pertinent information, are listed for major vessels. Former names of vessels and years of operation under the former names appear in parentheses. A number in brackets following a vessel's name indicates how many vessels, including the one listed, have carried that name.

KEY TO TYPE OF VESSEL

2B ....Brigantine	DV ....Drilling Vessel	PV ....Patrol Vessel
2S ....2-Masted Schooner	DW ....Scow	RR............................Roll On/Roll Off
3S ....3-Masted Schooner	ES .... Excursion Ship	RT .... Refueling Tanker
4S ....4-Masted Schooner	EV .... Environmental Response	RV............................Research Vessel
AC.............................Auto Carrier	FB ....Fireboat	SB ....Supply Boat
AT ....Articulated Tug	FD.........................Floating Dry Dock	SC .... Sand Carrier
ATB ....Articulated Tug/Barge	GC .... General Cargo	SR ....Search & Rescue
BC...............................Bulk Carrier	GL..................................... Gate Lifter	SU ....Self-Unloader
BK..................Bulk Carrier/Tanker	GU .... Grain Self-Unloader	SV ....Survey Vessel
BT ....Buoy Tender	HL...............................Heavy Lift Vessel	TB ....Tugboat
CA ....Catamaran	IB ....Ice Breaker	TF ....Train Ferry
CC .... Cement Carrier	IT .... Integrated Tug	TK .... Tanker
CF ....Car Ferry	ITB...............Integrated Tug/Barge	TS ....Tall Ship
CO ....Container Vessel	MB ....Mailboat	TT ....Tractor Tugboat
CS ....Crane Ship	MU ....Museum Vessel	TV...........................Training Vessel
DB ....Deck Barge	PA .... Passenger Vessel	TW ....Towboat
DH ....Hopper Barge	PB .... Pilot Boat	WB ....Workboat
DR ....Dredge	PF ....Passenger Ferry	
DS................................Spud Barge	PK......................Package Freighter	

KEY TO PROPULSION

B...Barge	R......................Steam – Triple Exp. Compound Engine
D...Diesel	S............................. Steam – Skinner "Uniflow" Engine
DE.. Diesel Electric	T...Steam – Turbine Engine
Q.....................Steam – Quad Exp. Compound Engine	W..Sailing Vessel (Wind)

Fleet Name Vessel Name	Vessel IMO #	Vessel Type	Year Built	Engine Type	Cargo Cap. or Gross*	Overall Length	Vessel Breadth	Vessel Depth

A

ABACO MARINE TOWING LLC, CLAYTON, NY

Bowditch		TB	1954	D	76*	71' 00"	22' 00"	8' 04"

Built: Missouri Valley Steel Inc., Leavenworth, KS (ST-1991, Oriskany, Hot Dog)

ALGOMA CENTRAL CORP., ST. CATHARINES, ON (algonet.com)

Adam L.*	7326245	SU	1973	D	29,200	680' 00"	78' 00"	42' 00"

*Built: American Shipbuilding Co., Toledo, OH (Roger M. Kyes '73-'89, Adam E. Cornelius {4} '89-'18) *New name likely*

Algolake	7423093	SU	1977	D	32,807	730' 00"	75' 00"	46' 06"

Built: Collingwood Shipyards, Collingwood, ON

Algoma Buffalo*	7620653	SU	1978	D	24,300	634' 10"	68' 00"	40' 00"

*Built: Bay Shipbuilding Co., Sturgeon Bay, WI (Buffalo {3} '78'-'18) *New name not official at press time*

Algoma Conveyor	9619268	BC	2018	D	39,400	740' 00"	78' 00"	48' 03"

Built: Nantong Mingde Heavy Industry Co. Ltd., Nantong City, China

Algoma Discovery	8505848	BC	1987	D	34,380	729' 00"	75' 09"	48' 05"

Built: 3 Maj Brodogradiliste d.d., Rijeka, Croatia (Malinska '87-'97, Daviken '97-'08)

Algoma Endurance	9773387	SU	2018	D	24,900	650' 08"	78' 00"	44' 09"

Built: 3 Maj Brodogradiliste d.d., Rijeka, Croatia

Algoma Enterprise	7726677	SU	1979	D	33,854	730' 00"	75' 11"	46' 07"

Built: Port Weller Dry Docks, Port Weller, ON (Canadian Enterprise '79-'11)

Algoma Equinox	9613927	BC	2013	D	39,400	740' 00"	78' 00"	48' 03"

Built: Nantong Mingde Heavy Industry Co. Ltd., Nantong City, China

Algoma Guardian	8505850	BC	1987	D	34,380	729' 00"	75' 09"	48' 05"

Built: 3 Maj Brodogradiliste d.d., Rijeka, Croatia (Omisalj '87-'97, Goviken '97-'08)

Fleet Name Vessel Name	Vessel IMO #	Vessel Type	Year Built	Engine Type	Cargo Cap. or Gross*	Overall Length	Vessel Breadth	Vessel Depth
Algoma Harvester	9613939	BC	2014	D	39,400	740' 00"	78' 00"	48' 03"

Built: Nantong Mingde Heavy Industry Co. Ltd., Nantong City, China

Algoma Innovator	9773375	SU	2017	D	24,900	650' 08"	78' 00"	44' 09"

Built: 3 Maj Brodogradiliste d.d., Rijeka, Croatia

Algoma Integrity	9405162	SU	2009	D	33,047	646' 07"	105' 06"	58' 02"

Built: Estaleiro Ilha S.A., Rio de Janeiro, Brazil; Vessel is too large for the St. Lawrence Seaway but is a frequent visitor to the St. Lawrence River (Gypsum Integrity '09-'15)

Algoma Mariner	9587893	SU	2011	D	37,399	740' 00"	77' 11"	49' 03"

Built: Chengxi Shipyard Co. Ltd., Jiangyin City, China (Laid down as Canadian Mariner {2})

Algoma Niagara	9619311	BC	2017	D	39,400	740' 00"	78' 00"	48' 02"

Built: Yangzijiang Shipbuilding Group Limited, Jingjiang City, Jiangsu Province, People's Republic of China

Algoma Olympic	7432783	SU	1976	D	33,859	730' 00"	75' 00"	46' 06"

Built: Port Weller Dry Docks, Port Weller, ON (Canadian Olympic '76-'11)

Algoma Sault	9619294	SU	2017	D	39,400	740' 00"	78' 00"	48' 02"

Built: Yangzijiang Shipbuilding Group Limited, Jingjiang City, Jiangsu Province, People's Republic of China

Algoma Spirit	8504882	BC	1986	D	34,380	729' 00"	75' 09"	48' 05"

Built: 3 Maj Brodogradiliste d.d., Rijeka, Croatia (Petka '86-'00, Sandviken '00-'08)

Algoma Strongfield	9613953	BC	2015	D	39,400	740' 00"	78' 00"	48' 03"

Built: Nantong Mingde Heavy Industry Co., Ltd., Nantong City, China (CWB Strongfield '15-'17)

Algoma Transport	7711737	SU	1979	D	32,678	730' 00"	75' 11"	46' 07"

Built: Port Weller Dry Docks, Port Weller, ON (Canadian Transport '79-'11)

Algorail {2}	6805531	SU	1968	D	23,810	640' 05"	72' 00"	40' 00"

Built: Collingwood Shipyards, Collingwood, ON

Algosteel {2}	6613299	SU	1966	D	26,949	730' 00"	75' 00"	39' 08"

Built: Davie Shipbuilding Co., Lauzon, QC; converted to a self-unloader by Port Weller Dry Docks, St. Catharines, ON, in '89 (A. S. Glossbrenner '66-'87, Algogulf {1} '87-'90)

Algoway {2}	7221251	SU	1972	D	23,812	646' 06"	72' 00"	40' 00"

Built: Collingwood Shipyards, Collingwood, ON

Algowood	7910216	SU	1981	D	32,253	740' 00"	75' 11"	46' 06"

Built: Collingwood Shipyards, Collingwood, ON; lengthened 10' in '00 at Port Weller Dry Docks, St. Catharines, ON

American Valor	5024738	SU	1953	T	26,200	767' 00"	70' 00"	36' 00"

Built: American Shipbuilding Co., Lorain, OH; lengthened 120' by Fraser Shipyard, Superior, WI, in '74; converted to a self-unloader in '82; entered long-term lay-up Nov. 13, 2008, at Toledo, OH (Armco '53-'06)

American Victory	5234395	SU	1942	T	26,700	730' 00"	75' 00"	39' 03"

Built: Bethlehem Shipbuilding and Drydock Co., Sparrows Point, MD; converted from saltwater tanker to a Great Lakes bulk carrier by Maryland Shipbuilding in '61; converted to a self-unloader by Bay Shipbuilding Co., Sturgeon Bay, WI, in '82; entered long-term lay-up Nov. 12, 2008, at Superior, WI (Laid down as Marquette, USS Neshanic [AO-71] '42-'47, Gulfoil '47-'61, Pioneer Challenger '61-'62, Middletown '62-'06)

Algoma Central workhorse Capt. Henry Jackman. (Jacob Northup)

Fleet Name Vessel Name	Vessel IMO #	Vessel Type	Year Built	Engine Type	Cargo Cap. or Gross*	Overall Length	Vessel Breadth	Vessel Depth
Capt. Henry Jackman	8006323	SU	1981	D	30,590	730' 00"	75' 11"	42' 00"
Built: Collingwood Shipyards, Collingwood, ON; converted to a self-unloader by Port Weller Dry Docks, St. Catharines, ON, in '96 (Lake Wabush '81-'87)								
John B. Aird	8002432	SU	1983	D	31,000	730' 00"	75' 10"	46' 06"
Built: Collingwood Shipyards, Collingwood, ON								
John D. Leitch	6714586	SU	1967	D	34,127	730' 00"	77' 11"	45' 00"
Built: Port Weller Dry Docks, Port Weller, ON; rebuilt with new mid-body, widened 3' by the builders in '02 (Canadian Century '67-'02)								
Radcliffe R. Latimer	7711725	SU	1978	D	36,668	740' 00"	77' 11"	49' 03"
Built: Collingwood Shipyards, Collingwood, ON; rebuilt with a new forebody at Chengxi Shipyard Co. Ltd., Jiangyin City, China, in '09 (Algobay '78-'94, Atlantic Trader '94-'97, Algobay '97-'12)								
Tim S. Dool	6800919	BC	1967	D	31,054	730' 00"	77' 11"	39' 08"
Built: Saint John Shipbuilding & Drydock Co., Saint John, NB; widened by 3' at Port Weller Dry Docks, St. Catharines, ON, in '96 (Senneville '67-'94, Algoville '94-'08)								
ALGOMA TANKERS LTD., ST. CATHARINES, ON – DIVISION OF ALGOMA CENTRAL CORP.								
Algocanada	9378591	TK	2008	D	11,453	426' 01"	65' 00"	32' 08"
Built: Eregli Shipyard, Zonguldak, Turkey								
Algoma Dartmouth	9327516	RT	2007	D	3,512	296' 11"	47' 11"	24' 11"
Built: Turkter Shipyard, Tuzla, Turkey; vessel is engaged in bunkering operations at Halifax, NS (Clipper Bardolino '07-'08, Samistal Due '08-'09)								
Algoma Hansa	9127186	TK	1998	D	16,775	472' 07"	75' 06"	40' 08"
Built: Alabama Shipyard Inc., Mobile, AL (Amalienborg '98-'98)								
Algonova {2}	9378589	TK	2008	D	11,453	426' 01"	65' 00"	32' 08"
Built: Eregli Shipyard, Zonguldak, Turkey (Eregli 04 '07-'08)								
Algoscotia	9273222	TK	2004	D	19,160	488' 03"	78' 00"	42' 00"
Built: Jiangnan Shipyard (Group) Co. Ltd., Shangahi, China								
Algosea {2}	9127198	TK	1998	D	17,258	472' 07"	75' 04"	40'08"
Built: Alabama Shipyard Inc., Mobile, AL (Aggersborg '98-'05)								
OPERATED BY ALGOMA CENTRAL CORP. FOR G3 CANADA LTD. (g3.ca)								
G3 Marquis	9613941	BC	2014	D	39,400	740' 00"	78' 00"	48' 03"
Built: Nantong Mingde Heavy Industry Co. Ltd., Nantong City, China (CWB Marquis '14-'16)								
ALPENA SHIPWRECK TOURS, ALPENA, MI (alpenashipwrecktours.com)								
Lady Michigan		ES	2010	D	90*	65' 00"	19' 00"	11' 00"

Federal Kumano sneaks up astern of Herbert C. Jackson. (Ben / Chanda McClain)

Fleet Name / Vessel Name	Vessel IMO #	Vessel Type	Year Built	Engine Type	Cargo Cap. or Gross*	Overall Length	Vessel Breadth	Vessel Depth
AMERICAN STEAMSHIP CO., WILLIAMSVILLE, NY *(americansteamship.com)*								
American Century	7923196	SU	1981	D	80,900	1,000' 00"	105' 00"	56' 00"
Built: Bay Shipbuilding Co., Sturgeon Bay, WI (Columbia Star '81-'06)								
American Courage	7634226	SU	1979	D	24,300	636' 00"	68' 00"	40' 00"
Built: Bay Shipbuilding Co., Sturgeon Bay, WI; spent '16-'17 in lay-up at Sturgeon Bay, WI (Fred R. White Jr. '79-'06)								
American Integrity	7514696	SU	1978	D	80,900	1,000' 00"	105' 00"	56' 00"
Built: Bay Shipbuilding Co., Sturgeon Bay, WI (Lewis Wilson Foy '78-'91, Oglebay Norton '91-'06)								
American Mariner	7812567	SU	1980	D	37,300	730' 00"	78' 00"	42' 00"
Built: Bay Shipbuilding Co., Sturgeon Bay, WI (Laid down as Chicago {3})								
American Spirit	7423392	SU	1978	D	62,400	1,004' 00"	105' 00"	50' 00"
Built: American Shipbuilding Co., Lorain, OH (George A. Stinson '78-'04)								
Burns Harbor {2}	7514713	SU	1980	D	80,900	1,000' 00"	105' 00"	56' 00"
Built: Bay Shipbuilding Co., Sturgeon Bay, WI								
H. Lee White {2}	7366362	SU	1974	D	35,400	704' 00"	78' 00"	45' 00"
Built: Bay Shipbuilding Co., Sturgeon Bay, WI								
Indiana Harbor	7514701	SU	1979	D	80,900	1,000' 00"	105' 00"	56' 00"
Built: Bay Shipbuilding Co., Sturgeon Bay, WI								
John J. Boland {4}	7318901	SU	1973	D	34,000	680' 00"	78' 00"	45' 00"
Built: Bay Shipbuilding Co., Sturgeon Bay, WI; spent 2015 in lay-up at Huron, Ohio (Charles E. Wilson '73-'00)								
Sam Laud	7390210	SU	1975	D	24,300	634' 10"	68' 00"	40' 00"
Built: Bay Shipbuilding Co., Sturgeon Bay, WI								
St. Clair {3}	7403990	SU	1976	D	44,800	770' 00"	92' 00"	52' 00"
Built: Bay Shipbuilding Co., Sturgeon Bay, WI								
Walter J. McCarthy Jr.	7514684	SU	1977	D	80,500	1,000' 00"	105' 00"	56' 00"
Built: Bay Shipbuilding Co., Sturgeon Bay, WI (Belle River '77-'90)								
AMHERSTBURG FERRY CO. INC, AMHERSTBURG, ON *(boblo.ca/amherstburg-ferry-company)*								
Columbia		PA/CF	1946	D	46*	65' 00"	28' 10"	8' 06"
Built: Champion Auto Ferries, Algonac, MI (Crystal O, St. Clair Flats)								
Ste. Claire V		PA/CF	1997	D	82*	86' 06"	32' 00"	6' 00"
Built: Les Ateliers Maurice Bourbonnais Ltée, Gatineau, QC (Courtney O., M. Bourbonnais)								
ANDRIE INC., MUSKEGON, MI *(andrietg.com)*								
A-390		TK	1982	B	2,346*	310' 00"	60' 00"	17' 00"
Built: St. Louis Shipbuilding & Steel Co., St. Louis, MO (Canonie 40 '82-'92)								

USCG Hollyhock was in the Fraser Shipyards drydock for a refit in 2017. (Jacob Northup)

Fleet Name / Vessel Name	Vessel IMO #	Vessel Type	Year Built	Engine Type	Cargo Cap. or Gross*	Overall Length	Vessel Breadth	Vessel Depth
A-397		TK	1962	B	2,928*	270' 00"	60' 01"	22' 05"
Built: Dravo Corp., Pittsburgh, PA (Auntie Mame '62-'91, Iron Mike '91-'93)								
A-410		TK	1955	B	3,793*	335' 00"	54' 00"	17' 00"
Built: Ingalls Shipbuilding Corp., Birmingham, AL (Methane '55-'63, B-6400 '63-'71, Kelly '71-'86, Canonie 50 '86-'93)								
Barbara Andrie	5097187	TB	1940	D	298*	122' 00"	29' 07"	16' 00"
Built: Pennsylvania Shipyards Inc., Beaumont, TX (Edmond J. Moran '40-'76)								
Endeavour		TK	2009	B	7,232*	360' 00"	60' 00"	24' 00"
Built: Jeffboat LLC, Jeffersonville, IN								
Karen Andrie {2}	6520454	TB	1965	D	516*	120' 00"	31' 06"	16' 00"
Built: Gulfport Shipbuilding, Port Arthur, TX (Sarah Hays '65-'93)								
Rebecca Lynn	6511374	TB	1964	D	433*	112' 07"	31' 06"	16' 00"
Built: Gulfport Shipbuilding, Port Arthur, TX (Kathrine Clewis '64-'96)								
Sarah Andrie	7114032	TB	1970	D	190*	99' 05"	32' 04"	6' 07"
Built: Main Iron Works, Houma, LA (Seminole Sun '70-'97, Declaration '97-'99, Caribe Service '99-'15)								
OPERATED BY ANDRIE INC. FOR LAFARGE HOLCIM								
G. L. Ostrander	7501106	AT	1976	D	198*	140' 02"	40' 01"	22' 03"
Built: Halter Marine, New Orleans, LA; paired with barge Integrity (Andrew Martin '76-'90, Robert L. Torres '90-'94, Jacklyn M '94-'04)								
Innovation	9082336	CC	2006	B	7,320*	460' 00"	70' 00"	37' 00"
Built: Bay Shipbuilding Co., Sturgeon Bay, WI								
Integrity	8637213	CC	1996	B	14,000	460' 00"	70' 00"	37' 00"
Built: Bay Shipbuilding Co., Sturgeon Bay, WI								
Samuel de Champlain	7433799	AT	1975	D	299*	140' 02"	39' 02"	20' 00"
Built: Mangone Shipbuilding, Houston, TX; paired with barge Innovation (Musketeer Fury '75-'78, Tender Panther '78-'79, Margarita '79-'83, Vortice '83-'99, Norfolk '99-'06)								
OPERATED BY ANDRIE INC. FOR OCCIDENTAL CHEMICAL CORP., MUSKEGON, MI								
Spartan	7047461	AT	1969	D	190*	121' 01"	32' 01"	10' 09"
Built: Burton Shipyard, Port Arthur, TX; paired with barge Spartan II (Lead Horse '69-'73, Gulf Challenger '73-'80, Challenger {2} '80-'93, Mark Hannah '93-'10)								
Spartan II		TK	1980	B	8,050	407' 01"	60' 00"	21' 00"
Built: Sturgeon Bay Shipbuilding Co., Sturgeon Bay, WI (Hannah 6301 '80-'10)								
APOSTLE ISLANDS CRUISES INC., BAYFIELD, WI *(apostleisland.com)*								
Ashland Bayfield Express		PA	1995	D	13*	49' 00"	18' 05"	5' 00"
Island Princess {2}		ES	1973	D	63*	65' 07"	20' 05"	7' 03"
ARNOLD FREIGHT COMPANY, ST. IGNACE, MI								
Corsair		CF	1955	D	98*	94' 06"	33' 01"	8' 01"
Built: Blount Marine Corp., Warren, RI								
ASHTON MARINE CO., NORTH MUSKEGON, MI *(ashtontugs.com)*								
Candace Elise	8016380	TB	1981	D	199*	100' 00"	32' 00"	14' 08"
Built: Modern Marine Power Inc., Houma LA (Perseverance '81-'83, Mr. Bill G '83-'90, El Rhino Grande '90-'97, Stephan Dann '97-'15)								
ASI GROUP LTD., ST. CATHARINES, ON *(asi-group.com)*								
ASI Clipper		SV	1939	D	64*	70' 00"	23' 00"	6' 06"
Built: Port Colborne Iron Works, Port Colborne, ON (Stanley Clipper '39-'94, Nadro Clipper '94-'08)								
ATLAS MARINE SERVICES LLC, FISH CREEK, WI								
Atlas		PA	1992	D	12*	30' 04"	11' 05"	5' 04"
Northern Lighter		GC	1973	D	5*	36' 00"	9' 09"	1' 06"
AZCON METALS, DULUTH, MN *(azcon.net)*								
J.B. Ford		CC	1904	R	8,000	440' 00"	50' 00"	28' 00
Built: American Shipbuilding Co., Lorain, OH; converted to a self-unloading cement carrier in '59; last operated Nov. 15, 1985; most recently used as a cement storage and transfer vessel at Superior, WI, and now awaiting scrapping at Duluth, MN (Edwin F. Holmes '04-'16, E. C. Collins '16-'59)								

B

B & L TUG SERVICE, THESSALON, ON								
C. West Pete		TB	1958	D	29*	65' 00"	17' 05"	6' 00"
Built: Erieau Shipbuilding & Drydock Co. Ltd., Erieau, ON								
BABCOCK WELDING & MARINE SERVICES, SARNIA, ON								
Lime Island		TB	1953	D	13*	42' 02"	12' 00"	5' 05"
Built: Knudson Brothers Shipbuilding, Sturgeon Bay, WI								
BAY CITY BOAT LINES LLC, BAY CITY, MI *(baycityboatlines.com)*								
Islander		ES	1946	D	39*	53' 04"	19' 09"	5' 04"

Great Republic navigates the Cuyahoga River at Cleveland, Ohio. (Nick Hunter)

John J. Boland on a peaceful afternoon on the St. Marys River. (Roger LeLievre)

Fleet Name Vessel Name	Vessel IMO #	Vessel Type	Year Built	Engine Type	Cargo Cap. or Gross*	Overall Length	Vessel Breadth	Vessel Depth
Princess Wenonah		ES	1954	D	96*	64' 09"	31' 00"	7' 03"
Built: Sturgeon Bay Shipbuilding Co., Sturgeon Bay, WI (William M. Miller '54-'98)								
BAY SHIPBUILDING CO., DIV. OF FINCANTIERI MARINE GROUP, STURGEON BAY, WI *(bayshipbuildingcompany.com)*								
Bayship		TB	1943	D	19*	45' 00"	12' 04"	5' 03"
Built: Sturgeon Bay Shipbuilding Co., Sturgeon Bay, WI (Sturshipco)								
BAYSAIL, BAY CITY, MI *(baysailbaycity.org)*								
Appledore IV		2S/ES	1989	W/D	48*	85' 00"	18' 08"	8' 08"
Built: Treworgy Yachts, Palm Coast, FL								
Appledore V		2S/ES	1992	W/D	34*	65' 00"	14' 00"	8' 06"
Built: Treworgy Yachts, Palm Coast, FL (Westwind, Appledore)								
BEAUSOLEIL FIRST NATION TRANSPORTATION, CHRISTIAN ISLAND, ON *(chimnissing.ca)*								
Indian Maiden		PA/CF	1987	D	91.5*	73' 06"	23' 00"	8' 00"
Built: Duraug Shipyard & Fabricating Ltd., Port Dover, ON								
Sandy Graham		PA/CF	1957	D	212*	125' 07"	39' 09"	8' 00"
Built: Barbour Boat Works Inc., New Bern, NC								
BEAVER ISLAND BOAT CO., CHARLEVOIX, MI *(bibco.com)*								
Beaver Islander		PF/CF	1963	D	95*	96' 03"	27' 02"	8' 03"
Built: Sturgeon Bay Shipbuilding, Sturgeon Bay, WI								
Emerald Isle {2}	8967840	PF/CF	1997	D	95*	130' 00"	38' 00"	12' 00"
Built: Washburn & Doughty Associates Inc., East Boothbay, ME								
BLUE HERON CO. LTD., TOBERMORY, ON *(blueheronco.com)*								
Blue Heron V		ES	1983	D	24*	54' 06"	17' 05"	7' 02"
Flowerpot		ES	1978	D	39*	47' 02"	15' 08"	5' 06"
Flowerpot Express		ES	2011	D	59*	49' 07"	16' 05"	4' 01"
Great Blue Heron		ES	1994	D	112*	79' 00"	22' 00"	6' 05"
BLUEWATER FERRY CO., SOMBRA, ON *(bluewaterferry.com)*								
Daldean		CF	1951	D	145*	75' 00"	35' 00"	7' 00"
Built: Erieau Shipbuilding & Drydock Co. Ltd., Erieau, ON								
Ontamich		CF	1939	D	55*	65' 00"	28' 10"	8' 06"
Built: Champion Auto Ferries, Harsens Island, MI (Harsens Island '39-'73)								
BRIGANTINE INC., KINGSTON, ONT. *(brigantine.ca)*								
St. Lawrence II		TV	1954	W/D	34*	72' 00"	15' 00"	8' 06"
BUFFALO DEPARTMENT OF PUBLIC WORKS, BUFFALO, NY *(emcotter.com)*								
Edward M. Cotter		FB	1900	D	208*	118' 00"	24' 00"	11' 06"
Built: Crescent Shipbuilding, Elizabeth, NJ (W. S. Grattan 1900-'53, Firefighter '53-'54)								

Atlantic Huron passing Mission Point on the St. Marys River. (Sam Hankinson)

Fleet Name Vessel Name	Vessel IMO #	Vessel Type	Year Built	Engine Type	Cargo Cap. or Gross*	Overall Length	Vessel Breadth	Vessel Depth
BUFFALO RIVER HISTORY TOURS, BUFFALO, NY *(buffaloriverhistorytours.com)*								
Harbor Queen		PA	2016	D	48*	63' 00"	24' 00"	10' 00"
River Queen		PA	2014	D	5*	45' 00"	12' 00"	3' 02"
BUFFALO SAILING ADVENTURES INC., BUFFALO, NY *(spiritofbuffalo.com)*								
Spirit of Buffalo		2S/ES	1992	D/W	34*	73' 00"	15' 06"	7' 02"
BUSCH MARINE INC., CARROLLTON, MI *(buschmarine.com)*								
BMT 3		DB	1965	B	280*	120' 01"	36' 01"	7' 06"
Edwin C. Busch		TB	1935	D	18*	42' 06"	11' 11"	5' 00"
Built: Manitowoc Shipbuilding Co., Manitowoc, WI (Stella B '35-'79, Paul L. Luedtke '79-'98, Joanne '98-'09)								
Gregory J. Busch	5156725	TB	1919	D	299*	151' 00"	27' 06"	14' 07"
Built: Whitney Bros. Co., Superior, WI (Humaconna '19-'77)								
STC 2004		DB	1963	B	1,230*	250' 00"	50' 00"	12' 00"

C

CALUMET RIVER FLEETING INC., CHICAGO, IL *(calumetriverfleeting.com)*								
Aiden William		TB	1954	D	120*	82' 00"	23' 06"	9' 09"
Built: Defoe Shipbuilding Co., Bay City, MI (John A. McGuire '54-'87, William Hoey {1} '87-'94, Margaret Ann '94-'08, Steven Selvick '08-'14)								
Audrie S		TW	1956	D	268*	102' 00"	28' 00"	8' 00"
Built: Calumet Shipyard & Drydock Co., Chicago, IL (Cindy D '56-'66, Katherine L. '66-'93, Daryl C. Hannah '93-'12)								
John M. Selvick	8993370	TB	1898	D	256*	118' 00"	24' 03"	16' 00"
Built: Chicago Shipbuilding Co., Chicago, IL (Fire tug Illinois {1} 1898-'41, John Roen III '41-'74)								
John Marshall	7223261	TB	1972	D	199*	111' 00"	30' 00"	9' 07"
Built: Main Iron Works, Houma, LA (Miss Lynn '72-'78, Newpark Sunburst '78-'83, Gulf Tempest '83-'89, Atlantic Tempest '89-'89, Catherine Turecamo '89-'14)								
Kimberly Selvick		TW	1975	D	93*	57' 07"	28' 00"	10' 00"
Built: Grafton Boat Co., Grafton, IL (Scout 1 '75-'02)								
Lake Trader		DB	1982	B	2,262*	250' 00"	72' 00"	17' 00"
Built: Forked Island Shipyard Inc., Abbeville, LA (TJ 2501, Primary 1)								
Mary E. Hannah		TB	1945	D	612*	149' 00"	33' 00"	16' 00"
Built: Marietta Manufacturing, Marietta, GA (U. S. Army LT-821 '45-'47, Brooklyn '47-'66, Lee Reuben '66-'75)								
Nathan S		TB	1962	D	198*	91' 05"	28' 05"	12' 05"
Built: Main Iron Works, Houma, LA (Donald C. Hannah '62-'09, Donald C. '09-'17)								
Niki S		TW	1971	D	39*	42' 00"	18' 00"	6' 00"
Built: Scully Bros. Boat Builders, Morgan City, LA (Miss Josie '71-'79, Matador VI '79-'08)								
Terry D		TB	1954	D	76*	66' 00"	19' 00"	9' 00"
Built: Liberty Dry Dock Inc., Brooklyn, N.Y. (Sanita '54-'77, Soo Chief '77-'81, Susan M. Selvick '81-'96, Nathan S. '96-'02, John M. Perry '02-'08, Zuccolo '08-'12, Carla Selvick '12-'14)								

Claude A. Desgagnés at Kahnawake, Que. *(René Beauchamp)*

Fleet Name Vessel Name	Vessel IMO #	Vessel Type	Year Built	Engine Type	Cargo Cap. or Gross*	Overall Length	Vessel Breadth	Vessel Depth

CANADA STEAMSHIP LINES INC., MONTREAL, QC – DIVISION OF THE CSL GROUP INC. *(cslships.com)*

Fleet Name / Vessel Name	IMO #	Type	Built	Engine	Cargo/Gross	Length	Breadth	Depth
Atlantic Huron {2}	8025680	SU	1984	D	34,860	736' 07"	77' 11"	46' 04"

Built: Collingwood Shipyards, Collingwood, ON; converted to a self-unloader in '89 and widened 3' in '03 at Port Weller Dry Docks, St. Catharines, ON (Prairie Harvest '84-'89, Atlantic Huron {2} '89-'94, Melvin H. Baker II {2} '94-'97)

Baie Comeau {3}	9639892	SU	2013	D	37,690	739' 10"	77' 11"	48' 05"

Built: Chengxi Shipyard Co. Ltd., Jiangyin City, China

Baie St. Paul {2}	9601027	SU	2012	D	37,690	739' 10"	77' 11"	48' 05"

Built: Chengxi Shipyard Co. Ltd., Jiangyin City, China

Cedarglen {2}	5103974	BC	1959	D	29,518	730' 00"	75' 09"	40' 04"

Built: Schlieker-Werft, Hamburg, Germany; rebuilt, lengthened with a new forebody at Davie Shipbuilding Co., Lauzon, QC, in '77 ([Stern Section] Ems Ore '59-'76, [Fore Section] Montcliffe Hall '76-'88, Cartierdoc '88-'02)

CSL Assiniboine	7413218	SU	1977	D	36,768	739' 10"	78' 00"	48' 05"

Built: Davie Shipbuilding Co., Lauzon, QC; rebuilt with a new forebody at Port Weller Dry Docks, St. Catharines, ON, in '05; repowered in '15 (Jean Parisien '77-'05)

CSL Laurentien	7423108	SU	1977	D	37,795	739' 10"	78' 00"	48' 05"

Built: Collingwood Shipyards, Collingwood, ON; rebuilt with new forebody in '01 at Port Weller Dry Docks, St. Catharines, ON; repowered in '15 (Stern section: Louis R. Desmarais '77-'01)

CSL Niagara	7128423	SU	1972	D	37,694	739' 10"	78' 00"	48' 05"

Built: Collingwood Shipyards, Collingwood, ON; rebuilt with a new forebody in '99 at Port Weller Dry Docks, St. Catharines, ON (Stern section: J. W. McGiffin '72-'99)

CSL St-Laurent	9665281	BC	2014	D	35,529	739' 10"	77' 11"	48' 05"

Built: Yangfan Shipbuilding Co. Ltd., Zhoushan City, China

CSL Tadoussac	6918716	SU	1969	D	30,051	730' 00"	77' 11"	41' 11"

Built: Collingwood Shipyards, Collingwood, ON; rebuilt with new mid-body, widened 3' at Port Weller Dry Docks, St. Catharines, ON, in '01 (Tadoussac {2} '69-'01)

CSL Welland	9665279	BC	2014	D	35,529	739' 10"	77' 11"	48' 05"

Built: Yangfan Shipbuilding Co. Ltd., Zhoushan City, China

Ferbec {2}	9259848	SU	2002	D	27,198	615' 01"	102' 08"	55' 00"

Built: COSCO KHI Ship Engineering Co. Ltd., Nantong, China; vessel is too large for the St. Lawrence Seaway but is a frequent visitor to the St. Lawrence River (Orientor 2 '02-10, CSL Melbourne '10-'17)

Frontenac {5}	6804848	SU	1968	D	26,822	729' 07"	75' 00"	39' 08"

Built: Davie Shipbuilding Co., Lauzon, QC; converted to a self-unloader by Collingwood Shipyards, Collingwood, ON, in '73

Oakglen {3}	7901148	BC	1980	D	35,067	729' 11"	75' 10"	47' 01"

Built: Boelwerf Vlaanderen Shipbuilding N.V., Temse, Belgium (Federal Danube '80-'95, Lake Ontario '95-'09)

Rt. Hon. Paul J. Martin	7324405	SU	1973	D	37,694	739' 07"	77' 11"	48' 04"

Built: Collingwood Shipyards, Collingwood, ON; rebuilt with a new forebody in '00 at Port Weller Dry Docks, St. Catharines, ON (Stern section: H. M. Griffith '73-'00)

Salarium	7902233	SU	1980	D	35,123	730' 00"	75' 11"	46' 06"

Built: Collingwood Shipyards, Collingwood, ON (Nanticoke '80-'09)

CSL St-Laurent sported the award-winning Sea Keeper mural in 2017 as a tribute to Canada's 150th anniversary and the 375th of the City of Montreal. (Vincent Tremblay)

Fleet Name Vessel Name	Vessel IMO #	Vessel Type	Year Built	Engine Type	Cargo Cap. or Gross*	Overall Length	Vessel Breadth	Vessel Depth
Spruceglen {2}	8119261	BC	1983	D	33,824	730' 01"	75' 09"	48' 00"
Built: Govan Shipyards, Glasgow, Scotland								
(Selkirk Settler '83-'91, Federal St. Louis '91-'91, Federal Fraser {2} '91-2001, Fraser '01-'02)								
Thunder Bay {2}	9601039	SU	2013	D	37,690	739' 10"	77' 11"	48' 05"
Built: Chengxi Shipyard Co. Ltd., Jiangyin City, China								
Whitefish Bay {2}	9639880	SU	2013	D	37,690	739' 10"	77' 11"	48' 05"
Built: Chengxi Shipyard Co. Ltd., Jiangyin City, China								

CANADIAN COAST GUARD (FISHERIES AND OCEANS CANADA), OTTAWA, ON *(www.ccg-gcc.gc.ca)*
CENTRAL AND ARCTIC REGION, MONTREAL, QC

Fleet Name Vessel Name	Vessel IMO #	Vessel Type	Year Built	Engine Type	Cargo Cap. or Gross*	Overall Length	Vessel Breadth	Vessel Depth
Cape Chaillon, Cape Commodore, Cape Discovery, Cape Dundas, Cape Hearne,								
Cape Providence, Cape Rescue		SR	2004	D	34*	47' 09"	14' 00"	4' 05"
Cape Lambton, Cape Mercy, Thunder Cape		SR	2000	D	34*	47' 09"	14' 00"	4' 05"
Cape Storm		SR	1999	D	34*	47' 09"	14' 00"	4' 05"
Caporal Kaeble V	9586045	PV	2012	D	253*	141' 07"	22' 09"	9' 09"
Built: Irving Shipbuilding Inc., Halifax, NS								
Caribou Isle		BT	1985	D	92*	75' 06"	19' 08"	7' 04"
Built: Breton Industrial & Marine Ltd., Port Hawkesbury, NS								
Constable Carrière	9586069	PV	2012	D	253*	141' 07"	22' 09"	9' 09"
Built: Irving Shipbuilding Inc., Halifax, NS								
Corporal Teather C.V.	9586057	PV	2012	D	253*	141' 07"	22' 09"	9' 09"
Built: Irving Shipbuilding Inc., Halifax, NS								
Cove Isle		BT	1980	D	80*	65' 07"	19' 08"	7' 04"
Built: Canadian Dredge & Dock Co. Ltd., Kingston, ON								
Griffon	7022887	IB	1970	D	2,212*	234' 00"	49' 00"	21' 06"
Built: Davie Shipbuilding Co., Lauzon, QC								
Kelso		RV	2009	D	63*	57' 07"	17' 01"	4' 09"
Built: ABCO Industries Ltd., Lunenburg, NS								
Limnos	6804903	RV	1968	D	489*	147' 00"	32' 00"	12' 00"
Built: Port Weller Dry Docks, St. Catharines, ON								
Private Robertson VC	9586033	PV	2012	D	253*	141' 07"	22' 09"	9' 09"
Built: Irving Shipbuilding Inc., Halifax, NS								
Samuel Risley	8322442	IB	1985	D	1,988*	228' 09"	47' 01"	21' 09"
Built: Vito Steel Boat & Barge Construction Ltd., Delta, BC								
QUEBEC REGION, QUÉBEC, QC *(Vessels over 100' only have been listed)*								
Amundsen	7510846	IB	1978	D	5,910*	295' 09"	63' 09"	31' 04"
Built: Burrard Dry Dock Co., North Vancouver, BC (Sir John Franklin '78-'03)								
Des Groseilliers	8006385	IB	1983	D	5,910*	322' 07"	64' 00"	35' 06"
Built: Port Weller Dry Docks, St. Catharines, ON								

Algolake, CSL Assiniboine, Algoma Harvester downbound and Baie St. Paul upbound above Port Huron/Sarnia. (Marc Dease)

Fleet Name / Vessel Name	Vessel IMO #	Vessel Type	Year Built	Engine Type	Cargo Cap. or Gross*	Overall Length	Vessel Breadth	Vessel Depth
F. C. G. Smith	8322686	SV	1985	D	439*	114' 02"	45' 11"	11' 02"
Built: Georgetown Shipyard, Georgetown, PEI								
Martha L. Black	8320432	IB	1986	D	3,818*	272' 04"	53' 02"	25' 02"
Built: Versatile Pacific Shipyards, Victoria, BC								
Pierre Radisson	7510834	IB	1978	D	5,910*	322' 00"	62' 10"	35' 06"
Built: Burrard Dry Dock Co., North Vancouver, BC								

CANAMAC CRUISES, TORONTO, ON

Fleet Name / Vessel Name	Vessel IMO #	Vessel Type	Year Built	Engine Type	Cargo Cap. or Gross*	Overall Length	Vessel Breadth	Vessel Depth
Stella Borealis		ES	1989	D	356*	118' 00"	26' 00"	7' 00"
Built: Duratug Shipyard & Fabricating Ltd., Port Dover, ON								

CARGILL GRAIN CO. LTD., BAIE COMEAU, QC
MANAGED BY GROUPE OCÉAN INC., QUÉBEC, QC

Fleet Name / Vessel Name	Vessel IMO #	Vessel Type	Year Built	Engine Type	Cargo Cap. or Gross*	Overall Length	Vessel Breadth	Vessel Depth
Pointe Comeau	7520322	TB	1976	D	391*	99' 09"	36' 01"	12' 01"
Built: Marystown Shipyard Ltd., Marystown, NL								

CARMEUSE NORTH AMERICA (ERIE SAND & GRAVEL), ERIE, PA *(carmeusena.com)*

Fleet Name / Vessel Name	Vessel IMO #	Vessel Type	Year Built	Engine Type	Cargo Cap. or Gross*	Overall Length	Vessel Breadth	Vessel Depth
J. S. St. John	5202524	SC	1945	D	415*	174' 00"	31' 09"	15' 00"
Built: Smith Shipyards & Engineering Corp., Pensacola, FL (USS YO-178 '45-'51, Lake Edward '51-'67)								

CAUSLEY MARINE CONTRACTING LLC, BAY CITY, MI

Fleet Name / Vessel Name	Vessel IMO #	Vessel Type	Year Built	Engine Type	Cargo Cap. or Gross*	Overall Length	Vessel Breadth	Vessel Depth
Jill Marie		TB	1891	D	24*	60' 00"	12' 06"	6' 00"
Built: Cleveland Shipbuilding Co., Cleveland, OH; oldest active commercial tug on the Great Lakes								
(Ciscoe 1891-1953, Capama-S '53-'97, Gail K '97-'07)								

CEMBA MOTOR SHIPS LTD., PELEE ISLAND, ON

Fleet Name / Vessel Name	Vessel IMO #	Vessel Type	Year Built	Engine Type	Cargo Cap. or Gross*	Overall Length	Vessel Breadth	Vessel Depth
Cemba		TK	1960	D	17*	50' 00"	15' 06"	7' 06"

CENTRAL MARINE LOGISTICS INC., GRIFFITH, IN *(centralmarinelogistics.com)*

Fleet Name / Vessel Name	Vessel IMO #	Vessel Type	Year Built	Engine Type	Cargo Cap. or Gross*	Overall Length	Vessel Breadth	Vessel Depth
Edward L. Ryerson	5097606	BC	1960	T	27,500	730' 00"	75' 00"	39' 00"
Built: Manitowoc Shipbuilding Co., Manitowoc, WI; in long-term lay-up at Superior, WI, since May 2009								
Joseph L. Block	7502320	SU	1976	D	37,200	728' 00"	78' 00"	45' 00"
Built: Bay Shipbuilding Co., Sturgeon Bay, WI								
Wilfred Sykes	5389554	SU	1949	T	21,500	678' 00"	70' 00"	37' 00"
Built: American Shipbuilding Co., Lorain, OH; converted to a self-unloader by Fraser Shipyards, Superior, WI, in '75								

CENTRAL MICHIGAN UNIVERSITY, COLLEGE OF SCIENCE & TECHNOLOGIES, MOUNT PLEASANT, MI

Fleet Name / Vessel Name	Vessel IMO #	Vessel Type	Year Built	Engine Type	Cargo Cap. or Gross*	Overall Length	Vessel Breadth	Vessel Depth
Chippewa		RV	2013	D	17*	34' 09"	12' 00"	6' 03"

CHAMPION'S AUTO FERRY, ALGONAC, MI *(hiferry.com)*

Fleet Name / Vessel Name	Vessel IMO #	Vessel Type	Year Built	Engine Type	Cargo Cap. or Gross*	Overall Length	Vessel Breadth	Vessel Depth
Champion		CF	1941	D	69*	65' 00"	25' 09"	5' 08"
Middle Channel		CF	1997	D	81*	79' 00"	30' 00"	6' 05"
North Channel		CF	1967	D	67*	75' 00"	30' 04"	6' 01"
South Channel		CF	1973	D	94*	79' 00"	30' 03"	6' 01"

CHARITY ISLAND TRANSPORT INC., AU GRES, MI *(charityisland.net)*

Fleet Name / Vessel Name	Vessel IMO #	Vessel Type	Year Built	Engine Type	Cargo Cap. or Gross*	Overall Length	Vessel Breadth	Vessel Depth
North Star		PA	1949	D	14*	50' 05"	14' 06"	3' 06"

CHICAGO DEPARTMENT OF WATER MANAGEMENT, CHICAGO, IL

Fleet Name / Vessel Name	Vessel IMO #	Vessel Type	Year Built	Engine Type	Cargo Cap. or Gross*	Overall Length	Vessel Breadth	Vessel Depth
James J. Versluis		TB	1957	D	126*	83' 00"	22' 00"	11' 02"
Built: Sturgeon Bay Shipbuilding Co., Sturgeon Bay, WI								

CHICAGO FIRE DEPARTMENT, CHICAGO, IL

Fleet Name / Vessel Name	Vessel IMO #	Vessel Type	Year Built	Engine Type	Cargo Cap. or Gross*	Overall Length	Vessel Breadth	Vessel Depth
Christopher Wheatley		FB	2011	D	300*	90' 00"	25' 00"	12' 02"
Built: Hike Metal Products Ltd., Wheatley, ON								
Victor L. Schlaeger		FB	1949	D	350*	92' 06"	24' 00"	11' 00"

CHICAGO'S FIRST LADY CRUISES, CHICAGO, IL *(cruisechicago.com)*

Fleet Name / Vessel Name	Vessel IMO #	Vessel Type	Year Built	Engine Type	Cargo Cap. or Gross*	Overall Length	Vessel Breadth	Vessel Depth
Chicago's Classic Lady		ES	2014	D	93*	98' 00"	32' 00"	6' 02"
Chicago's Fair Lady		ES	1979	D	82*	72' 04"	23' 01"	7' 01"
Chicago's First Lady		ES	1991	D	62*	96' 00"	22' 00"	9' 00"
Chicago's Leading Lady		ES	2011	D	92*	92' 07"	32' 00"	6' 09"
Chicago's Little Lady		ES	1999	D	70*	69' 02"	22' 08"	7' 00"

CHICAGO FROM THE LAKE LTD., CHICAGO, IL *(chicagoline.com)*

Fleet Name / Vessel Name	Vessel IMO #	Vessel Type	Year Built	Engine Type	Cargo Cap. or Gross*	Overall Length	Vessel Breadth	Vessel Depth
Ft. Dearborn		ES	1985	D	72*	64' 10"	22' 00"	7' 03"
Innisfree		ES	1980	D	35*	61' 09"	15' 06"	5' 07"
Marquette {6}		ES	1957	D	39*	50' 07"	15' 00"	5' 05"

CITY OF TORONTO, TORONTO, ON *(toronto.ca/parks)*

Fleet Name / Vessel Name	Vessel IMO #	Vessel Type	Year Built	Engine Type	Cargo Cap. or Gross*	Overall Length	Vessel Breadth	Vessel Depth
Ned Hanlan II		TB	1966	D	22*	41' 06"	14' 01"	5' 05"
Built: Erieau Shipbuilding & Drydock Co. Ltd., Erieau, ON								
Ongiara	6410374	PA/CF	1963	D	180*	78' 00"	12' 04"	9' 09"
Built: Russel Brothers Ltd., Owen Sound, ON								

Fleet Name Vessel Name	Vessel IMO #	Vessel Type	Year Built	Engine Type	Cargo Cap. or Gross*	Overall Length	Vessel Breadth	Vessel Depth
Sam McBride		PF	1939	D	387*	129'00"	34'11"	6'00"
Built: Toronto Dry Dock Co. Ltd., Toronto, ON								
Thomas Rennie		PF	1951	D	387*	129'00"	32'11"	6'00"
Built: Toronto Dry Dock Co. Ltd., Toronto, ON								
Trillium		PF	1910	R	564*	150'00"	30'00"	8'04"
Built: Poulson Iron Works, Toronto, ON; last sidewheel-propelled vessel on the Great Lakes								
William Inglis		PF	1935	D	238*	99'00"	24'10"	6'00"
Built: John Inglis Co. Ltd., Toronto, ON (Shamrock {2} '35-'37)								

CJC CRUISES INC., GRAND LEDGE, MI (detroitprincess.com)

Detroit Princess		PA	1993	D	1,430*	222'00"	62'00"	11'01"
Built: Leevac Shipyards Inc., Jennings, LA (Players Riverboat Casino II '93-'04)								

CLEARWATER MARINE LLC, HOLLAND, MI (clearwatermarinellc.com)

G.W. Falcon		TB	1936	D	22*	49'07"	13'08"	6'02"
Built: Fred E. Alford, Waukegan, IL (Lillie B. '36-'57)								

CLEVELAND FIRE DEPARTMENT, CLEVELAND, OH

Anthony J. Celebrezze		FB	1961	D	42*	66'00"	17'00"	5'00"
Built: Paasch Marine Services Inc., Erie, PA								

CLINTON RIVER CRUISE CO., MOUNT CLEMENS, MI (clintonrivercruisecompany.com)

Captain Paul II		PA	1960	D	14*	44'07"	11'00"	4'00"
Clinton		PA	1949	D	10*	63'07"	15'03"	4'08"
Clinton Friendship		PA	1984	D	43*	64'08"	22'00"	4'05"

COLLINGWOOD CHARTERS, COLLINGWOOD, ON (collingwoodcharters.ca)

Huronic		PA	1999	D	60	56'03"	19'00"	6'04"

CONSTRUCTION POLARIS INC., L'ANCIENNE-LORETTE, QC (constructionpolaris.com)

Point Viking	5118840	TB	1962	D	207*	98'05"	27'10"	13'05"
Built: Davie Shipbuilding Co., Lauzon, QC (Foundation Viking '62-'75)								

COOPER MARINE LTD., SELKIRK, ON

Ella G. Cooper		PB	1972	D	21*	43'00"	14'00"	6'05"
Janice C. No. 1		TB	1980	D	33*	57'00"	20'00"	6'00"
J.W. Cooper		PB	1984	D	25*	48'00"	14'07"	5'00"
Kimberley A. Cooper		TB	1974	D	17*	40'00"	13'05"	4'05"
Mrs. C.		PB	1991	D	26*	50'00"	14'05"	4'05"
Stacey Dawn		TB	1993	D	14*	35'09"	17'04"	3'05"
Wilson T. Cooper		DB	2009	D	58*	56'08"	23'06"	5'08"

CORPORATION OF THE TOWNSHIP OF FRONTENAC ISLANDS, WOLFE ISLAND, ON (frontenacislands.ca)

Howe Islander		CF	1946	D	13*	53'00"	12'00"	3'00"
Built: Canadian Dredge & Dock Co. Ltd., Kingston, ON								
Simcoe Islander		PF	1964	D	24*	47'09"	18'00"	3'06"
Built: Canadian Dredge & Dock Co. Ltd., Kingston, ON								

COBBY MARINE (1985) INC., KINGSVILLE, ON

Vida C.		TB	1960	D	17*	46'03"	15'05"	3'02"

CROISIÈRES AML INC., QUÉBEC CITY, QC (croisieresaml.com)

AML Alize		ES	1980	D	39*	41'00"	15'01"	6'01"
Built: Julien Tremblay, Arvida, QC								
AML Cavalier Maxim	5265904	ES	1962	D	752*	191'02"	42'00"	11'07"
Built: John I. Thornycroft & Co., Wollston, Southampton, England (Osborne Castle '62-'78, Le Gobelet D' Argent '78-'88, Gobelet D' Argent '88-'89, Le Maxim '89-'93)								
AML Grand Fleuve		ES	1987	D	499*	145'00"	30'00"	5'06"
Built: Kanter Yacht Co., St. Thomas, ON								
AML Levant	9056404	ES	1991	D	380*	112'07"	29'0"	10'02"
Built: Goelette Marie Clarisse Inc., LaBaleine, QC (Famille Dufour)								
AML Louis Jolliet	5212749	ES	1938	R	2,436*	170'01"	70'00"	17'00"
Built: Davie Shipbuilding Co., Lauzon, QC								
AML Suroît		ES	2002	D	171*	82'00"	27'00"	6'00"
Built: RTM Construction, Petite Rivière-St-François, QC (Le Coudrier de l'Isle '02-'14)								
AML Zephyr		ES	1992	D	171*	82'00"	27'00"	6'00"
Built: Katamarine International, Paspebiac, QC (Le Coudrier de l'Anse '92-'14)								

CROISIÈRES M/S JACQUES-CARTIER INC., TROIS-RIVIERES, QC (msjacquescartier.com)

Jacques Cartier		ES	1924	D	589*	132'05"	35'00"	9'08"
Built: Davie Shipbuilding Co., Lauzon, QC (rebuilt ' 75, '18)								

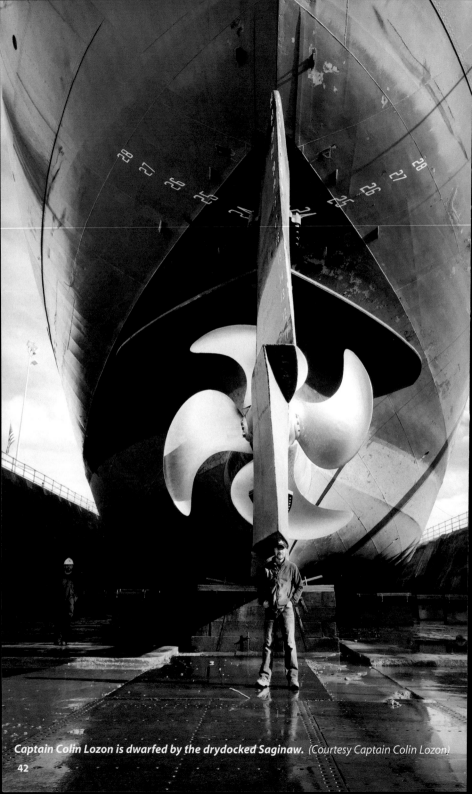

Captain Colin Lozon is dwarfed by the drydocked Saginaw. (Courtesy Captain Colin Lozon)

CRUISE TORONTO INC., TORONTO ON *(cruisetoronto.com)*

Fleet Name / Vessel Name	Vessel IMO #	Vessel Type	Year Built	Engine Type	Cargo Cap. or Gross*	Overall Length	Vessel Breadth	Vessel Depth
Obsession III		ES	1967	D	160*	66' 00"	25' 00"	6' 01"

Built: Halter Marine, New Orleans, LA (Mystique)

CTMA GROUP (NAVIGATION MADELEINE INC.), CAP-AUX-MEULES, QC *(ctma.ca)*

C.T.M.A. Vacancier	7310260	PA/RR	1973	D	11,481*	388' 04"	70' 02"	43' 06"

Built: J.J. Sietas KG Schiffswerft, Hamburg, Germany (Aurella '80-'82, Saint Patrick II '82-'98, Egnatia II '98-'00, Ville de Sete '00-'01, City of Cork '01-'02)

C.T.M.A. Voyageur	7222229	PA/RR	1972	D	4,526*	327' 09"	52' 06"	31' 07"

Built: Trosvik Versted A/S, Brevik, Norway (Anderida '72-'81, Truck Trader '81-'84, Sealink '84-'86, Mirela '86-'86)

Madeleine	7915228	PA	1981	D	10,024*	381' 04"	60' 06"	41' 00"

Built: Verolme Cork Dockyard Ltd., Cobh, Ireland (Isle of Inishturk)

D

DAN MINOR & SONS INC., PORT COLBORNE, ON

Andrea Marie I		TB	1986	D	87*	75' 02"	24' 07"	7' 03"

Built: Ralph Hurley, Port Burwell, ON

Jeanette M.		TB	1981	D	31*	70' 00"	20 01"	6' 00"

Built: Hike Metal Products, Wheatley, ON

Susan Michelle		TB	1995	D	89*	79' 10"	20' 11"	6' 02"

Built: Vic Powell Welding Ltd., Dunnville, ON

Welland		TB	1954	D	94*	86' 00"	20' 00"	8' 00"

Built: Russel-Hipwell Engines, Owen Sound, ON

DANN MARINE TOWING, CHESAPEAKE CITY, MD *(dannmarine.com)*

Calusa Coast	7942295	TB	1978	D	186*	110' 00"	30' 01"	11' 00"

Built: Bollinger Shipyards, Lockport, LA (Marc G., Katrina G.); paired with barge Delaware

Delaware	1588255	TK	2006	B	98*	292' 00"	60' 00"	24' 00"

Vessel owned by Kirby Offshore Marine Operating LLC, Houston, TX

Zeus	9506071	TB	1964	D	98*	104' 02"	29' 03"	13' 05"

Built: Houma Shipbuilding Co., Houma, LA; paired with barge Robert F. Deegan

DEAN CONSTRUCTION CO. LTD., WINDSOR, ON *(deanconstructioncompany.com)*

Americo Dean		TB	1956	D	15*	45' 00"	15' 00"	5' 00"

Built: Erieau Shipyard, Erieau, ON

Annie M. Dean		TB	1981	D	58*	50' 00"	19' 00"	5' 00"

Built: Dean Construction Co., LaSalle, ON

Bobby Bowes		TB	1944	D	11*	37' 04"	10' 02"	3' 06"

Built: Russel Brothers Ltd., Owen Sound, ON

Canadian Jubilee		DR	1978	B	896*	149' 09"	56' 01"	11' 01"
Neptune III		TB	1939	D	23*	53' 10"	15' 06"	5' 00"

Built: Herb Colley, Port Stanley, ON

DEAN MARINE & EXCAVATING INC., MOUNT CLEMENS, MI *(deanmarineandexcavating.com)*

Andrew J.		TB	1950	D	25*	47' 00"	15' 07"	8' 00"

Built: J.F. Bellinger & Sons, Jacksonville, FL

CSL Laurentien at Duluth, Minn. *(David Schauer)*

Fleet Name / Vessel Name	Vessel IMO #	Vessel Type	Year Built	Engine Type	Cargo Cap. or Gross*	Overall Length	Vessel Breadth	Vessel Depth
Kimberly Anne		TB	1965	D	65*	55' 02"	18' 08"	8' 00"
Built: Main Iron Works, Houma, LA (Lady Lisa, Lucy, Miss Alma)								
Madison R.	5126615	TB	1958	D	194*	103' 00"	26' 06"	12' 00"

DETROIT CITY FIRE DEPARTMENT, DETROIT, MI

Curtis Randolph		FB	1979	D	85*	77' 10"	21' 06"	9' 03"
Built: Peterson Builders Inc., Sturgeon Bay, WI								

DEWEY MARINE LEASING LLC, ROCHESTER, NY (deweymarineleasing.com)

Ronald J. Dahlke		TB	1903	D	58*	63' 04"	17' 06"	9' 00"
Built: Johnston Bros., Ferrysburg, MI (Bonita '03-'14, Chicago Harbor No. 4 '14-'60, Eddie B. '60-'69, Seneca Queen '69-'70, Ludington '70-'96, Seneca Queen '96-'04)								

DIAMOND JACK'S RIVER TOURS, DETROIT, MI (diamondjack.com)

Diamond Belle		ES	1958	D	93*	93' 06"	25' 00"	7' 00"
Built: Hans Hansen Welding Co., Toledo, OH (Mackinac Islander {2} '58-'90, Sir Richard '90-'91)								
Diamond Jack		ES	1955	D	82*	72' 00"	25' 00"	7' 03"
Built: Christy Corp., Sturgeon Bay, WI (Emerald Isle {1} '55-'91)								
Diamond Queen		ES	1956	D	94*	92' 00"	25' 00"	7' 02"
Built: Marinette Marine Corp., Marinette, WI (Mohawk '56-'96)								

DISCOVERY WORLD AT PIER WISCONSIN, MILWAUKEE, WI (discoveryworld.org)

Denis Sullivan	1100209	TV/ES	2000	W/D	99*	138' 00"	22' 08"	10' 06"

DONJON MARINE CO. INC., HILLSIDE, NJ (donjon.com)

Elizabeth Anna		TB	1958	D	37*	53' 08"	17' 00"	5' 07"
Built: Diesel Shipbuilding Co., Jacksonville, FL; stationed at Erie, PA (Catherine M. Brown '58-'11, Bear '11-'14)								
Rebecca Ann		TB	1994	D	52*	60' 00	18' 07"	7' 00"
Built: Empire Harbor Marine Inc., Thomson, NY (Herbert P. Brake '94-'14)								

DONKERSLOOT MARINE DEVELOPMENT CORP., NEW BUFFALO, MI (donkerslootmarine.com)

Miss Jamie Lynn		DR	1989	D	254*	120' 00"	34' 00"	5' 06"

DUC D' ORLEANS CRUISE BOAT, CORUNNA, ON (ducdorleans.com)

Duc d' Orleans II		ES	1987	D	120*	71' 03"	23' 02"	7' 07"
Built: Blount Marine Corp., Warren, RI (Spirit of Newport '87-'06)								

DUNDEE ENERGY LTD., TORONTO, ON (dundee-energy.com)
Vessels are engaged in oil and gas exploration on Lake Erie

Dr. Bob	8771992	DV	1973	B	1,022*	160' 01"	54' 01"	11' 01"
Built: Cenac Shipyard Co. Inc., Houma, LA (Mr. Chris '73-'03)								
J.R. Rouble	8767020	DV	1958	D	562*	123' 06"	49' 08"	16' 00"
Built: American Marine Machinery Co., Nashville, TN (Mr. Neil)								

Gulls escort the Great Lakes Towing tug Nebraska. (Paul C. LaMarre III)

Fleet Name Vessel Name	Vessel IMO #	Vessel Type	Year Built	Engine Type	Cargo Cap. or Gross*	Overall Length	Vessel Breadth	Vessel Depth
Miss Libby		DV	1972	B	924*	160' 01"	54' 01"	11' 01"
Built: Service Machine & Shipbuilding Corp., Morgan City, LA								
Sarah No. 1		TB	1969	D	43*	72' 01"	17' 03"	6' 08"
Built: Halter Marine, New Orleans, LA (Auries)								

DUROCHER MARINE, DIV. OF KOKOSING CONSTRUCTION CO., CHEBOYGAN, MI *(kokosing.biz)*

Champion {3}		TB	1974	D	125*	75' 00"	23' 05"	9' 05"
Built: Service Machine & Shipbuilding Co., Amelia, LA								
General {2}		TB	1954	D	119*	71' 00"	19' 06"	10' 00"
Built: Missouri Valley Bridge & Iron Works, Leavenworth, KS (U. S. Army ST-1999 '54-'61, USCOE Au Sable '61-'84,								
Challenger {3} '84-'87)								
Nancy Anne		TB	1969	D	73*	60' 00"	20' 00"	8' 00"
Built: Houma Shipbuilding Co., Houma, LA								
Ray Durocher		TB	1943	D	20*	45' 06"	12' 05"	7' 06"
Valerie B.		TB	1981	D	101*	65' 00"	25' 06"	10' 00"
Built: Rayco Shipbuilders & Repairers, Bourg, LA (Mr. Joshua, Michael Van)								

E

EASTERN UPPER PENINSULA TRANSPORTATION AUTHORITY, SAULT STE. MARIE, MI *(eupta.net)*

Drummond Islander III		CF	1989	D	96*	108' 00"	37' 00"	7' 02"
Built: Moss Point Marine Inc., Escatawpa, MS								
Drummond Islander IV		CF	2000	D	97*	148' 00"	40' 00"	12' 00"
Built: Basic Marine Inc., Escanaba, MI								
Neebish Islander II		CF	1946	D	90*	89' 00"	25' 09"	5' 08"
Built: Lock City Machine/Marine, Sault Ste. Marie, MI (Sugar Islander '46-'95)								
Sugar Islander II		CF	1995	D	90*	114' 00"	40' 00"	10' 00"
Built: Basic Marine Inc., Escanaba, MI								

ECOMARIS, MONTREAL, QC *(ecomaris.org)*

Roter Sand		TV/2S	1999	W/D	28*	65' 02"	17' 07"	8' 03"

EMPRESS OF CANADA ENTERPRISES LTD., TORONTO, ON *(empressofcanada.com)*

Empress of Canada		ES	1980	D	399*	116' 00"	28' 00"	6' 06"
Built: Hike Metal Products, Wheatley, ON (Island Queen V {2} '80-'89)								

ERIE ISLANDS PETROLEUM INC., PUT-IN-BAY, OH *(putinbayfuels.com)*

Cantankerus		TK	1955	D	43*	56' 00"	14' 00"	6' 06"
Built: Marinette Marine Corp., Marinette, WI								

***Erie Trader* arrives at Duluth Superior under a setting sun.** *(Jack Hurt)*

Fleet Name Vessel Name	Vessel IMO #	Vessel Type	Year Built	Engine Type	Cargo Cap. or Gross*	Overall Length	Vessel Breadth	Vessel Depth
ESSROC CANADA INC., PICTON, ON								
Metis	5233585	CC	1956	B	5,800	331' 00"	43' 09"	26' 00"

Built: Davie Shipbuilding Co., Lauzon, QC; lengthened 72', deepened 3'6" in '59 and converted to a self-unloading cement barge in '91 by Kingston Shipbuilding & Dry Dock Co., Kingston, ON

F-G

Fleet Name Vessel Name	Vessel IMO #	Vessel Type	Year Built	Engine Type	Cargo Cap. or Gross*	Overall Length	Vessel Breadth	Vessel Depth
FITZ SUSTAINABLE FORESTRY MANAGEMENT LTD., MANITOWANING, ON								
Wyn Cooper		TB	1973	D	25*	48' 00"	13' 00"	4' 00"

Built: Place Gas & Oil Co. Ltd., Toronto, ON

FRASER SHIPYARDS INC., SUPERIOR, WI *(frasershipyards.com)*								
FSY II		TB	2013	D	32*	45' 00"	13' 00"	6' 05"

Built: Fraser Shipyards Inc., Superior, WI

FSY III		TB	1959	D	30*	47' 04"	13' 00"	6' 06"

Built: Fraser-Nelson Shipyard & Drydock Co., Superior, WI (Susan A. Fraser '59-'78, Maxine Thompson '78-'14)

FSY IV		TB	1956	D	24*	43' 00"	12' 00"	5' 06"

Built: Fraser-Nelson Shipyard & Drydock Co., Superior, WI (Wally Kendzora '56-'14)

GAELIC TUGBOAT CO., DETROIT, MI *(gaelictugboat.com)*								
Patricia Hoey {2}	5285851	TB	1949	D	146*	88' 06"	25' 06"	11' 00"

Built: Alexander Shipyard Inc., New Orleans, LA (Propeller '49-'82, Bantry Bay '82-'91)

Shannon	8971669	TB	1944	D	145*	101' 00"	25' 08"	13' 00"

Built: Consolidated Shipbuilding Corp., Morris Heights, NY (USS Connewango [YT/YTB/YTM-388] '44-'77)

William Hoey	5029946	TB	1951	D	149*	88' 06"	25' 06"	11' 00"

Built: Alexander Shipyard Inc., New Orleans, LA (Atlas '51-'84, Susan Hoey {1} '84-'85, Atlas '85-'87, Carolyn Hoey '87-'13)

GALCON MARINE LTD., TORONTO, ON *(galconmarine.com)*								
Barney Drake (The)		TB	1954	D	10*	31' 02"	9' 05"	3' 04"

Built: Toronto Drydock Co. Ltd., Toronto ON (T.T.&S. No. 9)

Kenteau		TB	1937	D	15*	54' 07"	16' 04"	4' 02"

Built: George Gamble, Port Dover, ON

Patricia D		TB	1958	D	12*	38' 08"	12' 00"	3' 08"

Built: Toronto Drydock Co. Ltd., Toronto, ON (Big Chief III)

William Rest		TB	1961	D	62*	65' 00"	18' 06"	10' 06"

Built: Erieau Shipbuilding & Drydock Co. Ltd., Erieau, ON

GANANOQUE BOAT LINE LTD., GANANOQUE, ON *(ganboatline.com)*								
Thousand Islander	7227346	ES	1972	D	200*	96' 11"	22' 01"	5' 05"
Thousand Islander II	7329936	ES	1973	D	200*	99' 00"	22' 01"	5' 00"
Thousand Islander III	8744963	ES	1975	D	376*	118' 00"	28' 00"	6' 00"
Thousand Islander IV	7947984	ES	1976	D	347*	110' 09"	28' 04"	10' 08"
Thousand Islander V	8745187	ES	1979	D	246*	88' 00"	24' 00"	5' 00"
GANNON UNIVERSITY, ERIE, PA *(gannon.edu)*								
Environaut		RV	1950	D	18*	48' 00"	13' 00"	4' 05"
GENESIS ENERGY, HOUSTON, TX *(genesisenergy.com)*								
Genesis Victory	8973942	TB	1981	D	398*	105' 00"	34' 00"	17' 00"

Built: Halter Marine, New Orleans, LA (Eric Candies '81-'05, Huron Service '05-'15)

GM 6506		TB	2007	B	5,778*	345' 06"	60' 00"	29' 00"

Built: Bollinger Marine Fabricators, Amelia, LA; paired with the tug Genesis Victory

GEO. GRADEL CO., TOLEDO, OH *(geogradelco.com)*								
George Gradel		TB	1956	D	128*	84' 00"	26' 00"	9' 02"

Built: Parker Brothers & Co. Inc., Houston, TX (Harbor Queen '56-'76, St. John '76-'16)

John Francis		TB	1965	D	99*	75' 00"	22' 00"	9' 00"

Built: Bollinger Shipbuilding Inc., Lockport, LA (Dad '65-'98, Creole Eagle '98-'03)

Josephine		TB	1957	D		86' 09"	20' 00"	7' 06"

Built: Willemsoord Naval Yard, Den Helder, Netherlands; recreational tug

Mighty Jake		TB	1969	D	15*	36' 00"	12' 03"	7' 03"

Built: Lone Star Marine Salvage, Houston, TX

Mighty Jessie		TB	1954	D	57*	61' 02"	18' 00"	7' 03"

Built: John J. Mathis Co., Camden, NJ

Mighty John III		TB	1962	D	24*	45' 00"	15' 00"	5' 10"

Built:Toronto Drydock Co., Toronto, ON (Niagara Queen '62-'99)

Norman G		DB	2016	B	578*	141' 01"	54' 00"	10' 00"
Pioneerland		TB	1943	D	53*	58' 00"	16' 08"	8' 00"

Built: Maritime Oil Transport Co., Houston, TX

Fleet Name / Vessel Name	Vessel IMO #	Vessel Type	Year Built	Engine Type	Cargo Cap. or Gross*	Overall Length	Vessel Breadth	Vessel Depth
Prairieland		TB	1955	D	35*	49' 02"	15' 02"	6' 00"
Built: Main Iron Works, Houma, LA								
Timberland		TB	1946	D	20*	41' 03"	13' 01"	7' 00"
Built:George S. VerDuin, Grand Haven, MI								

GILLEN MARINE CONSTRUCTION LLC, MEQUON, WI *(gillenmarine.com)*

Kristin J.		TB	1963	D	60*	52' 06"	19' 01"	7' 04"
Built: St. Charles Steel Works, Thibodaux, LA (Jason A. Kadinger '63-'06)								

GOODTIME CRUISE LINE INC., CLEVELAND, OH *(goodtimeiii.com)*

Goodtime III		ES	1990	D	95*	161' 00"	40' 00"	11' 00"

GRAND PORTAGE / ISLE ROYALE TRANSPORTATION LINES, GRAND PORTAGE, MN *(isleroyaleboats.com)*

Sea Hunter III		ES	1985	D	47*	65' 00"	16' 00"	7' 05"
Voyageur II		ES	1970	D	40*	63' 00"	18' 00"	5' 00"

GRAND RIVER NAVIGATION CO. – SEE LOWER LAKES TRANSPORTATION CO.

GRAND VALLEY STATE UNIVERSITY, ROBERT B. ANNIS WATER RESOURCES, MUSKEGON, MI *(gvsu.edu/wri)*

D. J. Angus		RV	1986	D	16*	45' 00"	14' 00"	4' 00"
W. G. Jackson		RV	1996	D	80*	64' 10"	20' 00"	5' 00"

GRAVEL & LAKE SERVICES LTD., THUNDER BAY, ON

Peninsula		TB	1994	D	261*	111' 00"	27' 00"	13' 00"
Built: Montreal Drydock Ltd., Montreal, QC; may become a museum (HMCS Norton [W-31] '44-'45, W.A.C. 1 '45-'46)								

GRAYFOX ASSOCIATION, PORT HURON, MI *(nscsgrayfox.org)*

Grayfox [TWR-825]		TV	1985	D	213*	120' 00"	25' 00"	12' 00"
Built: Marinette Marine Corp., Marinette, WI; based at Port Huron, MI (USS TWR-825 '85-'97)								

GREAT LAKES DOCK & MATERIALS LLC, MUSKEGON, MI *(greatlakesdock.com)*

Defiance		TW	1965	D	39*	48' 00"	18' 00"	6' 03"
Built: Harrison Bros. Drydock, Mobile, AL								
Duluth		TB	1954	D	87*	70' 01"	19' 05"	9' 08"
Built: Missouri Valley Bridge & Iron Works, Leavenworth, KS (U. S. Army ST-2015 '54-'62)								
Ethan George		TB	1940	D	27*	42' 05"	12' 08"	6' 06"
Built: Sturgeon Bay Shipbuilding, Sturgeon Bay, WI (Holland, Captain Roy)								
Fischer Hayden		TB	1967	D	64*	54' 00"	22' 01"	7' 01"
Built: Main Iron Works Inc., Houma, LA (Gloria G. Cheramie, Joyce P. Crosby)								
Meredith Ashton	8951487	TB	1981	D	127*	68' 08"	26' 01"	9' 04"
Built: Service Marine Group Inc., Amelia, LA (The Rock, Specialist, Alpha)								
Sarah B.		TB	1953	D	23*	45' 00"	13' 00"	7' 00"
Built: Nashville Bridge Co., Nashville, TN (ST-2161 '53-'63, Tawas Bay '63-'03)								

GREAT LAKES FLEET INC., DULUTH, MN (KEY LAKES INC., MANAGER)

Arthur M. Anderson	5025691	SU	1952	T	25,300	767' 00"	70' 00"	36' 00"
Built: American Shipbuilding Co., Lorain, OH; lengthened 120' in '75 and converted to a self-unloader in '82 at Fraser Shipyards, Superior, WI; entered possible long-term lay-up at Duluth, MN, on 1-15-'17								
Cason J. Callaway	5065392	SU	1952	T	25,300	767' 00"	70' 00"	36' 00"
Built: Great Lakes Engineering Works, River Rouge, MI; lengthened 120' in '74 and converted to a self-unloader in '82 at Fraser Shipyards, Superior, WI								
Edgar B. Speer	7625952	SU	1980	D	73,700	1,004' 00"	105' 00"	56' 00"
Built: American Shipbuilding Co., Lorain, OH								
Edwin H. Gott	7606061	SU	1979	D	74,100	1,004' 00"	105' 00"	56' 00"
Built: Bay Shipbuilding Co., Sturgeon Bay, WI; converted from shuttle self-unloader to deck-mounted self-unloader at Bay Shipbuilding, Sturgeon Bay, WI, in '96								
Great Republic	7914236	SU	1981	D	25,600	634' 10"	68' 00"	39' 07"
Built: Bay Shipbuilding Co., Sturgeon Bay, WI (American Republic '81-'11)								
John G. Munson {2}	5173670	SU	1952	D	25,550	768' 03"	72' 00"	36' 00"
Built: Manitowoc Shipbuilding Co., Manitowoc, WI; lengthened 102' at Fraser Shipyards, Superior, WI, in '76; repowered in '16								
Philip R. Clarke	5277062	SU	1952	T	25,300	767' 00"	70' 00"	36' 00"
Built: American Shipbuilding Co., Lorain, OH; lengthened 120' in '74 and converted to a self-unloader in '82 at Fraser Shipyards, Superior, WI								
Presque Isle {2}	7303877	IT	1973	D	1,578*	153' 03"	54' 00"	31' 03"
Built: Halter Marine, New Orleans, LA; paired with the self-unloading barge Presque Isle								
Presque Isle {2}		SU	1973	B	57,500	974' 06"	104' 07"	46' 06"
Built: Erie Marine Inc., Erie, PA								
[ITB Presque Isle OA dimensions together]					1,000' 00"	104' 07"	46' 06"	
Roger Blough	7222138	SU	1972	D	43,900	858' 00"	105' 00"	41' 06"
Built: American Shipbuilding Co., Lorain, OH								

GREAT LAKES GROUP, CLEVELAND, OH *(thegreatlakesgroup.com)*

THE GREAT LAKES TOWING CO., CLEVELAND, OH – DIVISION OF THE GREAT LAKES GROUP

Fleet Name / Vessel Name	Vessel IMO #	Vessel Type	Year Built	Engine Type	Cargo Cap. or Gross*	Overall Length	Vessel Breadth	Vessel Depth
Arizona		TB	1931	D	98*	74' 08"	19' 09"	11' 06"
Arkansas {2}		TB	1909	D	97*	74' 08"	19' 09"	11' 06"
(Yale '09-'48)								
California		TB	1926	DE	97*	74' 08"	19' 09"	11' 06"
Cleveland		TB	2017	D	N/A*	65' 08"	24' 00"	11' 00"
Built: Great Lakes Shipyard, Cleveland, OH								
Colorado		TB	1928	D	98*	78' 08"	20' 00"	12' 04"
Erie		TB	1971	D	243*	102' 03"	29' 00"	16' 03"
(YTB 810 {Anoka} '71-'15)								
Favorite		FD	1983			90' 00"	50' 00"	5' 00"
Florida		TB	1926	D	99*	71' 00"	20' 02"	11' 02"
(Florida '26-'83, Pinellas '83-'84)								
Huron	8980907	TB	1974	D	243*	102' 03"	29' 00"	16' 03"
(YTB 833 {Shabonee} '74-'02, Daniel McAllister '02-'15)								
Idaho		TB	1931	DE	98*	78' 08"	20' 00"	12' 04"
Illinois {2}		TB	1914	D	98*	71' 00"	20' 00"	12' 05"
Indiana		TB	1911	DE	97*	74' 08"	19' 09"	11' 06"
Iowa		TB	1915	D	97*	74' 08"	19' 09"	11' 06"
Kansas		TB	1927	D	97*	74' 08"	19' 09"	11' 06"
Kentucky {2}		TB	1929	D	98*	78' 08"	20' 00"	12' 04"
Louisiana		TB	1917	D	97*	74' 08"	19' 09"	11' 06"
Maine {1}		TB	1921	D	96*	71' 00"	20' 01"	11' 02"
(Maine {1} '21-'82, Saipan '82-'83, Hillsboro '83-'84)								
Massachusetts		TB	1928	D	98*	78' 08"	20' 00"	12' 04"
Minnesota		TB	1911	D	98*	78' 08"	20' 00"	12' 04"
Mississippi		TB	1916	DE	97*	74' 08"	19' 09"	11' 06"
Missouri {2}		TB	1927	D	149*	88' 04"	24' 06"	12' 03"
(Rogers City {1} '27-'56, Dolomite {1} '56-'81, Chippewa {7} '81-'90)								
Nebraska		TB	1929	D	98*	78' 08"	20' 00"	12' 05"
New Jersey		TB	1924	D	98*	78' 08"	20' 00"	12' 04"
(New Jersey '24-'52, Petco-21 '52-'53)								
New York		TB	1913	D	98*	78' 08"	20' 00"	12' 04"
North Carolina {2}		TB	1952	DE	145*	87' 09"	24' 01"	10' 07"
(Limestone '52-'83, Wicklow '83-'90)								
North Dakota		TB	1910	D	97*	74' 08"	19' 09"	11' 06"
(John M. Truby '10-'38)								
Oklahoma		TB	1913	DE	97*	74' 08"	19' 09"	11' 06"
(T. C. Lutz {2} '13-'34)								
Ontario		TB	1964	D	243*	102' 03"	29' 00"	16' 03"
(YTB 770 {Dahlonega} '64-'01, Jeffrey K. McAllister '01-'15)								
Pennsylvania {3}		TB	1911	D	98*	78' 08"	20' 00"	12' 04"
Rhode Island		TB	1930	D	98*	78' 08"	20' 00"	12' 04"
South Carolina		TB	1925	D	102*	79' 06"	21' 01"	11' 03"
(Welcome {2} '25-'53, Joseph H. Callan '53-'72, South Carolina '72-'82, Tulagi '82-'83)								
Superior {3}		TB	1912	D	147*	82' 00"	22' 00"	10' 07"
(Richard Fitzgerald '12-'46)								
Texas		TB	1916	DE	97*	74' 08"	19' 09"	11' 06"
Vermont		TB	1914	D	98*	71' 00"	20' 00"	12' 05"
Virginia {2}		TB	1914	DE	97*	74' 08"	19' 09"	11' 06"
Washington		TB	1925	DE	97*	74' 08"	19' 09"	11' 06"
Wisconsin {4}		TB	1897	D	105*	83' 00"	21' 02"	9' 06"
(America {3}, Midway)								
Wyoming		TB	1929	D	104*	78' 08"	20' 00"	12' 04"

GREAT LAKES MARITIME ACADEMY, TRAVERSE CITY, MI *(nmc.edu/maritime)*

Fleet Name / Vessel Name	Vessel IMO #	Vessel Type	Year Built	Engine Type	Cargo Cap. or Gross*	Overall Length	Vessel Breadth	Vessel Depth
Anchor Bay		TV	1953	D	23*	45' 00"	13' 00"	7' 00"
Built: Roamer Boat Co., Holland, MI (ST-2158 '53-'62)								
State of Michigan	8835451	TV	1985	D	1,914*	224' 00"	43' 00"	20' 00"
Built: Tacoma Boatbuilding Co., Tacoma, WA (USNS Persistent '85-'98, USCG Persistent '98-'02)								

GREAT LAKES OFFSHORE SERVICES INC., PORT DOVER, ON

Fleet Name / Vessel Name	Vessel IMO #	Vessel Type	Year Built	Engine Type	Cargo Cap. or Gross*	Overall Length	Vessel Breadth	Vessel Depth
H. H. Misner		TB	1946	D	28*	66' 09"	16' 04"	4' 05"
Built: George Gamble, Port Dover, ON								

GREAT LAKES SCHOONER CO., TORONTO, ON *(greatlakesschooner.com)*

Fleet Name / Vessel Name	Vessel IMO #	Vessel Type	Year Built	Engine Type	Cargo Cap. or Gross*	Overall Length	Vessel Breadth	Vessel Depth
Challenge		ES	1980	W/D	76*	96' 00"	16' 06"	8' 00"
Built: Kanter Yachts Co, Port Stanley, ON								

Gaelic tugs Patricia Hoey and William Hoey in the Rouge River at Detroit, with Philip R. Clarke backing into the dock in the background. (Christopher Dark)

James R. Barker is helped through early winter ice on the St. Marys River by USCG Mackinaw, January 2018. (Joseph Komjathy)

Fleet Name Vessel Name	Vessel IMO #	Vessel Type	Year Built	Engine Type	Cargo Cap. or Gross*	Overall Length	Vessel Breadth	Vessel Depth
Kajama		ES	1930	W/D	263*	128' 09"	22' 09"	11' 08"
Built: Nobiskrug, Rendsburg, Germany								

GREAT LAKES SCIENCE CENTER – U.S. GEOLOGICAL SURVEY, ANN ARBOR, MI *(glsc.usgs.gov)*

Arcticus		RV	2014	D	148*	77' 03"	26' 11"	11' 00"
Kaho		RV	2011	D	55*	70' 02"	18' 00"	5' 00"
Kiyi		RV	1999	D	290*	107' 00"	27' 00"	12' 02"
Muskie		RV	2011	D	55*	70' 02"	18' 00"	7' 09"
Sturgeon		RV	1977	D	325*	100'00"	25' 05"	10' 00"

GREAT LAKES SHIPWRECK HISTORICAL SOCIETY, SAULT STE. MARIE, MI *(shipwreckmuseum.com)*

David Boyd		RV	1982	D	26*	47' 00"	17' 00"	3' 00"*

GREAT LAKES WATER STUDIES INSTITUTE, TRAVERSE CITY, MI *(nmc.edu/resources/water-studies)*

Northwestern {2}		RV	1969	D	12*	55' 00"	15' 00"	6' 06"
Built: Paasch Marine Services Inc., Erie, PA (USCOE North Central '69-'98)								

GROUPE DESGAGNÉS INC., QUÉBEC CITY, QC *(groupedesgagnes.com)*
OPERATED BY SUBSIDIARY TRANSPORT DESGAGNÉS

Acadia Desgagnés	9651541	GC	2013	D	7,875	393' 04"	59' 07"	34' 05"
Built: Shandong Baibuting Shipbuilding Co. Ltd., Shandong, China (BBT Ocean '12-'13, Sider Tis '13-'17)								
Argentia Desgagnés	9409895	GC	2007	D	6,369	390' 08"	60' 03"	32' 08"
Built: Ustaoglu Shipyard, Zonguldak, Turkey (Ofmar '07-'17)								
Claude A. Desgagnés	9488059	GC	2011	D	12,671	454' 05"	69' 11"	36' 01"
Built: Sanfu Ship Engineering, Taizhou Jiangsu, China (Elsborg '11-'12)								
Nordika Desgagnés	9508316	GC	2010	D	12,974	469' 05"	74' 08"	43' 06"
Built: Xingang Shipbuilding Heavy Industry, Tianjin, China (BBC Oder '10-'17)								
Rosaire A. Desgagnés	9363534	GC	2007	D	12,575	453' 00"	68' 11"	36' 01"
Built: Quingshan/Jiangdong/Jiangzhou Shipyards, Jiangzhou, China (Beluga Fortification '07-'07)								
Sedna Desgagnés	9402093	GC	2009	D	12,413	456' 00"	68' 11"	36' 01"
Built: Quingshan/Jiangdong/Jiangzhou Shipyards, Jiangzhou, China (Beluga Festivity '09-'09)								
Taiga Desgagnés	9303302	GC	2007	D	12,936	469' 05"	74' 08"	43' 06"
Built: Tianjin Xingang Shipyard, Tianjin, China (BBC Amazon '07-'17)								
Zélada Desgagnés	9402081	GC	2008	D	12,413	441' 00"	68' 11"	36' 01"
Built: Quingshan/Jiangdong/Jiangzhou Shipyards, Jiangzhou, China (Beluga Freedom '09-'09)								

THE FOLLOWING VESSELS CHARTERED TO PETRO-NAV INC., MONTREAL, QC,
A SUBSIDIARY OF GROUPE DESGAGNÉS INC.

Damia Desgagnés	9766437	TK	2016	D	15,182	442' 11"	77' 01"	37' 01"
Built: Besiktas Gemi Insa A.S., Istanbul, Turkey								
Dara Desgagnés	9040089	TK	1992	D	10,511	405' 10"	58' 01"	34' 09"
Built: MTW Shipyard, Wismar, Germany (Elbestern '92-'93, Diamond Star, '93-'10)								
Esta Desgagnés	9040077	TK	1992	D	10,511	405' 10"	58' 01"	34' 09"
Built: MTW Shipyard, Wismar, Germany (Emsstern '92-'92, Emerald Star '92-'10)								
Jana Desgagnés	9046564	TK	1993	D	10,511	405' 10"	58' 01"	34' 09"
Built: MTW Shipyard, Wismar, Germany (Jadestern '93-'94, Jade Star '94-'10)								
Maria Desgagnés	9163752	TK	1999	D	13,199	393' 08"	68' 11"	40' 05"
Built: Qiuxin Shipyard, Shanghai, China (Kilchem Asia '99-'99)								
Mia Desgagnés	9772278	TK	2017	D	12,061	442' 11"	77' 01"	37' 01"
Built: Besiktas Gemi Insa A.S., Istanbul, Turkey								
Paul A. Desgagnés		TK	2017	D	12,061	442' 11"	77' 01"	37' 01"
Built: Besiktas Gemi Insa A.S., Istanbul, Turkey								
Sarah Desgagnés	9352171	TK	2007	D	18,000	483'11"	73' 06"	41' 04"
Built: Gisan Shipyard, Tuzla, Turkey (Besiktas Greenland '07-'08)								

THE FOLLOWING VESSELS CHARTERED TO RELAIS NORDIK INC., RIMOUSKI, QC *(relaisnordik.com)*
A SUBSIDIARY OF GROUPE DESGAGNÉS INC.

Bella Desgagnés	9511519	PF/RR	2012	D	1,054	312' 00"	63' 06"	22' 08"
Built: Brodogradil Kraljevica d.d., Kraljevica, Croatia								
Nordik Express	7391290	GC/CF	1974	D	1,697	219' 11"	44' 00"	16' 01"
Built: Todd Pacific Shipyards Corp., Seattle, WA (Theriot Offshore IV '74-'77, Scotoil 4 '77-'79, Tartan Sea '79-'87)								

TRANSPORT MARITIME ST-LAURENT INC., A SUBSIDIARY OF GROUPE DESGAGNÉS INC.

Espada Desgagnés	9334698	TK	2006	D	42,810*	750' 00"	105' 08"	67' 01"
Built: Brodosplit, Split, Croatia (Stena Poseidon '06-'14)								
Laurentia Desgagnés	9334703	TK	2007	D	42,810*	750' 00"	105' 08"	67' 01"
Built: Brodosplit, Split, Croatia (laid down as Neste Polaris, Palva '07-'14)								

GROUPE MARITIME VERREAULT INC., LES MÉCHINS, QC *(verreaultnavigation.com)*

Epinette II		TB	1965	D	75*	61' 03"	20' 01"	8' 05"
Built: Russel Brothers Ltd., Owen Sound, ON								

Fleet Name / Vessel Name	Vessel IMO #	Vessel Type	Year Built	Engine Type	Cargo Cap. or Gross*	Overall Length	Vessel Breadth	Vessel Depth
Grande Baie		TT	1972	D	194*	86' 06"	30' 00"	12' 00"

Built: Prince Edward Island Lending Authority, Charlottetown, PEI

GROUPE OCÉAN INC., QUÉBEC CITY, QC (groupocean.com)

Fleet Name / Vessel Name	Vessel IMO #	Vessel Type	Year Built	Engine Type	Cargo Cap. or Gross*	Overall Length	Vessel Breadth	Vessel Depth
Andre H.	5404172	TB	1963	D	317*	126' 00"	28' 06"	12' 10"

Built: Davie Shipbuilding Co., Lauzon, QC (Foundation Valiant '63-'73, Point Valiant {1} '73-'95)

Avantage	6828882	TB	1969	D	362*	116' 10"	32' 09"	16' 03"

Built: J. Boel En Zonen, Temse, Belgium (Sea Lion '69-'97)

Basse-Cote	8644620	DB	1932	B	400	201' 00"	40' 00"	12' 00"

Built: Department of Marine and Fisheries Government Shipyard, Sorel, QC (Louis D. '32-'93)

Duga	7530030	TB	1977	D	382*	114' 02"	32' 10"	16' 05"

Built: Langsten Slip & Båtbyggeri A/S, Lansten, Norway

Escorte	8871027	TT	1964	D	120*	85' 00"	23' 07"	7' 05"

Built: Jakobson Shipyard, Oyster Bay, NY (USS Menasha [YTB / YTM-773, YTM-761] '64-'92, Menasha {1} '92-'95)

Jerry G.	8959788	TB	1960	D	202*	91' 06"	27' 03"	12' 06"

Built: Davie Shipbuilding Co., Lauzon, QC

Josee H.		PB	1961	D	66*	63' 50"	16' 02"	9' 50"

Built: Ferguson Industries Ltd., Pictou, NS (Le Bic '61-'98)

Kim R.D.		TB	1954	D	36*	48' 08"	14' 01"	5' 01"

Built: Port Dalhousie Shipyard Co., Port Dalhousie, ON (Constructor '54-'86)

La Prairie	7393585	TB	1975	D	110*	73' 09"	25' 09"	11' 08"

Built: Georgetown Shipyard, Georgetown, PEI

Le Phil D.		TB	1961	D	38*	56' 01"	16' 00"	5' 08"

Built: Russel Brothers Ltd., Owen Sound, ON (Expanse)

Mega	7347641	TB	1975	D	768*	125' 03"	42' 03"	22' 09"

Built: Oy Wartsila AB, Helsinki, Finland; mated with articulated barge Motti

Motti	9072434	DB	1993	B	5,195*	403' 04"	78' 02"	7' 07"

Built: Kvaerner Masa Yards, Turku, Finland

Océan Abys	8644644	DB	1948	B	1,000	140' 00"	40' 00"	9' 00"

Built: Marine Industries Ltd., Sorel, QC (Omni No. 1 '48-'94)

Océan A. Gauthier	7305904	TT	1973	D	390*	98' 11"	36' 00"	12' 04"

Built: Star Shipyards Ltd., New Westminster, BC (Vachon '73-'17)

Océan Arctique	9261607	TB	2005	D	512*	102' 08"	39' 05"	17' 00"

Built: Industries Ocean Inc., Ile-Aux-Coudres, QC (Stevns Arctic '05-'13)

Océan A. Simard	8000056	TT	1980	D	286*	92' 00"	34' 00"	13' 07"

Built: Georgetown Shipyards Ltd., Georgetown, PEI (Alexis-Simard '80-'11)

Océan Basques	7237212	TB	1972	D	396*	98' 04"	32' 08"	16' 04"

Built: Canadian Shipbuilding & Engineering Co., Collingwood, ON (Pointe Aux-Basques '72-'13)

Océan Bertrand Jeansonne	9521526	TB	2008	D	402*	94' 05"	36' 05"	17' 02"

Built: East Isle Shipyard, Georgetown, PEI

Océan Bravo	7025279	TB	1970	D	320*	110' 00"	28' 06"	17' 00"

Built: Davie Shipbuilding Co., Lauzon, QC (Takis V. '70-'80, Donald P '80-'80, Nimue '80-'83, Donald P. '83-'98)

Océan Brochu	7305909	TT	1973	D	390*	98' 11"	36' 00"	12' 04"

Built: Star Shipyards Ltd., New Westminster, BC (Brochu '73-'17)

Océan Cape Crow		TB	1951	D	14*	37' 08"	10' 05"	5' 00"

Built: Russel-Hipwell Engines, Owen Sound, ON (Cape Crow '51-'16)

Océan Cartier	8668248	TB	2007	D	350*	90' 05"	36' 07"	13' 08"

Built: Shanghai Harbor Foxing, Shanghai, China (Hai Gang 107 '07-'14, Svitzer Wombi '14-'15, Svitzer Cartier '15-'17)

Océan Catatug 1		TW	2016	D	55*	52' 00"	30' 00"	8' 07"

Built: Industries Ocean Inc., Ile-Aux-Coudres, QC

Océan Catatug 2		TW	2016	D	52*	52' 00"	30' 00"	8' 07"

Built: Industries Ocean Inc., Ile-Aux-Coudres, QC

Océan Charlie	7312024	TB	1973	D	448*	123' 02"	31' 07"	16' 01"

Built: Davie Shipbuilding Co., Lauzon, QC (Leonard W. '73-'98)

Océan Clovis T.	9533036	TB	2009	D	381*	94' 60"	36' 50"	17' 10"

Built: East Isle Shipyard, Georgetown, PEI (Svitzer Njal '09-'17)

Océan Cote-Nord			2001	D	79*	75' 01"	18' 00"	10' 06"

Built: Industries Ocean Inc., Ile-Aux-Coudres, QC (Cote-Nord '01-'14)

Océan Echo II	6913091	AT	1969	D	438*	104' 08"	34' 05"	18' 00"

Built: Port Weller Dry Docks, Port Weller, ON (Atlantic '69-'75, Laval '75-'96)

Océan Express		PB	1999	D	29*	47' 02"	14' 00"	7' 05"

Built: Industries Ocean Inc., Charlevoix, QC (H-2000 '99-'00)

Océan Georgie Bain	9553892	TB	2009	D	204*	75' 02"	29' 09"	12' 09"

Built: Industries Ocean Inc., Ile-Aux-Coudres, QC

Océan Golf	5146354	TB	1959	D	159*	103' 00"	25' 10"	11' 09"

Built: P.K. Harris & Sons, Appledore, England (launched as Stranton; Helen M. McAllister '59-'97)

Océan Guide		PB	2001	D	29*	47' 02"	14' 00"	7' 05"

Built: Industries Ocean Inc., Charlevoix, QC

Fleet Name / Vessel Name	Vessel IMO #	Vessel Type	Year Built	Engine Type	Cargo Cap. or Gross*	Overall Length	Vessel Breadth	Vessel Depth
Océan Henry Bain	9420916	TB	2006	D	402*	94' 08"	30' 01"	14' 09"
Built: East Isle Shipyard, Georgetown, PEI								
Océan Intrepide	9203423	TT	1998	D	302*	80' 00"	30' 01"	14' 09"
Built: Industries Ocean Inc., Ile-Aux-Coudres, QC								
Océan Iroquois		WB	1974	D	20*	37' 09"	10' 00"	6' 06"
Built: Sigama Ltd., Cap-de-la-Madeline, QC (SLS Iroquois '74-??, S/VM Iroquis ??-'09)								
Océan Jupiter	9220160	TT	1998	D	302*	80' 00"	30' 01"	14' 09"
Built: Industries Ocean Inc., Ile-Aux-Coudres, QC								
Océan K. Rusby	9345556	TB	2005	D	402*	94' 08"	30' 01"	14' 09"
Built: East Isle Shipyard, Georgetown, PEI								
Océan Lima		TB	1977	D	15*	34' 02"	11' 08"	4' 00"
(VM/S St. Louis III '77-'10)								
Océan Maisonneuve		SV	1974	D	56*	58' 03"	20' 03"	6' 05"
Built: Fercraft Marine, St. Catherine d'Alexandrie, QC (VM/S Maisonneuve '74-'16)								
Océan Nigiq		TB	2008	D	12*	31' 05"	13' 05"	6' 00"
Built: Industrie Océan, Ile-aux-Coudres, QC								
Océan Pierre Julien	9688142	TB	2013	D	204*	75' 01"	30' 01"	12' 09"
Built: Industries Ocean Inc., Ile-Aux-Coudres, QC								
Océan Raymond Lemay	9420904	TB	2006	D	402*	94' 08"	30' 01"	14' 09"
Built: East Isle Shipyard, Georgetown, PEI								
Ocean Raynald T.	9533048	TB	2009	D	381*	94' 60"	36' 50"	17' 10"
Built: East Isle Shipyard, Georgetown, PEI (Stevns Iceflower '09-'09, Svitzer Nerthus '09-'17)								

Wintry view of John D. Leitch at Mission Point, Sault Ste. Marie, Mich. (Joy Fett)

Fleet Name Vessel Name	Vessel IMO #	Vessel Type	Year Built	Engine Type	Cargo Cap. or Gross*	Overall Length	Vessel Breadth	Vessel Depth
Océan Ross Gaudreault	9542221	TB	2011	D	402*	94' 04"	36' 05"	17' 00"
Built: East Isle Shipyard, Georgetown, PEI								
Océan Sept-Iles	7901162	TB	1980	D	427*	98' 04"	36' 01"	13' 01"
Built: Canadian Shipbuilding & Engineering Co., Collingwood, ON (Pointe Sept-Iles '80-'13)								
Océan Serge Genois	9553907	TB	2010	D	204*	75' 01"	30' 01"	12' 09"
Built: Industries Ocean Inc., Ile-Aux-Coudres, QC								
Océan Stevns	9224960	TB	2002	D	512*	102' 08"	39' 05"	17' 00"
Built: Industries Ocean Inc., Ile-Aux-Coudres, QC (Stevns Ocean '02-'13)								
Océan Taiga	9679488	TB	2016	D	710*	112' 00"	42' 06"	26' 07"
Built: Industries Ocean Inc., Ile-Aux-Coudres, QC								
Océan Traverse Nord	9666534	DR	2012	B	1,165*	210' 00"	42' 06"	14' 07"
Built: Industries Ocean Inc., Ile-Aux-Coudres, QC								
Océan Tundra	9645504	TB	2013	D	710*	118' 01"	42' 03"	22' 09"
Built: Industries Ocean Inc., Ile-Aux-Coudres, QC								
Océan Yvan Desgagnés	9542207	TB	2010	D	402*	94' 04"	36' 05"	17' 00"
Built: East Isle Shipyard, Georgetown, PEI								
Omni-Atlas	8644668	CS	1913	B	479*	133' 00"	42' 00"	10' 00"
Built: Sir William Arrol & Co. Ltd., Glasgow, Scotland								
Omni-Richelieu	6923084	TB	1969	D	144*	83' 00"	24' 06"	13' 06"
Built: Pictou Industries Ltd., Pictou, NS (Port Alfred II '69-'82)								
R. F. Grant		TB	1934	D	78*	71' 00"	17' 00"	8' 00"
Service Boat No. 1		PB	1965	D	55*	57' 08"	16' 01"	7' 06"

Fleet Name / Vessel Name	Vessel IMO #	Vessel Type	Year Built	Engine Type	Cargo Cap. or Gross*	Overall Length	Vessel Breadth	Vessel Depth
Service Boat No. 2		TB	1934	D	78*	65' 02"	17' 00"	8' 01"
Service Boat No. 4		PB	1959	D	26*	39' 01"	14' 02"	6' 03"

GROUPE RIVERIN MARITIME INC., SAGUENAY, QC

Jean-Joseph	8817382	GC	1990	D	1,999*	257' 08"	41' 00"	21' 06"

Built: Ferus Smit, Westerbroek, Netherlands (Bothniaborg '90-'04, Westerborg '04-'06, Maple '06-'08, Myras '08-'13, Hav Sund '13-'15)

H

HAMILTON PORT AUTHORITY, HAMILTON, ON *(hamiltonport.ca)*

Judge McCombs		TB	1948	D	10*	33' 01"	10' 03"	4' 00"

Built: Northern Shipbuilding & Repair Co. Ltd., Bronte, ON (Bronte Sue '48-'50)

HAMILTON HARBOUR QUEEN CRUISES, HAMILTON, ON *(hamiltonharbourqueen.ca)*

Hamilton Harbour Queen		ES	1956	D	252*	100' 00"	40' 00"	4' 05"

Built: Russel-Hipwell Engines, Owen Sound, ON (Johnny B. '56-'89, Garden City '89-'00, Harbour Princess '00-'05)

HARBOR LIGHT CRUISE LINES INC., TOLEDO, OH *(sandpiperboat.com)*

Sandpiper		ES	1984	D	37*	65' 00"	16' 00"	3' 00"

HARBOR BOAT CRUISE CO., TORONTO, ON *(rivergambler.ca)*

River Gambler		ES	1992	D	332*	100' 06"	16' 00"	4' 07"

Built: Jacques Beauchamp, Windsor, ON

HEDDLE MARINE SERVICE INC., HAMILTON, ON *(heddlemarine.com)*

Hamilton Energy	6517328	RT	1965	D	1,282	201' 05"	34' 01"	14' 09"

Built: Grangemouth Dockyard Co., Grangemouth, Scotland; laid up at Hamilton, ON (Partington '65-'79, Shell Scientist '79-'81, Metro Sun '81-'85)

King Fish 1		TB	1955	D	24*	47' 09"	13' 00"	5' 03"

Built: Russel Hipworth Engines Ltd., Owen Sound, ON (Anglo Duchess '55-'84, Duchess V '84-'??)

Lac Manitoba		TB	1944	D	51*	64' 00"	16' 07"	7' 10"

Built: Central Bridge Co., Trenton, ON; being rebuilt at Hamilton, ON (Tanac 75 '44-'52, Manitoba '52-'57)

Provmar Terminal	5376521	TK	1959	B	7,300	403' 05"	55' 06"	28' 05"

Built: Sarpsborg Mekaniske, Verksted, Norway; last operated in 1984; laid up at Hamilton, ON (Varangnes '59-'70, Tommy Wiborg '70-'74, Ungava Transport '74-'85)

HERITAGE MARINE, KNIFE RIVER, MN *(heritagemarinetug.com)*

Edward H. {2}	8990471	TB	1970	D	196*	102' 08"	29' 00"	16' 03"

Built: Peterson Builders Inc., Sturgeon Bay, WI (YTB-809-Agawam '70-'02, Fort Point '02-'17)

Helen H.	8624670	TB	1967	D	138*	82' 03"	26' 08"	10' 05"

Built: Bludworth Shipyard, Corpus Christi, TX (W. Douglas Masterson '67-'11)

Nancy J.	6504838	TB	1964	D	186*	92' 17"	29' 05"	14' 00"

Built: Main Iron Works, Houma, La (Horace, Point Comfort-'14)

Nels J. {2}		TB	1952	D	197*	101' 00"	26' 07"	12' 06"

Built: National Steel and Shipbuilding Co., San Diego, CA (LT-2078 '52-'64, YTM-748-Yuma '64-'80, Delaware '80-'89, Mobile Point '89-'95, Delaware '95-'08, Mobile Point '08-'09, Lesli M '09-'12, Taurus '12-'17)

HORNBLOWER CANADA CO., NIAGARA FALLS, ON *(niagaracruises.com)*

Niagara Guardian		PA	2013	D	38*	68' 09"	15' 07"	7' 05"
Niagara Thunder		PA	2014	D	185*	83' 02"	35' 09"	8' 09"
Niagara Wonder		PA	2014	D	185*	83' 02"	35' 09"	8' 09"

HORNE TRANSPORTATION LTD., WOLFE ISLAND, ON *(wolfeisland.com/ferry.php)*

William Darrell		CF	1952	D	66*	66' 00"	28' 00"	6' 00"

HUFFMAN EQUIPMENT RENTAL INC., EASTLAKE, OH

Benjamin Ridgway		TW	1969	D	51*	53' 00"	18' 05"	7' 00"
Bert Huffman		TW	1979	D	34*	38' 00"	13' 06"	5' 02"
Hamp Thomas		TB	1968	D	22*	43' 00"	13' 00"	4' 00"
Paddy Miles		TB	1934	D	16*	45' 04"	12' 04"	4' 07"

HURON LADY CRUISES, PORT HURON, MI *(huronlady.com)*

Huron Lady II		ES	1993	D	82*	65' 00"	19' 00"	10' 00"

(Lady Lumina '93-'99)

HYDRO-QUEBEC, MONTREAL, QC

Des Chenaux		TB	1953	D	46*	51' 08"	16' 00"	7' 08"

Built: Chantiers Manseau Ltd., Sorel, QC

R.O. Sweezy		TB	1991	D	29*	41' 09"	14' 00"	5' 07"

Built: Jean Fournier, Quebec City, QC (Citadelle I '91-'92)

Fleet Name / Vessel Name	Vessel IMO #	Vessel Type	Year Built	Engine Type	Cargo Cap. or Gross*	Overall Length	Vessel Breadth	Vessel Depth
ILLINOIS & MICHIGAN OIL LLC, JOLIET, IL								
Daniel E		TW	1967	D	70*	70' 00"	18' 06"	6' 08"
Built: River Enterprises Inc., Morris, IL (Foster M. Ford '67-'84)								
David E		TW	1952	D	236*	95' 00"	30' 00"	8' 06"
Built: Sturgeon Bay Shipbuilding & Drydock Co., Sturgeon Bay, WI (Irving Crown '52-'01)								
Derek E		TB	1907	D	85*	72' 06"	20' 01"	10' 06"
Built: Benjamin T. Cowles, Buffalo, NY (John Kelderhouse '07-'13, Sachem '13-'90)								
Lisa E		TB	1963	D	75*	65' 06"	20' 00"	8' 06"
Built: Main Iron Works Inc., Houma, LA (Dixie Scout '63-'90)								
INFINITY AND OVATION YACHT CHARTERS LLC, ST. CLAIR SHORES, MI *(infinityandovation.com)*								
Infinity		PA	2001	D	82*	117' 00"	22' 00"	6' 00"
Ovation		PA	2005	D	97*	138' 00"	27' 00"	7' 00"

Fleet Name / Vessel Name	Vessel IMO #	Vessel Type	Year Built	Engine Type	Cargo Cap. or Gross*	Overall Length	Vessel Breadth	Vessel Depth
INLAND LAKES MANAGEMENT INC., ALPENA, MI								
Alpena {2}	5206362	CC	1942	T	13,900	519' 06"	67' 00"	35' 00"
Built: Great Lakes Engineering Works, River Rouge, MI; shortened by 120' and converted to a self-unloading cement carrier at Fraser Shipyards, Superior, WI, in '91 (Leon Fraser '42-'91)								
J.A.W. Iglehart	5139179	CC	1936	T	12,500	501' 06"	68' 03"	37' 00"
Built: Sun Shipbuilding and Drydock Co., Chester, PA; converted from a saltwater tanker to a self-unloading cement carrier at American Shipbuilding Co., South Chicago, IL , in '65; last operated Oct. 29, 2006; in use as a cement storage/transfer vessel at Superior, WI (Pan Amoco '36-'55, Amoco '55-'60, H. R. Schemm '60-'65)								
S.T. Crapo	5304011	CC	1927	B	8,900	402' 06"	60' 03"	29' 00"
Built: Great Lakes Engineering Works, River Rouge, MI; last operated Sept. 4, 1996; in use as a cement storage and transfer vessel at Green Bay, WI								
INLAND SEAS EDUCATION ASSOCIATION, SUTTONS BAY, MI *(schoolship.org)*								
Inland Seas		RV	1994	W	41*	61' 06"	17' 00"	7' 00"
Built: Treworgy Yachts, Palm Coast, FL								
Utopia		RV	1946	W	49*	65' 0"	18' 00"	6' 08"
INLAND TUG & BARGE LTD., BROCKVILLE, ON								
Katanni		TB	1991	D	19*	34' 08"	14' 05"	5' 05"
Built: Duratug Shipyard & Fabricating Ltd., Port Dover, ON								
INTERLAKE STEAMSHIP CO., MIDDLEBURG HEIGHTS, OH *(interlakesteamship.com)*								
Dorothy Ann	8955732	AT/TT	1999	D	1,090*	124' 03"	44' 00"	24' 00"
Built: Bay Shipbuilding Co., Sturgeon Bay, WI; paired with self-unloading barge Pathfinder								
Herbert C. Jackson	5148143	SU	1959	D	24,800	690' 00"	75' 00"	37' 06"
Built: Great Lakes Engineering Works, River Rouge, MI; converted to a self-unloader at Defoe Shipbuilding Co., Bay City, MI, in '75; repowered in '16								
Hon. James L. Oberstar	5322518	SU	1959	D	31,000	806' 00"	75' 00"	37' 06"
Built: American Shipbuilding Co., Lorain, OH; lengthened 96' in '72; converted to a self-unloader in '81 at Fraser Shipyards, Superior, WI; repowered in '09 (Shenango II '59-'67, Charles M. Beeghly '67-'11)								
James R. Barker	7390260	SU	1976	D	63,300	1,004' 00"	105' 00"	50' 00"
Built: American Shipbuilding Co., Lorain, OH								
John Sherwin {2}	5174428	BC	1958	B	31,500	806' 00"	75' 00"	37' 06"
Built: American Steamship Co., Lorain, OH; lengthened 96' at Fraser Shipyards, Superior, WI, in '73; last operated Nov. 16, 1981; in long-term lay-up at DeTour, MI								
Kaye E. Barker	5097450	SU	1952	D	25,900	767' 00"	70' 00"	36' 00"
Built: American Shipbuilding Co., Toledo, OH; lengthened 120' at Fraser Shipyards, Superior, WI, in '76; converted to a self-unloader at American Shipbuilding Co., Toledo, OH, in '81; repowered in '12 (Edward B. Greene '52-'85, Benson Ford {3} '85-'89)								
Lee A. Tregurtha	5385625	SU	1942	D	29,360	826' 00"	75' 00"	39' 00"
Built: Bethlehem Shipbuilding and Drydock Co., Sparrows Point, MD; converted from a saltwater tanker to a Great Lakes bulk carrier in '61; lengthened 96' in '76 and converted to a self-unloader in '78, all at American Shipbuilding Co., Lorain, OH; repowered in '06 (laid down as Mobiloil; launched as Samoset; USS Chiwawa [AO-68] '42-'46, Chiwawa '46-'61, Walter A. Sterling '61-'85, William Clay Ford {2} '85-'89)								
Mesabi Miner	7390272	SU	1977	D	63,300	1,004' 00"	105' 00"	50' 00"
Built: American Shipbuilding Co., Lorain, OH								
Pathfinder {3}	5166768	SU	1953	B	10,577	606' 00"	70' 03"	36' 03"
Built: Great Lakes Engineering Works, River Rouge, MI; converted from a powered vessel to a self-unloading barge at Bay Shipbuilding Co., Sturgeon Bay, WI, in '98 (J. L. Mauthe '53-'98)								
Paul R. Tregurtha	7729057	SU	1981	D	68,000	1,013' 06"	105' 00"	56' 00"
Built: American Shipbuilding Co., Lorain, OH; largest vessel on the lakes (William J. DeLancey '81-'90)								
Stewart J. Cort	7105495	SU	1972	D	58,000	1,000' 00"	105' 00"	49' 00"
Built: Erie Marine Inc., Erie, PA; built for Bethlhem Steel Corp., first 1,000-footer on the Great Lakes								

Fleet Name Vessel Name	Vessel IMO #	Vessel Type	Year Built	Engine Type	Cargo Cap. or Gross*	Overall Length	Vessel Breadth	Vessel Depth
ISLAND FERRY SERVICES CORP., CHEBOYGAN, MI								
Polaris		PF	1952	D	99*	60' 02"	36' 00"	8' 06"
ISLE ROYALE LINE INC., COPPER HARBOR, MI *(isleroyale.com)*								
Isle Royale Queen IV		PA/PK	1980	D	93*	98' 09"	22' 01"	7' 00"
Built: Neuville Boat Works Inc., New Iberia, LA (American Freedom, John Jay, Shuttle V, Danielle G, Harbor Commuter V)								

J-K

J.W. WESTCOTT CO., DETROIT, MI *(jwwestcott.com)*								
Joseph J. Hogan		MB	1957	D	16*	40' 00"	12' 05"	5' 00"
(USCOE Ottawa '57-'95)								
J. W. Westcott II		MB	1949	D	14*	46' 01"	13' 03"	4' 05"
Built: Paasch Marine Service, Erie, PA; floating post office has its own U.S. ZIP code, 48222								
JEFF FOSTER, SUPERIOR, WI								
Sundew		IB	1944	DE	1,025*	180' 00"	37' 05"	17' 04"
Built: Marine Ironworks and Shipbuilding Corp., Duluth, MN; former U.S. Coast Guard cutter WLB-404 was decommissioned in 2004 and turned into a marine museum; returned to private ownership in 2009								
JUBILEE QUEEN CRUISE LINES, TORONTO, ON *(jubileequeencruises.ca)*								
Jubilee Queen		ES	1986	D	269*	122' 00"	23' 09"	5' 05"
(Pioneer Princess III '86-'89)								
KEHOE MARINE CONSTRUCTION CO., LANSDOWNE, ON *(kehoemarine.com)*								
Halton		TB	1942	D	15*	42' 08"	14' 00"	5' 08"
Built: Muir Bros. Dry Dock Co. Ltd., Port Dalhousie, ON (Wokboat No. 8)								
Houghton		TB	1944	D	15*	45' 00"	13' 00"	6' 00"
Built: Port Houston Iron Works, Houston, TX (ST-573 '44-'48)								
Sawyer 1		TB	1946	D	11*	35' 02"	10' 02"	4' 04"
Built: Russel Bros. Ltd., Owen Sound, ON (Coulonge)								
KELLEYS ISLAND BOAT LINES, MARBLEHEAD, OH *(kelleysislandferry.com)*								
Carlee Emily		PA/CF	1987	D	98*	101' 00"	34' 06"	10' 00"
Built: Blount Marine Corp., Warren, RI (Endeavor '87-'02)								
Juliet Alicia		PA/CF	1969	D	95*	88' 03"	33' 00"	6' 08"
Built: Blount Marine Corp., Warren, RI (Kelley Islander)								
Shirley Irene		PA/CF	1991	D	68*	160' 00"	46' 00"	9' 00"
Built: Ocean Group Shipyard, Bayou La Batre, AL								
KINDRA LAKE TOWING LP, CHICAGO, IL *(kindralake.com)*								
Buckley		TW	1958	D	94*	95' 00"	26' 00"	11' 00"
Built: Parker Bros. Shipyard, Houston, TX (Linda Brooks '58-'67, Eddie B. {2} '67-'95)								

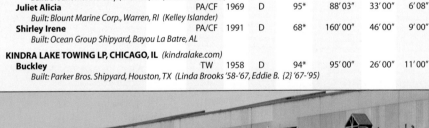

Bulk carrier Oakglen loading at Superior, Wis. *(Nick Stenstrup)*

Fleet Name / Vessel Name	Vessel IMO #	Vessel Type	Year Built	Engine Type	Cargo Cap. or Gross*	Overall Length	Vessel Breadth	Vessel Depth
Ellie		TB	1970	D	29*	39' 07"	16' 00"	4' 06"
Built: Big River Shipbuilding Inc., Vicksburg, MS (Miss Bissy '09)								
Morgan		TB	1974	D	134*	90' 00"	30' 00"	10' 06"
Built: Peterson Builders Inc., Sturgeon Bay, WI (Donald O'Toole '74-'86, Bonesey B. '86-'95)								
Old Mission		TB	1945	D	94*	85' 00"	23' 00"	10' 04"
Built: Sturgeon Bay Shipbuilding, Sturgeon Bay, WI (U. S. Army ST-880 '45-'47, USCOE Avondale '47-'64, Adrienne B. '64-'95)								
Tanner		TW	1977	D	62*	56' 06"	22' 03"	6' 06"
Built: Thrift Shipbuilding Inc., Sulphur, LA; Owned by Jamattca Inc., Chicago, IL (J.H. Tanner 76-'00)								

KING CO. (THE), HOLLAND, MI

Fleet Name / Vessel Name	Vessel IMO #	Vessel Type	Year Built	Engine Type	Cargo Cap. or Gross*	Overall Length	Vessel Breadth	Vessel Depth
Barry J		TB	1943	D	26*	46' 00"	13' 00"	7' 00"
Built: Sturgeon Bay Shipbuilding & Dry Dock Co., Sturgeon Bay, WI								
Buxton II		DR	1976	B	147*	130' 02"	28' 01"	7' 00"
Built: Barbour Boat Works Inc., Holland, MI								
Carol Ann		TB	1981	D	86*	61' 05"	24' 00"	8' 07"
Built: Rodriguez Boat Builders, Bayou La Batre, AL								
John Henry		TB	1954	D	66*	65' 04"	19' 04"	9' 06"
Built: Missouri Valley Steel, Leavenworth, KS (U. S. Army ST-2013 '54-'80)								
Julie Dee		TB	1937	D	64*	68' 08"	18' 01"	7' 06"
Built: Herbert Slade, Beaumont, TX (Dernier, Jerry O'Day, Cindy B)								
Matt Allen		TB	1961	D	146*	80' 04"	24' 00"	11' 03"
Built: Nolty Theriot Inc., Golden Meadow, LA (Gladys Bea '61-'73, American Viking '73-'83, Maribeth Andrie '83-'05)								
Miss Edna		TB	1935	D	13*	36' 08"	11' 02"	4' 08"
Built: Levingston Shipbuilding, Orange, TX								

KINGSTON 1,000 ISLANDS CRUISES, KINGSTON, ON (1000islandscruises.on.ca)

Fleet Name / Vessel Name	Vessel IMO #	Vessel Type	Year Built	Engine Type	Cargo Cap. or Gross*	Overall Length	Vessel Breadth	Vessel Depth
Island Belle I		ES	1988	D	150*	65' 00"	22' 00"	8' 00"
Built: Kettle Creek Boat Works, Port Stanley, ON (Spirit of Brockville '88-'91)								
Island Queen III		ES	1975	D	300*	96' 00"	26' 00"	11' 00"
Built: Marlin Yacht Co., Summerstown, ON								
Papoose III		ES	1968	D	110*	64' 08"	23' 03"	7' 03"
Built: Hike Metal Products Ltd., Wheatley, ON (Peche Island II ('68'-'93)								

L

LAFARGE CANADA INC., MISSISSAUGA, ON
THE FOLLOWING VESSEL MANAGED BY ALGOMA CENTRAL CORP.

Fleet Name / Vessel Name	Vessel IMO #	Vessel Type	Year Built	Engine Type	Cargo Cap. or Gross*	Overall Length	Vessel Breadth	Vessel Depth
English River	5104382	CC	1961	D	7,450	404' 03"	60' 00"	36' 06"
Built: Canadian Shipbuilding and Engineering Ltd., Collingwood, ON; converted to a self-unloading cement carrier by Port Arthur Shipbuilding, Port Arthur (now Thunder Bay), ON, in '74								

LAFARGE – SEE ANDRIE INC. (andrie.com)

Group Océan's dredge Océan Traverse Nord. (Jeff Cameron)

Fleet Name / Vessel Name	Vessel IMO #	Vessel Type	Year Built	Engine Type	Cargo Cap. or Gross*	Overall Length	Vessel Breadth	Vessel Depth

LAKE ERIE ISLAND CRUISES LLC, SANDUSKY, OH *(goodtimeboat.com)*

Goodtime I		ES	1960	D	81*	111' 00"	29' 08"	9' 05"

    Built: Blount Marine Corp., Warren, RI

LAKE EXPRESS LLC, MILWAUKEE, WI *(lake-express.com)*

Lake Express	9329253	PA/CF	2004	D	96*	179' 02"	57' 07"	16' 00"

    Built: Austal USA, Mobile, AL; high-speed ferry service from Milwaukee, WI, to Muskegon, MI; capacity is 250 passengers, 46 autos

LAKE MICHIGAN CARFERRY, LUDINGTON, MI *(ssbadger.com)*

Badger	5033583	PA/CF	1953	S	4,244*	410' 06"	59' 06"	24' 00"

    Built: Christy Corp., Sturgeon Bay, WI; traditional ferry service from Ludington, MI, to Manitowoc, WI; capacity is 520 passengers, 180 autos; last coal-fired steamship on the Great Lakes; listed on the National Register of Historic Places in 2016; last vessel in Great Lakes service powered by Skinner Unaflow engines

Spartan		PA/CF	1952	S	4,244*	410' 06"	59' 06"	24' 00"

    Built: Christy Corp., Sturgeon Bay, WI; last operated Jan. 20, 1979; in long-term lay-up at Ludington, MI

LAKEHEAD TUG BOATS INC., THUNDER BAY, ON *(lakeheadtugs.com)*

George N. Carleton		TB	1943	D	97*	82' 00"	21' 00"	11' 00"

    Built: Russel Brothers Ltd., Owen Sound, ON (HMCS Glenlea [W-25] '43-'45, Bansaga '45-'64)

Robert John		TB	1945	D	98*	82' 00"	20' 01"	11' 00"

    Built: Canadian Dredge & Dock Co., Kingston, ON (HMCS Gleneagle [W-40] '45-'46, Bansturdy '46-'65)

Teclutsa		TB	1973	D	235*	102' 85"	30' 00"	15' 00"

    Built: Marinette Marine Ltd., Marinette, WI (YTB-822 – USS Pawhuska '73-'95)

LAKES PILOTS ASSOCIATION, PORT HURON, MI *(lakespilots.com)*

Huron Belle		PB	1979	D	38*	50' 00"	15' 07"	7' 09"

    Built: Gladding-Hearn Shipbuilding, Somerset, MA; pilot service at Detroit, MI

Huron Maid		PB	1977	D	26*	46' 00"	12' 05"	3' 05"

    Built: Hans Hansen Welding Co., Toledo, OH; pilot service at Port Huron, MI

Huron Spirit		PB	2016	D	47*	52' 05"	16' 07"	8' 01"

    Built: Gladding Hearn Shipbuilding, Somerset, MA; pilot service at Port Huron, MI

LAMBTON MARINE LTD., PORT LAMBTON, ON

Mary Ellen I		TB	2008	D	18*	41' 08"	14' 02"	7' 0"

LAURENTIAN PILOTAGE AUTHORITY, MONTREAL, QC *(pilotagestlaurent.gc.ca)*

Grandes Eaux		PB	2008	D	63*	62' 06"	17' 02"	9' 05"
Taukamaim		PB	2012	D	82*	72' 01"	19' 05"	10' 05"

    Both vessels offer pilot service at Les Escoumins, QC, on the St. Lawrence River

James R. Barker departs CN Duluth with the first load of new Mustang ore pellets for delivery to ArcelorMittal in Indiana Harbor in June 2017. (Paul Scinocca)

LEGEND CRUISES LLC, STURGEON BAY, WI *(ridethefireboat.com)*

Fleet Name / Vessel Name	Vessel IMO #	Vessel Type	Year Built	Engine Type	Cargo Cap. or Gross*	Overall Length	Vessel Breadth	Vessel Depth
Fred A. Busse		ES	1937	D	99*	92' 00"	22' 04"	9' 06"

Built: Defoe Boat & Motor Works, Bay City, MI; former Chicago fireboat offers cruises at Sturgeon Bay, WI

LES BARGES DE MATANE INC., MATANE, QC *(bargesmatane.com)*

Fleet Name / Vessel Name	Vessel IMO #	Vessel Type	Year Built	Engine Type	Cargo Cap. or Gross*	Overall Length	Vessel Breadth	Vessel Depth
Point Vim	518852	TB	1962	D	207*	98' 06"	26' 18"	12' 02"

Built: Davie Shipbuilding Co., Lauzon, QC (Foundation Vim '62-'74)

LOWER LAKES TOWING LTD., PORT DOVER, ON *(randlogisticsinc.com)*
A SUBSIDIARY OF RAND LOGISTICS INC., NEW YORK, NY

Fleet Name / Vessel Name	Vessel IMO #	Vessel Type	Year Built	Engine Type	Cargo Cap. or Gross*	Overall Length	Vessel Breadth	Vessel Depth
Cuyahoga	5166392	SU	1943	D	15,675	620' 00"	60' 00"	35' 00"

Built: American Shipbuilding Co., Lorain, OH; converted to a self-unloader by Manitowoc Shipbuilding Co., Manitowoc, WI, in '74; repowered in '01 (J. Burton Ayers '43-'95)

Kaministiqua	8119285	BC	1983	D	34,500	730' 01"	75' 09"	48' 00"

Built: Govan Shipyards, Glasgow, Scotland (Saskatchewan Pioneer '83-'95, Lady Hamilton '95-'06, Voyageur Pioneer '06-'08)

Manitoba {3}	6702301	BC	1967	D	19,093	607' 09"	62' 00"	36' 00"

Built: Collingwood Shipyards, Collingwood, ON (Mantadoc '67-'02, Teakglen '02-'05, Maritime Trader '05-'11); Entered long-term lay-up on April 17, 2016 at Montreal QC and is expected to be scrapped

Manitoulin {6}	8810918	SU	1991	D	25,000	662' 09"	77' 09"	44' 11"

Former saltwater tanker rebuilt for Great Lakes service in 2015 with a new self-unloading bow section. **Bow section** *built 2014-15 at Chengxi Shipyards, Jiangyin, China.* **Stern section** *built in 1991 at Uljanik Shipyard, Pula, Croatia. (Trelsi '91-'01, Euro Swan '01-'11, Lalandia Swan '11-'15)*

Michipicoten {2}	5102865	SU	1952	D	22,300	698' 00"	70' 00"	37' 00"

Built: Bethlehem Shipbuilding & Drydock Co., Sparrows Point, MD; lengthened 72' by American Shipbuilding Co., S. Chicago, IL, in '57; converted to a self-unloader by American Shipbuilding Co., Toledo, OH, in '80; repowered in '11 (Elton Hoyt 2nd '52-'03)

Mississagi	5128467	SU	1943	D	15,800	620' 06"	60' 00"	35' 00"

Built: Great Lakes Engineering Works, River Rouge, MI; converted to a self-unloader by Fraser Shipyards, Superior, WI, in '67; repowered in '85 (Hill Annex '43-'43, George A. Sloan '43-'01)

Ojibway	5105831	BC	1952	D	20,668	642' 03"	67' 00"	35' 00"

Built: Defoe Shipbuilding Co., Bay City, MI; repowered in '05 (Charles L. Hutchinson {3} '52-'62, Ernest R. Breech '62-'88, Kinsman Independent '88-'05, Voyageur Independent '05-'08)

Robert S. Pierson	7366403	SU	1974	D	19,650	630' 00"	68' 00"	36' 11"

Built: American Shipbuilding Co., Lorain, OH (Wolverine {2} '74- '08)

Saginaw {3}	5173876	SU	1953	D	20,200	639' 03"	72' 00"	36' 00"

Built: Manitowoc Shipbuilding Co., Manitowoc, WI, repowered in '08 (John J. Boland {3} '53-'99)

Tecumseh {2}	7225855	BC	1973	D	29,510	641' 00"	78' 00"	45' 03"

Built: Lockheed Shipbuilding & Construction Co., Seattle, WA (Sugar Islander '73-'96, Islander '96-'96, Judy Litrico '96-'06, Tina Litrico '06-'11)

Algoma DIscovery passes Joseph L. Block. *(Ben/Chanda McClain)*

Fleet Name / Vessel Name	Vessel IMO #	Vessel Type	Year Built	Engine Type	Cargo Cap. or Gross*	Overall Length	Vessel Breadth	Vessel Depth
GRAND RIVER NAVIGATION CO., NEW YORK, NY, OWNER – AN AFFILIATE OF LOWER LAKES TOWING LTD.								
Ashtabula	8637495	SU	1982	B	17,982	610' 01"	78' 01"	49' 08"
Built: Bay Shipbuilding Co., Sturgeon Bay, WI (Mary Turner '82-'12)								
Calumet {3}	7329314	SU	1973	D	19,650	630' 00"	68' 00"	36' 11"
Built: American Shipbuilding Co., Lorain, OH (William R. Roesch '73-'95, David Z. Norton {3} '95-'07, David Z. '07-'08)								
CTC No. 1		CC	1943	R	16,300	620' 06"	60' 00"	35' 00"
Built: Great Lakes Engineering Works, River Rouge, MI; last operated Nov. 12, 1981; former cement storage/transfer vessel is laid up at South Chicago, IL; may be returned to service at a future date (launched as McIntyre; Frank Purnell {1} '43-'64, Steelton {3} '64-'78, Hull No. 3 '78-'79, Pioneer {4} '79-'82)								
Defiance	8109761	ATB	1982	D	196*	145' 01"	44' 00"	21' 00"
Built: Marinette Marine Corp., Marinette, WI; paired with barge Ashtabula (April T. Beker '82-'87, Beverly Anderson '82-'12)								
Invincible	7723819	ATB	1979	D	180*	100' 00"	35' 00"	22' 06"
Built: Atlantic Marine Inc., Fort George Island, FL (R. W. Sesler '79-'91)								
James L. Kuber	5293341	SU	1953	B	25,500	703' 08"	70' 00"	36' 00"
Built: Great Lakes Engineering Works, River Rouge, MI; lengthened 120' by Fraser Shipyards, Superior, WI, in '75; converted to a self-unloader by Bay Shipbuilding, Sturgeon Bay, WI, in '83; converted to a barge by the owners in '07 (Reserve '53-'08)								
Manistee	5294307	SU	1943	D	14,900	620' 06"	60' 03"	35' 00"
Built: Great Lakes Engineering Works, River Rouge, MI; converted to a self-unloader by Manitowoc Shipbuilding Co., Manitowoc, WI, in '64; repowered in '76; entered long-term lay-up at Toledo, Ohio, in December 2015 (launched as Adirondack. Richard J. Reiss {2} '43-'86, Richard Reiss '86-'05)								
Manitowoc	7366398	SU	1973	D	19,650	630' 00"	68' 00"	36' 11"
Built: American Shipbuilding Co., Lorain, OH (Paul Thayer '73-'95, Earl W. Oglebay '95-'07, Earl W. '07-'08)								
Menominee	5336351	SU	1952	B	22,300	616' 10"	70' 00"	37' 00"
Built: Bethlehem Steel Corp., Sparrows Point, MD; lengthened 72' by American Shipbuilding, South Chicago, IL, in '58; converted to a self-unloader by Fraser Shipyards, Superior, WI, in '80; converted to a barge by Erie Shipbuilding, Erie, PA, in '06; (Sparrows Point '52-'90, Buckeye {3} '90-'06, Lewis J. Kuber '06-'17)								
Olive L. Moore	8635227	AT	1928	D	524*	125' 00"	39' 02"	13' 09"
Built: Manitowoc Shipbuilding Co., Manitowoc, WI (John F. Cushing '28-'66, James E. Skelly '66-'66)								
Victory	8003292	TB	1980	D	194*	140' 00"	43' 01"	18' 00"
Built: McDermott Shipyard Inc., Amelia, LA; paired with barge James L. Kuber								
LUEDTKE ENGINEERING CO., FRANKFORT, MI *(luedtke-eng.com)*								
Alan K. Luedtke		TB	1944	D	149*	86' 04"	23' 00"	10' 03"
Built: Allen Boat Co., Harvey, LA; inactive at Ludington, MI (U. S. Army ST-527 '44-'55, USCOE Two Rivers '55-'90)								
Ann Marie		TB	1954	D	81*	71' 00"	19' 05"	9' 06"
Built: Smith Basin & Drydock, Pensacola, FL (ST-1449 '54-'80, Lewis Castle '80-'98, Apache '98-'01)								
Chris E. Luedtke		TB	1936	D	18*	42' 05"	11' 09"	5' 00"
Built: Manitowoc Shipbuilding, Manitowoc, WI (Manshipco '36-'80)								
Erich R. Luedtke		TB	1939	D	18*	42' 05"	11' 09"	5' 00"
Built: Manitowoc Shipbuilding, Manitowoc, WI								

Algosteel laid up at Goderich, Ont., with the tugs Donald Bert and Dover. *(Philip Nash)*

Fleet Name Vessel Name	Vessel IMO #	Vessel Type	Year Built	Engine Type	Cargo Cap. or Gross*	Overall Length	Vessel Breadth	Vessel Depth
Gretchen B		TB	1943	D	18*	41' 09"	12' 05"	6' 00"
Built: Sturgeon Bay Shipbuilding, Sturgeon Bay, WI (ST-175 '43-'46, Jane T '46-'70)								
Karl E. Luedtke		TB	1928	D	32*	55' 02"	14' 09"	6' 00"
Built: Leathem D. Smith Dock Co., Sturgeon Bay, WI (Betty D. '28-'32, Killarney '32-'35)								
Krista S		TB	1954	D	93*	67' 09"	20' 01"	7' 07"
Built: Arnold V. Walker Shipyard, Pascagoula, MS (Sea Traveler '54-'87, Sea Wolf '87-'01, Jimmy Wray '01-'08)								
Paul L. Luedtke		TB	1988	D	97*	75' 00"	26' 00"	9' 06"
Built: Terrebonne Fabricators Inc., Houma, LA (Edward E. Gillen III '88-'13)								

M

MCM MARINE INC., SAULT STE. MARIE, MI *(mcmmarine.com)*

Fleet Name Vessel Name	Vessel IMO #	Vessel Type	Year Built	Engine Type	Cargo Cap. or Gross*	Overall Length	Vessel Breadth	Vessel Depth
Beaver State		TB	1935	D	18*	43' 06"	12' 00"	5' 02"
Drummond Islander II		TB	1961	D	97*	65' 00"	36' 00"	9' 00"
Built: Marinette Marine Corp., Marinette, WI; former carferry was built to serve DeTour / Drummond Island, MI								
Madison		TB	1975	D	17*	33' 08"	13' 05"	4' 07"
Mohawk		TB	1945	D	46*	65' 00"	19' 00"	10' 06"
Built: Robert Jacob Shipbuilding, City Island, NY (YTL-440 '45-'75)								
No. 55		DR	1927	DE	721*	165' 00"	42' 08"	12' 00"
No. 56		DS	1928	DE	1,174*	165' 00"	42' 04"	15' 07"
Peach State		TB	1961	D	19*	42' 01"	12' 04"	5' 03"
Sioux		DS	1954	B	504*	120' 00"	50' 00"	10' 00"

MacDONALD MARINE LTD., GODERICH, ON *(www.mactug.com)*

Fleet Name Vessel Name	Vessel IMO #	Vessel Type	Year Built	Engine Type	Cargo Cap. or Gross*	Overall Length	Vessel Breadth	Vessel Depth
Debbie Lyn		TB	1950	D	10*	45' 00"	14' 00"	10' 00"
Built: Matheson Boat Works, Goderich, ON (Skipper '50-'60)								
Donald Bert		TB	1953	D	11*	45' 00"	14' 00"	10' 00"
Built: Matheson Boat Works, Goderich, ON								
Dover		TB	1931	D	70*	84' 00"	17' 00"	6' 00"
Built: Canadian Mead-Morrison Co. Ltd., Welland, ON (Earleejune, Iveyrose)								
Ian Mac		TB	1955	D	12*	45' 00"	14' 00"	10' 00"
Built: Matheson Boat Works, Goderich, ON								

MADELINE ISLAND FERRY LINE INC., LaPOINTE, WI *(madferry.com)*

Fleet Name Vessel Name	Vessel IMO #	Vessel Type	Year Built	Engine Type	Cargo Cap. or Gross*	Overall Length	Vessel Breadth	Vessel Depth
Bayfield {2}		PA/CF	1952	D	83*	120' 00"	43' 00"	10' 00"
Built: Chesapeake Marine Railway, Deltaville, VA (Charlotte '52-'99)								
Island Queen {2}		PA/CF	1966	D	90*	75' 00"	34' 09"	10' 00"
Madeline		PA/CF	1984	D	94*	90' 00"	35' 00"	8' 00"
Nichevo II		PA/CF	1962	D	89*	65' 00"	32' 00"	8' 09"

MAID OF THE MIST STEAMBOAT CO. LTD., NIAGARA FALLS, ON *(maidofthemist.com)*

Fleet Name Vessel Name	Vessel IMO #	Vessel Type	Year Built	Engine Type	Cargo Cap. or Gross*	Overall Length	Vessel Breadth	Vessel Depth
Maid of the Mist VI		ES	1990	D	155*	78' 09"	29' 06"	7' 00"
Maid of the Mist VII		ES	1997	D	160*	80' 00"	30' 00"	7' 00"

Paul R. Tregurtha departing Duluth for Lake Superior. (Aidan Kemp)

Fleet Name Vessel Name	Vessel IMO #	Vessel Type	Year Built	Engine Type	Cargo Cap. or Gross*	Overall Length	Vessel Breadth	Vessel Depth
MALCOLM MARINE, ST. CLAIR, MI *(malcolmmarine.com)*								
Capt. Keith		TB	1955	D	39*	53' 03"	15' 06"	6' 04"
Built: Diamond Manufacturing, Savannah GA (Richard Merritt '55-'13)								
Debbie Lee		TB	1955	D	13*	32' 00"	11' 00"	4' 04"
Built: U.S. Coast Guard, Baltimore, MD (CG-40397, Hooligan, Shy Poke)								
Manitou {2}	8971695	TB	1942	D	199*	110' 00"	26' 02"	15' 06"
Built: U.S. Coast Guard, Curtis Bay, MD (USCGC Manitou [WYT-60] '43-'84)								
MANITOU ISLAND TRANSIT, LELAND, MI *(manitoutransit.com)*								
Manitou Isle		PA/PK	1946	D	39*	52' 00"	14' 00"	8' 00"
(Namaycush '46-'59)								
Mishe Mokwa		PA/CF	1966	D	49*	65' 00"	17' 06"	8' 00"
MARINE NAVIGATION AND TRAINING ASSOCIATION, INC. , CHICAGO, IL *(manatra.org)*								
Manatra [YP-671]		TV	1974	D	67*	80' 05"	17' 09"	5' 04"
Name stands for MArine NAvigation and TRaining Association (USS YP-671 '74-'89)								
MARINE RECYCLING CORP., PORT COLBORNE & PORT MAITLAND, ON *(marinerecycling.ca)*								
Charlie E.		TB	1943	D	32*	63' 00"	16' 06"	7' 06"
Built: W.F. Kolbe & Co. Ltd., Port Dover, ON (Kolbe '43-'86, Lois T. '86-'02)								
MARINE SERVICES INC., OAK PARK, MI								
Tenacious	5238004	TB	1960	D	149*	79' 01"	25' 06"	12' 06"
Built: Ingalls Shipbuilding Corp., Pascagoula, MS (Mobil 8 '60-'91, Tatarrax '91-'93, Nan McKay '93-'95)								
Titan		TB	1940	D	31*	56' 03"	15' 08"	7' 00"
MARINE TECH LLC, DULUTH, MN *(marinetechduluth.com)*								
Callie M.		TB	1910	D	51*	64' 03"	16' 09"	8' 06"
Built: Houma Shipbuilding Co., Houma, LA (Chattanooga '10-'79, Howard T. Hagen '79-'94, Nancy Ann '94-'01)								
Jean C.	8651879	TB	1944	D	142*	86' 00"	23' 00"	10' 03"
Built: Equitable Equipment Co., Madisonville, LA (ST-707 '44-'60, Forney '60-'07, Edward H. '07-'17)								
Miss Laura		TB	1943	D	146*	81' 01"	24' 00"	9' 10"
Built: Lawley & Son Corp., Neponset, MA (DPC-3 '43-'46, DS-43 '46-'50, Fresh Kills '50-'69, Richard K. '69-'93, Leopard '93-'03)								
MARIPOSA CRUISES, TORONTO, ON *(mariposacruises.com)*								
Capt. Matthew Flinders	8883355	ES	1982	D	746*	144' 00"	40' 00"	8' 06"
Built: North Arm Slipway Pty. Ltd., Port Adelaide, Australia								
Klancy II		ES	1989	D	124*	60' 02"	20' 00"	8' 02"
Northern Spirit I	8870073	ES	1983	D	489*	136' 00"	31' 00"	9' 00"
Built: Blount Marine Corp., Warren, RI (New Spirit '83-'89, Pride of Toronto '89-'92)								

Chief Engineer Mark Sipper (right) and First Assistant Engineer Mark McTaggart inspect Stewart J. Cort's propeller. (Mike Sipper)

Fleet Name Vessel Name	Vessel IMO #	Vessel Type	Year Built	Engine Type	Cargo Cap. or Gross*	Overall Length	Vessel Breadth	Vessel Depth
Oriole	8800054	ES	1987	D	200*	75' 00"	23' 00"	9' 00"
Rosemary		ES	1960	D	52*	68' 00"	15' 06"	6' 08"
Showboat		ES	1988	D	135*	74' 00"	21' 00"	4' 00"

MARTIN GAS & OIL INC., BEAVER ISLAND, MI

Petroqueen		TK	2015	B	112*	70' 00"	24' 00"	8' 00"

Built: Basic Marine Inc., Escanaba, MI

Shamrock		TB	1933	D	60*	64' 00"	18' 00"	7' 03"

Built: Pennsylvania Shipyard Inc., Beaumont, TX

MAXIMUS CORP., BLOOMFIELD HILLS, MI (boblosteamers.com)

Ste. Claire		PA	1910	R	870*	197' 00"	65' 00"	14' 00"

Built: Toledo Ship Building Co., Toledo, OH; former Detroit to Bob-Lo Island passenger steamer last operated Sept. 2, 1991; undergoing long-term restoration at Detroit, MI

McASPHALT MARINE TRANSPORTATION LTD., TORONTO, ON (mcasphalt.com)

Everlast	7527332	ATB	1976	D	1,361*	143' 04"	44' 04"	21' 04"

Built: Hakodate Dock Co., Hakodate, Japan; paired with barge Norman McLeod (Bilibino '77-'96)

John J. Carrick	9473444	TK	2008	B	11,613	407' 06"	71' 07"	30' 00"

Built: Penglai Bohai Shipyard Co. Ltd., Penglai, China

Leo A. McArthur	9473262	ATB	2009	D	1,299	122' 00"	44' 03"	26' 02

Built: Penglai Bohai Shipyard Co. Ltd., Penglai, China; paired with barge John J. Carrick (Victorious '09-'17)

Norman McLeod	8636219	TK	2001	B	6,809*	379' 02"	71' 06"	30' 02"

Built: Jinling Shipyard, Nanjing, China

McKEIL MARINE LTD., BURLINGTON, ON (mckeil.com)

Alouette Spirit	8641537	DB	1969	B	10,087*	425' 01"	74' 02"	29' 05"

Built: Gulfport Shipbuilding Co., Port Arthur, TX (KTC 135 '69-'04, Lambert's Spirit '04-'05)

Beverly M 1	9084047	TB	1994	D	450*	114' 06"	34' 04"	17' 04"

Built: Imamura Shipbuilding, Kure, Japan (Shek O, Hunter, Pacific Typhoon)

Blain M	7907099	RV	1981	D	925*	165' 05"	36' 00"	19' 09"

Built: Ferguson Industries, Picton, ON (Wilfred Templeman '81-'11)

Bonnie B III	7017662	TB	1969	D	308*	107' 00"	32' 00"	18' 00"

(Esso Oranjestad '69-'85, Oranjestad '85-'86, San Nicolas '86-'87, San Nicolas I '87-'88)

Carrol C. 1	7017674	TB	1969	D	307*	107' 00"	32' 00"	18' 00"

Built: Gulfport Shipbuilding Corp., Port Arthur, TX (Esso San Nicolas '69-'86, San Nicolas '86-'87, Carrol C '87-'88)

Evans McKeil	8983416	TB	1936	D	284*	110' 06"	25' 06"	14' 08"

Built: Panama Canal Co., Balboa, Panama (Alhajuela '36-'70, Barbara Ann {2} '70-'89)

Evans Spirit	9327774	GC	2007	D	14,650	459' 02"	68' 11"	34' 09"

Built: Royal Niestern Sander, Delfzijl, Netherlands (Spavalda '07-'16)

Sam Laud unloading at the Verplank Lakeside Dock in Muskegon, Mich. (Sam Hankinson)

Fleet Name / Vessel Name	Vessel IMO #	Vessel Type	Year Built	Engine Type	Cargo Cap. or Gross*	Overall Length	Vessel Breadth	Vessel Depth
Florence M	5118797	TB	1961	D	236*	90' 00"	28' 08"	11' 04"
Built: P.K. Harris, Appledore, UK (Foundation Vibert '61-'73, Point Vibert '73-'06)								
Florence Spirit	9314600	BC	2004	D	13,988	477' 07"	69' 07"	37' 01"
Built: Kyokuyo Shipyard Corp., Shimonoseki, Japan (Arklow Willow '04-'16)								
Huron Spirit	8646642	SU	1995	B	4,542*	328' 01"	82' 25"	23' 06"
Built: Jiangdu Shipyard, Tiangsu Province, China (Mulege '95-'14)								
Jarrett M	5030086	TB	1945	D	96*	82' 00"	20' 00"	10' 00"
Built: Russel Brothers Ltd., Owen Sound, ON (Atomic '45-'06)								
Kaliutik		TB	1998	D	83*	65' 00"	22' 00"	8' 00"
Built: Dovercraft Marine, Nanticoke, ON								
Lambert Spirit	8641525	DB	1968	B	9,645	400' 01"	70' 02"	27' 06"
Built: Avondale Shipyards Inc., Avondale, LA (KTC 115 '68-'06)								
Leonard M.	8519215	TB	1986	D	457*	103' 07"	36' 01"	19' 02"
Built: McTay Marine, Bromborough, England (Point Halifax '86-'12)								
Lois M.	9017616	TT	1991	D	453*	35' 09"	11' 65"	5' 07"
Built: Matsuura Tekko Zosen, Higashino, Japan (Lambert '91-'14)								
McKeil Spirit	9347023	CC	2007	D	14,650	459' 02"	68' 11"	34' 0"
Built: Royal Niestern Sander, Delfzijl, The Netherlands; converted to a self-discharging cement carrier '17 (Ardita '07-'18)								
Molly M. 1	5118838	TB	1962	D	207*	98' 06"	27' 10"	12' 02"
Built: Davie Shipbuilding Co., Lauzon, QC (Foundation Vigour '62-'74, Point Vigour '74-'07)								
Niagara Spirit	8736021	DB	1984	D	9,164*	340' 01"	78' 02"	19' 06"
Built: FMC Corp., Portland, OR (Alaska Trader '84-'99, Timberjack '99-'08)								
Nunavut Spirit	8636673	DB	1983	B	6,076*	400' 00"	105' 00"	20' 06"
Built: FMC Corp., Portland, OR (Barge 5001)								
Salvor	5427019	TB	1963	D	407*	120' 00"	31' 00"	18' 06"
Built: Jakobson Shipyard, Oyster Bay, NY (Esther Moran '63-'00)								
Sharon M I	9084059	TB	1993	D	450*	107' 04"	34' 04"	17' 03"
Built: Inamura Shipbuilding, Kure, Japan (Mai Po, Pacific Tempest)								
Stephen B. Roman	6514900	CC	1965	D	7,600	488' 09"	56' 00"	35' 06"
Built: Davie Shipbuilding Co., Lauzon, QC; converted to a self-unloading cement carrier by Collingwood Shipyards, Collingwood, ON, in '83 (Fort William '65-'83)								
Stormont	8959893	TB	1953	D	108*	80' 00"	20' 00"	15' 00"
Built: Canadian Dredge & Dock Co., Kingston, ON								
S/VM 86		DB	1958	B	487*	168' 01"	40' 00"	10' 00"
Built: Canadian Shipbuilding & Engineering Ltd., Collingwood, ON (S.L.S. 86)								
Tim McKeil	9017604	TB	1991	D	453*	107' 07"	34' 04"	17' 03"
Built: Matsuura Tekko Zosen, Higashino, Japan (Pannawonica 1 '91-'14)								
Tobias	9642253	DB	2012	B	8,870*	393' 09"	105' 07"	26' 07"
Built: Damen Shipyards Gorinchem, Gorinchem, Netherlands								
Tony MacKay	7227786	TB	1973	D	366*	117' 00"	30' 02"	14' 05"
Built: Richard Dunston Ltd., Hessle, England (Point Carroll '73-'01)								
Viateur's Spirit		DB	2004	D	253*	141' 01"	52' 03"	5' 01"
Built: Port Weller Dry Dock, Port Weller, ON (Traverse René Lavasseur '04-'06)								
Wilf Seymour	5215789	TB	1961	D	442*	122' 00"	31' 00"	17' 00"
Built: Gulfport Shipbuilding, Port Arthur, TX (M. Moran '61-'70, Port Arthur '70-'72, M. Moran '72-'00, Salvager '00-'04)								
Wyatt M.	8974178	TB	1948	D	123*	85' 00"	20' 00"	10' 00"
Built: Russel Brothers Ltd., Owen Sound, ON (P. J. Murer '48-'81, Michael D. Misner '81-'93, Thomas A. Payette '93-'96, Progress '96-'06)								
MAMMOET-McKEIL LTD., AYR, ON – A SUBSIDIARY OF McKEIL MARINE LTD.								
Dowden Spirit		DB	2014	B	2,130*	250' 02"	72' 01"	16' 04"
Built: Glovertown Shipyards Ltd., Glovertown, NL								
Glovertown Spirit	9662174	DB	2012	B	2,073*	243' 07"	77' 02"	14' 09"
Built: Damen Shipyards, Gorichem, Netherlands								
MM Newfoundland		DB	2011	B	2,165*	260' 00"	72' 00"	16' 01"
Built: Signal International, Pascagoula, MS								
MONTREAL BOATMEN LTD., PORT COLBORNE, ON – A SUBSIDIARY OF McKEIL MARINE LTD.								
Aldo H.		PB	1979	D	37*	56' 04"	15' 04"	6' 02"
Boatman No. 3		PB	1965	D	13*	33' 08"	11' 00"	6' 00"
Boatman No. 6		PB	1979	D	39*	56' 07"	18' 07"	6' 03"
Primrose		DR	1915	B	916*	136' 06"	42' 00"	10' 02"
McMULLEN & PITZ CONSTRUCTION CO., MANITOWOC, WI (mcmullenandpitz.net)								
Dauntless		TB	1937	D	25*	52' 06"	15' 06"	5' 03"
McNALLY INTERNATIONAL INC., HAMILTON, ON (mcnallycorp.com)								
A SUBSIDIARY OF WEEKS MARINE INC., CRANFORD, NJ								
Bagotville		TB	1964	D	62*	65' 00"	18' 05"	8' 03"
Built: Verreault Navigation, Les Méchins, QC								

Fleet Name Vessel Name	Vessel IMO #	Vessel Type	Year Built	Engine Type	Cargo Cap. or Gross*	Overall Length	Vessel Breadth	Vessel Depth
Beaver Delta II		TB	1959	D	14*	35' 08"	12' 00"	4' 04"
Built: Allied Builders Ltd., Vancouver, BC (Halcyon Bay)								
Beaver Gamma		TB	1960	D	17*	37' 01"	12' 09"	6' 00"
Built: Diesel Sales & Service Ltd., Burlington, ON (Burlington Bertie)								
Carl M.		TB	1957	D	21*	47' 00"	14' 06"	6' 00"
D.L. Stanyer		TB	2014	D	14*	40' 03"	11' 08"	6' 02"
Built: Chantier Naval Forillon, Gaspé, QC								
Jamie L.		TB	1988	D	25*	36' 04"	14' 07"	5' 09"
(Baie Ste-Anne '88-'96, T-1 '96-'98, Baie Ste-Anne II '98-'05)								
J.F. Whalen		TB	2014	D	14*	40' 03"	11' 08"	6' 02"
Built: Chantier Naval Forillon, Gaspé, QC								
Lac Como		TB	1944	D	63*	65' 00"	16' 10"	7' 10"
Built: Canadian Bridge Co., Walkerville, ON (Tanac 74 '44-'64)								
Lac Vancouver		TB	1943	D	65*	60' 09"	16' 10"	7' 08"
Built: Central Bridge Co., Trenton, ON (Vancouver '43-'74)								
Mister Joe		TB	1964	D	70*	61' 00"	19' 00"	7' 02"
Built: Russel Brothers Ltd., Owen Sound, ON (Churchill River '64-'01)								
Oshawa		TB	1969	D	24*	42' 09"	13' 08"	5' 04"
Paula M.		TB	1959	D	12*	48' 02"	10' 05"	3' 01"
Sandra Mary		TB	1962	D	97*	80' 00"	21' 00"	10' 09"
Built: Russel Brothers Ltd., Owen Sound, ON (Flo Cooper '62-'00)								
Whitby		TB	1978	D	24*	42' 19"	13' 08"	6' 05"
Willmac		TB	1959	D	16*	40' 00"	13' 00"	3' 07"

MERCURY CRUISES, CHICAGO, IL *(mercurycruises.com)*

Skyline Queen		ES	1959	D	45*	61' 05"	16' 10"	6' 00"

MICHELS CORP., BROWNSVILLE, WI *(michels.us)*

Edith J.		TB	1962	D	18*	43' 02"	13' 00"	5' 04"

MICHIGAN DEPARTMENT OF NATURAL RESOURCES, LANSING, MI *(michigan.gov/dnr)*

Channel Cat		RV	1968	D	24*	46' 00"	13' 06"	4' 00"
Lake Char		RV	2006	D	26*	56' 00"	16' 00"	4' 05"
Steelhead		RV	1967	D	70*	63' 00"	16' 04"	6' 06"
Tanner		RV	2016	D	26*	57' 00"	16' 00"	4' 05"

MICHIGAN TECHNOLOGICAL UNIVERSITY, HOUGHTON, MI *(mtu.edu/greatlakes/fleet/agassiz)*

Agassiz		RV	2002	D	14*	36' 00"	13' 00"	4' 00"

MIDLAND TOURS INC., PENETANGUISHENE, ON *(midlandtours.com)*

Miss Midland	7426667	ES	1974	D	106*	68' 07"	19' 04"	6' 04"
Serendipity Princess		ES	1992	D	93*	64' 09"	23' 00"	4' 07"

MIDWEST MARITIME CORP., FRANKLIN, WI

Leona B.		TB	1972	D	99*	59' 08"	24' 01"	10' 03"
(Kings Squire '72-'89, Juanita D. '78-'89, Peggy Ann '89-'93, Mary Page Hannah {2} '93-'04)								

MILLER BOAT LINE, PUT-IN-BAY, OH *(millerferry.com)*

Islander {3}		PA/CF	1983	D	92*	90' 03"	38' 00"	8' 03"
Put-in-Bay {3}		PA/CF	1997	D	97*	136' 00"	38' 06"	9' 06"
Built: Sturgeon Bay Shipbuilding Co., Sturgeon Bay, WI; lengthened 40' at Cleveland, OH, in '09								
South Bass		PA/CF	1989	D	95*	96' 00"	38' 06"	9' 06"
Wm. Market		PA/CF	1993	D	95*	96' 00"	38' 06"	8' 09"
Built: Peterson Builders Inc., Sturgeon Bay, WI								

MILWAUKEE BOAT LINE LLC, MILWAUKEE, WI *(mkeboat.com)*

Iroquois		PA	1922	D	91*	61' 09"	21' 00"	6' 04"
Vista King		ES	1978	D	60*	78' 00"	23' 00"	5' 02"
Voyageur		PA	1988	D	94*	67' 02"	21' 00"	7' 04"

MILWAUKEE HARBOR COMMISSION, MILWAUKEE, WI *(city.milwaukee.gov/port)*

Harbor Seagull		TB	1961	D	23*	44' 05"	16' 04"	5' 00"
Joey D.		TB	2011	D	65*	60' 00"	20' 06"	6' 06"
Built: Great Lakes Shipyard, Cleveland, OH								

MILWAUKEE METROPOLITAN SEWERAGE DISTRICT, MILWAUKEE, WI

Pelagos		RV	1989	D	32*	42' 09"	13' 08"	6' 06"

MILWAUKEE RIVER CRUISE LINE, MILWAUKEE, WI *(edelweissboats.com)*

Edelweiss II		ES	1989	D	95*	73' 08"	20' 00"	2' 08"
Harbor Lady		ES	1996	D	76*	80' 08"	20' 00"	6' 00"
Lakeside Spirit		ES	1992	D	25*	63' 00"	15' 00"	4' 00"
Miss Wisconsin		ES	1994	D	51*	72' 06"	20' 00"	5' 04"

Fleet Name / Vessel Name	Vessel IMO #	Vessel Type	Year Built	Engine Type	Cargo Cap. or Gross*	Overall Length	Vessel Breadth	Vessel Depth
MINISTRY OF TRANSPORTATION, DOWNSVIEW, ON (mto.gov.on.ca)								
Frontenac Howe Islander		PF/CF	2004	D	130*	100'00"	32'03"	5'05"
Built: Heddle Marine Service Inc., Hamilton, ON; 15-car cable ferry to Howe Island, east of Kingston, ON								
Frontenac II	5068875	PA/CF	1962	D	666*	181'00"	45'00"	10'00"
Built: Chantier Maritime de St-Laurent, St-Laurent, QC (Charlevoix {2}'62-'92); ferry from Millhaven, ON, to Amherst Island								
Glenora	5358074	PA/CF	1952	D	189*	127'00"	33'00"	9'00"
Built: Port Arthur Shipbuilding Co., Port Arthur, ON (St. Joseph Islander '52-'74); ferry from Adolphustown to Glenora, ON								
Jiimaan	9034298	PA/CF	1992	D	2,807*	176'09"	42'03"	13'06"
Built: Port Weller Dry Docks, Port Weller, ON; ferry from Leamington/Kingsville, ON, to Pelee Island								
Pelee Islander	5273274	PA/CF	1960	D	334*	145'00"	32'00"	10'00"
Built: Erieau Shipbuilding & Drydock Co. Ltd., Erieau, ON; ferry from Leamington/Kingsville, ON, to Pelee Island								
Pelee Islander II		PA/CF	2018	D	N/A	222'00"	N/A	N/A
Built: Asenav, Santiago, Chile; new ferry from Leamington/Kingsville, ON due to enter service in 2018								
Quinte Loyalist	5358062	PA/CF	1954	D	204*	127'00"	32'00"	8'00"
Built: Erieau Shipbuilding & Drydock Co. Ltd., Erieau, ON; service to Wolfe Island/Kingston and Glenora/Adolphustown, ON								
Wolfe Islander III	7423079	PA/CF	1975	D	985*	205'00"	68'00"	6'00"
Built: Port Arthur Shipbuilding Co., Port Arthur, ON; ferry from Kingston, ON, to Wolfe Island, ON								
MJO CONTRACTING INC., HANCOCK, MI (mjocontracting.com)								
Lily North		TB	1986	D	85*	60'00"	16'00"	10'02"
MONTREAL PORT AUTHORITY, MONTREAL, QC (port-montreal.com)								
Denis M		TB	1942	D	21*	46'07"	12'08"	4'01"
Built: Russel Brothers Ltd., Owen Sound, ON (Marcel D.)								
Maisonneuve	7397749	PA	1972	D	84*	63'10"	20'07"	9'03"
Built: Fercraft Marine Inc., Ste. Catherine D'Alexandrie, QC								
MUNISING BAY SHIPWRECK TOURS INC., MUNISING, MI (shipwrecktours.com)								
Miss Munising		ES	1967	D	50*	60'00"	14'00"	4'04"
MUSIQUE AQUATIQUE CRUISE LINES INC., TORONTO, ON (citysightseeingtoronto.com)								
Harbour Star		ES	1978	D	45*	63'06"	15'09"	3'09"
MUSKOKA STEAMSHIPS & DISCOVERY CENTRE, GRAVENHURST, ON (realmuskoka.com)								
Segwun		PA	1887	R	308*	128'00"	24'00"	7'06"
Built: Melancthon Simpson, Toronto, ON (Nipissing {2} 1887-'25)								
Wenonah II	8972003	PA	2001	D	447*	127'00"	28'00"	6'00"
Built: McNally Construction Inc., Belleville, ON								

Taïga Desgagnés upbound past bridges 7A and 7B at Kahnawake, Que. (Joe Delaronde)

MYSTIC BLUE CRUISES INC., CHICAGO, IL (mysticbluecruises.com)

Fleet Name Vessel Name	Vessel IMO #	Vessel Type	Year Built	Engine Type	Cargo Cap. or Gross*	Overall Length	Vessel Breadth	Vessel Depth
Mystic Blue		PA	1998	D	97*	138' 09"	36' 00"	10' 05"

N

NADRO MARINE SERVICES LTD., PORT DOVER, ON (nadromarine.com)

Fleet Name Vessel Name	Vessel IMO #	Vessel Type	Year Built	Engine Type	Cargo Cap. or Gross*	Overall Length	Vessel Breadth	Vessel Depth
Ecosse	8624682	TB	1979	D	142*	91' 00"	26' 00"	8' 06"

    Built: Hike Metal Products Ltd., Wheatley, ON (R & L No. 1 '79-'96)

Intrepid III		TB	1976	D	39*	66' 00"	17' 00"	7' 06"

    Built: Halter Marine Ltd., Chalmette, LA

Lac St-Jean		DB	1971	B	771*	150' 00"	54' 09"	10' 06"

    Built: Canadian Vickers Ltd., Montreal, QC

Seahound		TB	1941	D	57*	65' 00"	18' 00"	8' 00"

    Built: Equitable Equipment Co., New Orleans, LA ([Unnamed] '41-'56, Sea Hound '56-'80, Carolyn Jo '80-'00)

Vac		TB	1942	D	36*	65' 00"	20' 04"	4' 03"

    Built: George Gamble, Port Dover, ON

Vigilant I	8994178	TB	1944	D	111*	79' 06"	20' 11"	10' 02"

    Built: Russell Brothers Ltd., Owen Sound, ON (HMCS Glenlivet [W-43] '44-'75, Glenlivet II '75-'77,
    Canadian Franko '77-'82, Glenlivet II '82-'00)

NAUTICA QUEEN CRUISE DINING, CLEVELAND, OH (nauticaqueen.com)

Nautica Queen		ES	1981	D	95*	124' 00"	31' 02"	8' 09"

    Built: Blount Marine Corp., Warren, RI (Bay Queen '81-'85, Arawanna Queen '85-'88, Star of Nautica '88-'92)

NAUTICAL ADVENTURES, TORONTO, ON (nauticaladventure.com)

Empire Sandy	5071561	ES/3S	1943	D/W	338*	140' 00"	32' 08"	14' 00"

    Built: Clellands Ltd., Wellington Quay-on-Tyne, England (Empire Sandy '43-'48, Ashford '48-'52, Chris M. '52-'79)

NEAS (NUNAVUT EASTERN ARCTIC SHIPPING), MONTREAL, QC (neas.ca)

    Vessels offer service between St. Lawrence River ports and the Canadian Arctic between July and November

Avataq	8801618	GC	1989	D	9,653	370' 07"	62' 00"	37' 00"

    Built: Miho Shipbuilding Co. Ltd., Shimizu Shizuoka Prefecture, Japan; operated by Spliethoff's, Amsterdam,
    Netherlands (Poleca, Mekhanik Volkosh, Tiger Speed, Lootsgracht)

Mitiq	9081306	GC	1995	D	12,754	447' 04"	62' 00"	38' 03"

    Built: Frisian Shipbuilding Welgelegen B.V., Harlingen, Netherlands; operated by Spliethoff's, Amsterdam,
    Netherlands (Emmagracht '95-'13)

Nunalik	9466996	HL	2009	D	12,837	453' 00"	68' 11"	36' 01"

    Built: Jiandong Shipyard, Jianfong, China (Beluga Fairy '09-'11, HHL Amazon '11-'16, Hemgracht '16-'17)

Detroit-based tug Cheyenne was brought from the East Coast in 2017. (Aaron Border)

Fleet Name / Vessel Name	Vessel IMO #	Vessel Type	Year Built	Engine Type	Cargo Cap. or Gross*	Overall Length	Vessel Breadth	Vessel Depth
Qamutik	9081289	GC	1995	D	12,760	446' 00"	62' 00"	38' 02"
Built: Frisian Shipbuilding Welgelegen B.V., Harlingen, Netherlands; operated by Spliethoff's, Amsterdam, (Edisongracht)								
Umiavut	8801591	GC	1988	D	9,653	370' 07"	63' 01"	37' 00"
Built: Miho Shipbuilding Co. Ltd., Shimizu Shizuoka Prefecture, Japan; operated by Spliethoff's, Amsterdam, Netherlands (completed as Newca; Kapitan Silin '88-'92, Lindengracht '92-'00)								

NEW YORK POWER AUTHORITY, LEWISTON, NY

Fleet Name / Vessel Name	Vessel IMO #	Vessel Type	Year Built	Engine Type	Cargo Cap. or Gross*	Overall Length	Vessel Breadth	Vessel Depth
Breaker		IB/TB	1962	D	29*	43' 03"	14' 03"	5' 00"
Daniel Joncaire		IB/TB	1979	D	25*	43' 03"	15' 00"	5' 00"
Joncaire II		IB/TB	2015	D	47*	45' 00"	19' 07"	6' 01"
William H. Latham		IB/TB	1987	D	77*	61' 00"		

NEW YORK DEPARTMENT OF ENVIRONMENTAL CONSERVATION, LAKE ONTARIO UNIT, ALBANY, NY

Fleet Name / Vessel Name	Vessel IMO #	Vessel Type	Year Built	Engine Type	Cargo Cap. or Gross*	Overall Length	Vessel Breadth	Vessel Depth
Seth Green		RV	1984	D	50*	47' 00"	17' 00"	8' 00"

NEW YORK STATE MARINE HIGHWAY TRANSPORTATION CO., TROY, NY (nysmarinehighway.com)

Fleet Name / Vessel Name	Vessel IMO #	Vessel Type	Year Built	Engine Type	Cargo Cap. or Gross*	Overall Length	Vessel Breadth	Vessel Depth
Benjamin Elliot		TB	1960	D	27*	47' 07"	15' 02"	7' 02"
Built: Gladding-Hearn Shipbuilding, Somerset, MA (El-Jean '60-'62)								
Frances	5119246	TB	1957	D	146*	84' 08"	24' 00"	9' 06"
Built: Jakobson Shipyard, Oyster Bay, NY (Frances Turecamo '57-'12)								
Margot	5222043	TB	1958	D	141*	90' 00"	25' 00"	10' 00"
Built: Jakobson Shipyard, Oyster Bay, NY (Hustler II '58-'62, Margot Moran '62-'90, Jolene Rose '90-'93)								

NOAA GREAT LAKES ENVIRONMENTAL RESEARCH LABORATORY, ANN ARBOR, MI (glerl.noaa.gov)

Fleet Name / Vessel Name	Vessel IMO #	Vessel Type	Year Built	Engine Type	Cargo Cap. or Gross*	Overall Length	Vessel Breadth	Vessel Depth
Huron Explorer		RV	1979	D	15*	41' 00"	14' 08"	4' 08"
Laurentian		RV	1974	D	129*	80' 00"	21' 06"	11' 00"
Shenehon		SV	1953	D	90*	65' 00"	17' 00"	6' 00"

NORTH CHANNEL TRANSPORT LLC., ALGONAC, MI

Fleet Name / Vessel Name	Vessel IMO #	Vessel Type	Year Built	Engine Type	Cargo Cap. or Gross*	Overall Length	Vessel Breadth	Vessel Depth
Islander {2}		PA/CF	1967	D	38*	41' 00"	15' 00"	3' 06"

NORTH SHORE SCENIC CRUISES, SILVER BAY, MN (scenicsuperior.com)

Fleet Name / Vessel Name	Vessel IMO #	Vessel Type	Year Built	Engine Type	Cargo Cap. or Gross*	Overall Length	Vessel Breadth	Vessel Depth
Wenonah		ES	1960	D	91*	70' 07"	19' 04"	9' 07"

NORTH SHORE MARINE TERMINAL & LOGISTICS, ESCANABA, MI (basicmarine.com)

Fleet Name / Vessel Name	Vessel IMO #	Vessel Type	Year Built	Engine Type	Cargo Cap. or Gross*	Overall Length	Vessel Breadth	Vessel Depth
Erika Kobasic	8654235	TB	1939	DE	226*	110' 00"	25' 01"	14' 03"
Built: Gulfport Shipbuilding, Port Arthur, TX (USCGC Arundel [WYT / WYTM-90] '39-'84, Karen Andrie '84-'90)								
Escort		TB	1969	D	26*	50' 00"	14' 00"	6' 03"
Built: Jakobson Shipyard, Oyster Bay, NY								
Krystal		TB	1954	D	23*	45' 02"	12' 08"	6' 00"
Built: Roamer Boat Co., Holland, MI (ST-2168 '54-'62, Thunder Bay '62-'02)								
Nickelena	8654247	TB	1973	D	240*	109' 00"	30' 07"	15' 08"
Built: Marinette Marine Corp., Marinette, WI (USS Chetek [YTB-827] '73-'96, Chetek '96-'00, Koziol '00-'08)								

NORTHERN MARINE TRANSPORTATION INC., SAULT STE. MARIE, MI

Fleet Name / Vessel Name	Vessel IMO #	Vessel Type	Year Built	Engine Type	Cargo Cap. or Gross*	Overall Length	Vessel Breadth	Vessel Depth
Linda Jean		PB	1950	D	17*	38' 00"	10' 00"	5' 00"
Pilot boat based at DeTour, MI								

NOVAALGOMA CEMENT CARRIERS LTD., ST. CATHARINES, ON (www.novaalgomacc.com)
A PARTNERSHIP BETWEEN ALGOMA CENTRAL CORP. AND NOVA MARINE HOLDINGS SA

Fleet Name / Vessel Name	Vessel IMO #	Vessel Type	Year Built	Engine Type	Cargo Cap. or Gross*	Overall Length	Vessel Breadth	Vessel Depth
NACC Toronto	9287302	CC	2003	D	TBA	447' 05"	69' 05"	37' 07
Built: Kyokuyo Shipyard Corp., Shimonoseki, Japan; converted to a cement carrier in '17 (Arklow Wave '03-'16)								
NACC Quebec	9546057	CC	2011	D	10,243	459' 01"	68' 09"	34' 0
Built: Tuzla Gemi Endustrisi A.S., Tulza, Turkey; converted to a cement carrier in '16 (Tenace '11-'16)								

O-P

OAK GROVE & MARINE TRANSPORTATION INC., CLAYTON, NY

Fleet Name / Vessel Name	Vessel IMO #	Vessel Type	Year Built	Engine Type	Cargo Cap. or Gross*	Overall Length	Vessel Breadth	Vessel Depth
Maple Grove		PK	1954	D	55*	73' 07"	20' 00"	9' 00"
(LCM 8168)								

ODYSSEY CRUISES, CHICAGO, IL (odysseycruises.com/chicago)

Fleet Name / Vessel Name	Vessel IMO #	Vessel Type	Year Built	Engine Type	Cargo Cap. or Gross*	Overall Length	Vessel Breadth	Vessel Depth
Odyssey II		ES	1993	D	88*	162' 05"	40' 00"	13' 05"

OFFSHORE DREDGING & CONSTRUCTION INC., MUSKEGON, MI

Fleet Name / Vessel Name	Vessel IMO #	Vessel Type	Year Built	Engine Type	Cargo Cap. or Gross*	Overall Length	Vessel Breadth	Vessel Depth
Andrew J.		TB	1972	D	31*	43' 08"	14' 03"	7' 05"

OHIO DEPARTMENT OF NATURAL RESOURCES, COLUMBUS, OH (dnr.state.oh.us)

Fleet Name / Vessel Name	Vessel IMO #	Vessel Type	Year Built	Engine Type	Cargo Cap. or Gross*	Overall Length	Vessel Breadth	Vessel Depth
Explorer II		RV	1999	D		53' 00"	15' 05"	4' 05"
Grandon		RV	1990	D	47*	47' 00"	16' 00"	5' 05"

*Alpena unloads powdered
cement at Detroit.*
(Christopher Dark)

*Michipicoten's sunrise arrival at Presque
Isle Harbor, Marquette, Mich.* *(Rod Burdick)*

Fleet Name Vessel Name	Vessel IMO #	Vessel Type	Year Built	Engine Type	Cargo Cap. or Gross*	Overall Length	Vessel Breadth	Vessel Depth
OLSON DREDGE & DOCK CO., ALGONAC, MI								
John Michael		TB	1913	D	41*	55' 04"	15' 01"	7' 06"

Built: Cowles Shipyard Co., Buffalo, NY (Colonel Ward '13-'23, Ross Coddington '24-'65, Joseph J. Olivieri '65-'80)

OLYMPIA CRUISE LINE INC., THORNHILL, ON *(torontocruises.com)*								
Enterprise 2000		ES	1998	D	370*	121' 06"	35' 00"	6' 00"
ONTARIO MINISTRY OF NATURAL RESOURCES, PETERBOROUGH, ON *(mnr.gov.on.ca)*								
Erie Explorer		RV	1981	D	72*	53' 05"	20' 01"	4' 08"

Built: Hopper Fisheries Ltd., Port Stanley, ON (Janice H.X. '81-'97)

Huron Explorer I		RV	2010	D	112*	62' 00"	21' 03"	6' 00"

Built: Hike Metal Products Ltd., Wheatley, ON

Keenosay		RV	1957	D	68*	51' 04"	20' 07"	2' 07"

Built: S.G. Powell Shipyard Ltd., Dunnville, ON

Nipigon Osprey		RV	1990	D	33*	42' 04"	14' 09"	6' 08"

Built: Kanter Yachts Corp., St. Thomas, ON

Ontario Explorer		RV	2009	D	84*	64' 09"	21' 03"	6' 00"

Built: Hike Metal Products Ltd., Wheatley, ON

ONTARIO POWER GENERATION INC., TORONTO, ON								
Niagara Queen II		IB	1992	D	58*	56' 01"	18' 00"	6' 08"

Built: Hike Metal Products Ltd., Wheatley, ON

OPEN LAKE GROUP LLC, DETROIT, MI								
Cheyenne	6515851	TB	1965	D	146*	84' 05"	25' 03"	12' 06"

Built: Ira S. Bushey and Sons Inc., Brooklyn, NY (Glenwood '65-'70)

OWEN SOUND TRANSPORTATION CO., OWEN SOUND, ON *(ontarioferries.com)*								
Chi-Cheemaun	7343607	PA/CF	1974	D	6,991*	365' 05"	61' 00"	21' 00"

Built: Canadian Shipbuilding and Engineering Ltd., Collingwood, ON

PERE MARQUETTE SHIPPING CO., LUDINGTON, MI *(pmship.com)*								
Pere Marquette 41	5073894	SU	1941	B	3,413*	403' 00"	58' 00"	23' 05"

Built: Manitowoc Shipbuilding Co., Manitowoc, WI; converted from powered train/car ferry to a self-unloading barge in '97 (City of Midland 41 '41-'97)

Undaunted	8963210	AT	1943	DE	569*	143' 00"	38' 00"	18' 00"

Built: Gulfport Boiler/Welding, Port Arthur, TX; paired with barge Pere Marquette 41
(USS Undaunted [ATR-126, ATA-199] '44-'63, USMA Kings Pointer '63-'93, Krystal K. '93-'97)

PICTON TERMINALS, PICTON, ON *(pictonterminals.ca)*								
Sheri Lynn S		TB	2017	D	55*	52' 03"	18' 02"	9' 05"

Built: Damen Shipyards, Gorinchem, Netherlands

PICTURED ROCKS CRUISES INC., MUNISING, MI *(picturedrocks.com)*								
Grand Island {2}		ES	1989	D	52*	68' 00"	16' 01"	7' 01"
Grand Portal		ES	2004	D	76*	64' 08"	20' 00"	8' 04"
Miners Castle		ES	1974	D	82*	68' 00"	16' 06"	6' 04"
Miss Superior		ES	1984	D	83*	68' 00"	16' 09"	10' 04"
Pictured Rocks		ES	1972	D	53*	55' 07"	13' 07"	4' 04"
Pictured Rocks Express		ES	1988	D	90*	82' 07"	28' 06"	4' 04"
PIONEER CRUISES, TORONTO, ON *(pioneercruises.com)*								
Pioneer Princess		ES	1984	D	96*	56' 00"	17' 01"	3' 09"
Pioneer Queen		ES	1968	D	110*	85' 00"	30' 06"	7' 03"

(Peche Island III '68-'71, Papoose IV '71-'96)

PLAUNT TRANSPORTATION CO. INC., CHEBOYGAN, MI *(bbiferry.com)*								
Kristen D		CF	1987	D	83*	94' 11"	36' 00"	4' 06"
PORT CITY CRUISE LINE INC., NORTH MUSKEGON, MI *(portcityprincesscruises.com)*								
Port City Princess		ES	1966	D	79*	64' 09"	30' 00"	5' 06"

Built: Blount Marine Corp., Warren, RI (Island Queen {1} '66-'87)

PORTOFINO ON THE RIVER, WYANDOTTE, MI *(portofinoontheriver.com)*								
Friendship		ES	1968	D	76*	85' 00"	23' 04"	7' 03"

Built: Hike Metal Products Ltd., Wheatley, ON (Peche Island V '68-'71, Papoose V '71-'82)

Portofino		ES	1997	D	76*	80' 08"	20' 00"	6' 00"

Built: Skipper Liner, LaCrosse, WI (Island Girl X, Naples Royal Princess, Romantics, Infinity, The Jude Thaddeus, Infinity, Jacksonville Princess II, Miami Magic)

PRESQUE ISLE BOAT TOURS, ERIE, PA *(piboattours.com)*								
Lady Kate {2}		ES	1952	D	11*	59' 03"	15' 00"	3' 09"

(G.A. Boeckling II, Cedar Point III, Island Trader '89-'97)

Fleet Name Vessel Name	Vessel IMO #	Vessel Type	Year Built	Engine Type	Cargo Cap. or Gross*	Overall Length	Vessel Breadth	Vessel Depth
PURE MICHIGAN BOAT CRUISES LLC, MUNISING, MI *(puremichiganboatcruises.com)*								
Isle Royale Queen III		PA	1959	D	88*	74' 03"	18' 04"	6' 05"
Built: T.D. Vinette Co., Escanaba, MI (Isle Royale Queen II)								
PURVIS MARINE LTD., SAULT STE. MARIE, ON *(purvismarine.com)*								
Adanac III		TB	1913	D	108*	80' 03"	19' 03"	9' 10"
Built: Western Drydock & Shipbuilding Co., Port Arthur, ON (Edward C. Whalen '13-'66, John McLean '66-'95)								
Anglian Lady	5141483	TB	1953	D	398*	132' 00"	31' 00"	14' 00"
Built: John I. Thorneycroft & Co., Southampton, England (Hamtun '53-'72, Nathalie Letzer '72-'88)								
Avenger IV	5401297	TB	1962	D	291*	120' 00"	30' 00"	19' 00"
Built: Cochrane & Sons Ltd., Selby, Yorkshire, England (Avenger '62-'85)								
G.L.B. No. 2		DB	1953	B	3,215	240' 00"	50' 00"	12' 00"
Built: Ingalls Shipbuilding Corp., Birmingham, AL (Jane Newfield '53-'66, ORG 6502 '66-'75)								
Malden		DB	1946	B	1,075	150' 00"	41' 09"	10' 03"
Built: Russel Brothers Ltd., Owen Sound, ON								
Martin E. Johnson		TB	1959	D	26*	47' 00"	16' 00"	7' 00"
Built: Russel Hipworth Engines Ltd, Owen Sound, ON								
Osprey		TB	1944	D	36*	45' 00"	13' 06"	7' 00"
Built: Kewaunee Shipbuilding and Engineering Corp., Kewaunee, WI (ST-606 '43-'46)								
PML 2501		TK	1980	B	1,954*	302' 00"	52' 00"	17' 00"
Built: Cenac Shipyard, Houma, LA (CTCO 2505 '80-'96)								
PML 9000		DB	1968	B	4,285*	400' 00"	76' 00"	20' 00"
Built: Bethlehem Steel – Shipbuilding Division, San Francisco, CA (Palmer '68-'00)								
PML Alton		DB	1933	B	150	93' 00"	30' 00"	8' 00"
Built: McClintic- Marshall, Sturgeon Bay, WI								
PML Ironmaster		DB	1962	B	7,437*	360' 00"	75' 00"	25' 00"
Built: Yarrows Ltd., Esquimalt, BC (G.T. Steelmaster, Ceres, American Gulf VII, Seaspan 241, G.T. Ironmaster)								
PML Tucci		CS	1958	B	601*	150' 00"	52' 00"	10' 00"
Built: Calumet Shipyard & Drydock Co., Chicago, IL (MCD '58-'73, Minnesota '73-'88, Candace Andrie '88-'08)								
PML Tucker		DS	1971	B	477*	140' 00"	50' 00"	9' 00"
Built: Twin City Shipyard, St. Paul, MN (Illinois '71-'02, Meredith Andrie '02-'08)								
Reliance	7393808	TB	1974	D	708*	148' 03"	35' 07"	21' 07"
Built: Ulstein Hatlo A/S, Ulsteinvik, Norway (Sinni '74-'81, Irving Cedar '81-'96, Atlantic Cedar '96-'02)								
Rocket		TB	1901	D	40*	73' 00"	16' 00"	7' 00"
Built: Buffalo Shipbuilding Co., Buffalo, NY								
Tecumseh II		DB	1976	B	2,500	180' 00"	54' 00"	12' 00"
Built: Bergeron Machine Shop Inc., New Orleans, LA								
Wilfred M. Cohen	7629271	TB	1947	D	284*	102' 06"	28' 00"	15' 00"
Built: Newport News Shipbuilding and Drydock Co., Newport News, VA (A. T. Lowmaster '48-'75)								
W. I. Scott Purvis	5264819	TB	1938	D	203*	96' 00"	26' 00"	10' 00"
Built: Marine Industries, Sorel, QC (Orient Bay '38-'75, Guy M. No. 1 '75-'90)								
W.J. Isaac Purvis	318726	TB	1962	D	71*	72' 00"	19' 00"	12' 00"
Built: McNamara Marine Ltd., Toronto, ON (Angus M. '62-'92, Omni Sorel '92-'02, Joyce B. Gardiner '02-'09)								
W. J. Ivan Purvis	5217218	TB	1938	D	190*	100' 00"	26' 00"	10' 00"
Built: Marine Industries, Sorel, QC (Magpie '38-'66, Dana T. Bowen '66-'75)								
PUT-IN-BAY BOAT LINE CO., PORT CLINTON, OH *(jet-express.com)*								
Jet Express		PF/CA	1989	D	93*	92' 08"	28' 06"	8' 04"
Jet Express II		PF/CA	1992	D	85*	92' 06"	28' 06"	8' 04"
Jet Express III		PF/CA	2001	D	70*	78' 02"	27' 06"	8' 02"
Jet Express IV		PF/CA	1995	D	71*	77' 02"	28' 05"	7' 07"

Q-R

Fleet Name Vessel Name	Vessel IMO #	Vessel Type	Year Built	Engine Type	Cargo Cap. or Gross*	Overall Length	Vessel Breadth	Vessel Depth
QUEBEC PORT AUTHORITY, QUÉBEC, QC *(portquebec.ca)*								
Le Cageux		TB	2011	D	24*	42' 06"	16' 01"	7' 07"
QUYON FERRY, QUYON, QC *(quyonferry.com)*								
Grant Beattie (The)		PF	2013		235*	115' 00"	46' 00"	7' 05"
RIO TINTO-ALCAN INC., LA BAIE, QC *(riotintoalcan.com)*								
Fjord Éternité	9364348	TT	2006	D	381*	94' 00"	36' 05"	16' 04"
Built: East Isle Shipyard, Georgetown, PEI (Stevns Icecap '06-'07, Switzer Nanna '07-'11, Stevns Icecap '10-'11)								
Fjord Saguenay	9351012	TT	2006	D	381*	94' 00"	36' 05"	16' 04"
Built: East Isle Shipyard, Georgetown, PEI (Stevns Iceflower '06-'07, Switzer Njord '07-'09, Stevns Iceflower '09-'09)								
ROCKPORT BOAT LINE LTD., ROCKPORT, ON *(rockportcruises.com)*								
Canada Spirit		ES	1976	D	325*	92' 00"	26' 00"	10' 00"
Built: Marlin Yacht Co., Summerstown, ON (Cayuga II '76-'82, Wayward Princess '82-'17)								

Fleet Name / Vessel Name	Vessel IMO #	Vessel Type	Year Built	Engine Type	Cargo Cap. or Gross*	Overall Length	Vessel Breadth	Vessel Depth
Chief Shingwauk		ES	1965	D	109*	70' 00"	24' 00"	4' 06"
Built: Hike Metal Products, Wheatley, ON								
Ida M.		ES	1970	D	29*	55' 00"	14' 00"	3' 00"
Ida M. II		ES	1973	D	121*	63' 02"	22' 02"	5' 00"
Sea Prince II		ES	1978	D	172*	83' 00"	24' 02"	6' 08"

ROEN SALVAGE CO., STURGEON BAY, WI *(roensalvage.com)*

Fleet Name / Vessel Name	Vessel IMO #	Vessel Type	Year Built	Engine Type	Cargo Cap. or Gross*	Overall Length	Vessel Breadth	Vessel Depth
Chas. Asher		TB	1967	D	39*	49' 02"	17' 06"	6' 10"
Built: Sturgeon Bay Shipbuilding Co., Sturgeon Bay, WI								
John R. Asher		TB	1943	D	93*	68' 09"	20' 00"	8' 00"
Built: Platzer Boat Works, Houston, TX (U. S. Army ST-71 '43-'46, Russell 8 '46-'64, Reid McAllister '64-'67, Donegal '67-'85)								
Louie S.		TB	1956	D	10*	37' 00"	12' 00"	4' 05"
Spuds		TB	1944	D	19*	42' 00"	12' 05"	5' 04"
Built: Roen Salvage Co., Sturgeon Bay, WI								
Stephan M. Asher		TB	1954	D	60*	65' 00"	19' 01"	5' 04"
Built: Burton Shipyard Inc., Port Arthur, TX (Captain Bennie '54-'82, Dumar Scout '82-'87)								
Timmy A.		TB	1953	D	12*	33' 06"	10' 08"	5' 02"
Built: M.D. Moody & Sons, Jacksonville, FL (Calhoun '53-'64)								

RYBA MARINE CONSTRUCTION CO., CHEBOYGAN, MI *(rybamarine.com)*

Fleet Name / Vessel Name	Vessel IMO #	Vessel Type	Year Built	Engine Type	Cargo Cap. or Gross*	Overall Length	Vessel Breadth	Vessel Depth
Amber Mae		TB	1922	D	67*	65' 00"	14' 01"	10' 00"
Built: Glove Shipyard Inc., Buffalo, NY (E. W. Sutton '22-'52, Venture '52- '00)								
Kathy Lynn	8034887	TB	1944	D	140*	85' 00"	24' 00"	9' 06"
Built: Decatur Iron & Steel Co., Decatur, AL (U. S. Army ST-693 '44-'79, Sea Islander '79-'91)								
Kristin Joelle	6604016	TB	1965	D	148*	75' 05"	24' 00"	8' 06"
(Vincent J.Robin IV, Betty Smith, Seacor Enterprise '91-'97, Leo '97-'98, Ybor '98-'99, Capt. Sweet '99-'01, Susan McAllister '01-'15, Michigan '15-'17)								
Rochelle Kaye		TB	1963	D	52*	51' 06"	19' 04"	7' 00"
Built: St. Charles Steel Works Inc., Thibodeaux, LA (Jaye Anne '63-?, Katanni ?-'97)								
Thomas R. Morrish		TB	1980	D	88*	64' 00"	14' 05"	8' 06"
Built: Houma Shipbuilding Co., Houma, LA (Lady Ora '80-'99, Island Eagle '99-'04, Captain Zeke '01-'14)								

S

SAIL DOOR COUNTY, SISTER BAY, WI *(saildoorcounty.com)*

Fleet Name / Vessel Name	Vessel IMO #	Vessel Type	Year Built	Engine Type	Cargo Cap. or Gross*	Overall Length	Vessel Breadth	Vessel Depth
Edith M. Becker		PA	1984	D/W	22*	62' 00"	24' 00"	8' 06"

SAND PRODUCTS CORP., MUSKEGON, MI

LAKE SERVICE SHIPPING, MUSKEGON, MI

Fleet Name / Vessel Name	Vessel IMO #	Vessel Type	Year Built	Engine Type	Cargo Cap. or Gross*	Overall Length	Vessel Breadth	Vessel Depth
McKee Sons	5216458	SU	1945	B	19,900	579' 02"	71' 06"	38' 06"
Built: Sun Shipbuilding and Drydock Co., Chester, PA; converted from a saltwater vessel to a self-unloading Great Lakes bulk carrier by Maryland Drydock, Baltimore, MD, in '52; completed as a self-unloader by Manitowoc Shipbuilding Co., Manitowoc, WI, in '53; converted to a self-unloading barge by Upper Lakes Towing, Escanaba, MI, in '91; laid up at Erie, PA, 2012-14 and Muskegon, MI, since Dec. 20, 2014 (USNS Marine Angel '45-'52)								

MICHIGAN-OHIO BARGE LLC, MUSKEGON, MI

Fleet Name / Vessel Name	Vessel IMO #	Vessel Type	Year Built	Engine Type	Cargo Cap. or Gross*	Overall Length	Vessel Breadth	Vessel Depth
Commander		CC	1957	B	TBA	390' 00"	71' 00"	27' 00"
Built: Todd Shipyards Corp., Houston, TX; converted to a cement carrier '17-'18 at Bay Shipbuilding Co., Sturgeon Bay, WI (M-211 '57-'81, Virginia '81-'88, C-11 '88-'93, Kellstone 1 '93-'04, Cleveland Rocks '04-'18)								

PORT CITY MARINE SERVICES, MUSKEGON, MI (portcitymarine.com)

Fleet Name / Vessel Name	Vessel IMO #	Vessel Type	Year Built	Engine Type	Cargo Cap. or Gross*	Overall Length	Vessel Breadth	Vessel Depth
Bradshaw McKee	7644312	ATB	1977	D	174*	121' 06"	34' 06"	18' 02"
Built: Toche Enterprises Inc., Ocean Springs, MS; paired with barge St. Marys Conquest (Lady Elda '77-'78, Kings Challenger '78-'78, ITM No. 1 '78-'81, Kings Challenger '81-'86, Susan W. Hannah '86-'11)								
Colleen McAllister	7338872	TB	1967	D	194*	124' 00"	31' 06"	13' 08"
Built: Gulfport Shipbuilding Corp., Port Arthur, TX (Ellena Hicks '67-'03)								
Katie G. McAllister	7046089	TB	1966	D	194*	124' 00"	31' 06"	13' 08"
Built: Gulfport Shipbuilding Corp., Port Arthur, TX (Libby Black '67-'03)								
Prentiss Brown	7035547	TB	1967	D	197*	123' 05"	31' 06"	19' 00"
Built: Gulfport Shipbuilding, Port Arthur, TX; paired with barge St. Marys Challenger (Betty Culbreath '67-'03, Micheala McAllister '03-'09)								
St. Marys Challenger	5009984	CC	1906	B	N/A	N/A	56' 00"	31' 00"
Built: Great Lakes Engineering Works, Ecorse, MI; repowered in '50; converted to a self-unloading cement carrier by Manitowoc Shipbuilding Co., Manitowoc, WI, in '67; converted to a barge by Bay Shipbuilding Co., Sturgeon Bay, WI, over the winter of 2013-'14 (William P. Snyder '06-'26, Elton Hoyt II {1} '26-'52, Alex D. Chisholm '52-'66, Medusa Challenger '66-'99, Southdown Challenger '99-'04)								
St. Marys Conquest	5015012	CC	1937	B	8,500	437' 06"	55' 00"	28' 00"
Built: Manitowoc Shipbuilding Co., Manitowoc, WI; converted from a powered tanker to a self-unloading cement barge by Bay Shipbuilding, Sturgeon Bay, WI, in '87 (Red Crown '37-'62, Amoco Indiana '62-'87, Medusa Conquest '87-'99, Southdown Conquest '99-'04)								

Fleet Name / Vessel Name	Vessel IMO #	Vessel Type	Year Built	Engine Type	Cargo Cap. or Gross*	Overall Length	Vessel Breadth	Vessel Depth
SEA SERVICE LLC, SUPERIOR, WI *(seaservicellc.com)*								
Sea Bear		PB	1959	D	28*	45' 08"	13' 08"	7' 00"
Provides pilot service at Duluth, MN								
SEAWAY MARINE GROUP LLC, CLAYTON, NY *(seawaymarinegroup.com)*								
Seaway Supplier		GC	1952	D	97*	73' 06"	21' 00"	9' 04"
(LCM-8010)								
SELVICK MARINE TOWING CORP., STURGEON BAY, WI *(selvickmarinetowing.com)*								
Cameron O		TB	1955	D	26*	50' 00"	15' 00"	7' 03"
Built: Peterson Builders Inc., Sturgeon Bay, WI (Escort II '55-'06)								
Donny S	7436234	TB	1950	DE	461*	143' 00"	33' 01"	14' 06"
Built: Levingston Shipbuilding, Orange, TX (U. S. Army ATA-230 '49-'72, G. W. Codrington '72-'52,								
William P. Feeley {2} '52-'72, William W. Stender '72-'76, Mary Page Hannah '76-'14)								
Jacquelyn Yvonne		TB	1943	D	29*	45' 02"	12' 10"	7' 08"
Built: Sturgeon Bay Shipbuilding, Sturgeon Bay, WI (ST-173 '43-'55, Manistee '55-'87, Robert W. Purcell '87-'17)								
Jimmy L		TB	1939	D	148*	110' 00"	25' 00"	13' 00"
Built: Defoe Shipbuilding Co., Bay City, MI (USCGC Naugatuck [WYT / WYTM-92] '39-'80, Timmy B. '80-'84)								
Sharon M. Selvick		TB	1943	D	28*	45' 05"	12' 10"	7' 01"
Built: Kewaunee Shipbuilding & Engineering, Kewaunee, WI (U. S. Army ST-585 '43-'49, USCOE Judson '49-'94)								
Susan L		TB	1944	D	133*	86' 00"	23' 00"	10' 04"
Built: Equitable Equipment Co., New Orleans, LA (U. S. Army ST-709 '44-'47, USCOE Stanley '47-'99)								
William C. Gaynor	8423818	TB	1956	D	187*	94' 00"	27' 00"	11' 09"
Built: Defoe Shipbuilding Co., Bay City, MI (William C. Gaynor '56-'88, Captain Barnaby '88-'02)								
William C. Selvick	5322623	TB	1944	D	142*	85' 00"	23' 00"	9' 07"
Built: Platzer Boat Works, Houston, TX (U. S. Army ST-500 '44-'49, Sherman H. Serre '49-'77)								
SHELL CANADA LIMITED, CALGARY, AB								
Juno Marie	9301641	RT	2004	D	2,191	262' 05"	45' 04"	22' 00"
Built: Miura Shipbuilding, Saiki, Japan; stationed at Montreal, QC (Alios Apollo '04-'10, Elin Apollo '10-'12, Milo '12-'16)								
SHEPLER'S MACKINAC ISLAND FERRY, MACKINAW CITY, MI *(sheplersferry.com)*								
Capt. Shepler		PF	1986	D	71*	84' 00"	21' 00"	7' 10"
Felicity		PF	1972	D	65*	65' 00"	18' 01"	8' 03"
Miss Margy		PF	2015	D	70*	85' 00"	22' 00"	
Sacré Bleu		PK	1959	D	98*	94' 10"	31' 00"	9' 09"
The Hope		PF	1975	D	87*	77' 00"	20' 00"	8' 03"
The Welcome		PF	1969	D	66*	60' 06"	16' 08"	8' 02"
Wyandot		PF	1979	D	83*	77' 00"	20' 00"	8' 00"
SHORELINE CHARTERS, GILLS ROCK, WI *(shorelinecharters.net)*								
The Shoreline		ES	1973	D	12*	33' 00"	11' 4"	3' 00"
SHORELINE CONTRACTORS INC., WELLINGTON, OH *(shorelinecontractors.com)*								
Eagle		TB	1943	D	31*	57' 07"	35' 09"	6' 08"
Built: Defoe Shipbuilding Co., Bay City, MI (Jack Boyce '43-'78, Jan B. '78-'79, Sea Search II '79-'86)								
General		TB	1964	D	125*	63' 08"	15' 04"	6' 05"
SHORELINE SIGHTSEEING CO., CHICAGO, IL *(shorelinesightseeing.com)*								
Blue Dog		ES	1981	D	31*	47' 07"	18' 00"	5' 05"
Bright Star		ES	2003	D	93*	79' 03"	23' 00"	7' 01"
Cap Streeter		ES	1987	D	28*	63' 06"	24' 04"	7' 07"
Cityview		ES	2014	D	76*	75' 06"	34' 06"	5' 04"
Evening Star	(Tug/barge)	ES	2001	D	93*	83' 00"	23' 00"	7' 00"
Marlyn		ES	1961	D	70*	65' 00"	25' 00"	7' 00"
Riverview		ES	2013	D	76*	75' 06"	34' 06"	5' 04"
Shoreline II		ES	1987	D	89*	75' 00"	26' 00"	7' 01"
Skyview	(Tug/barge)	ES	2016	D	90*	94' 05"	35' 00"	7' 05"
Star of Chicago {2}		ES	1999	D	73*	64' 10"	22' 08"	7' 05"
Voyageur		ES	1983	D	98*	65' 00"	35' 00"	7' 00"
SNC-LAVALIN, MONTREAL, QC *(snclavalin.com)*								
Intense		TB	2016	D	21*	41' 00"	14' 04"	7' 08"
Built: Besiktas Tersane A.S., Istanbul, Turkey								
Turbulent		TB	2016	D	38*	48' 06"	19' 00"	9' 02"
Built: Besiktas Tersane A.S., Istanbul, Turkey								
SOCIÉTÉ DES TRAVERSIERS DU QUÉBEC CITY, QUÉBEC, QC *(traversiers.gouv.qc.ca)*								
Alphonse-Desjardins	7109233	PA/CF	1971	D	1,741*	214' 00"	71' 06"	20' 00"
Built: Davie Shipbuilding Co., Lauzon, QC								

Fleet Name / Vessel Name	Vessel IMO #	Vessel Type	Year Built	Engine Type	Cargo Cap. or Gross*	Overall Length	Vessel Breadth	Vessel Depth
Armand-Imbeau	7902269	PA/CF	1980	D	1,285*	203' 07"	72' 00"	18' 04"
Built: Marine Industries Ltd., Sorel, QC								
Armand-Imbeau II	9703215	PA/CF	2018	D	5,000*	301' 08"		
Built: Davie Shipbuilding Co., Lauzon, QC								
Catherine-Legardeur	8409355	PA/CF	1985	D	1,348*	205' 09"	71' 10"	18' 10"
Built: Davie Shipbuilding Co., Lauzon, QC								
F.-A.-Gauthier	9669861	PA/CF	2015	DE	15,901*	436' 03"	73' 05"	26' 02"
Built: Fincantieri Castellammare di Stabia, Naples, Italy								
Felix-Antoine-Savard	9144706	PA/CF	1997	D	2,489*	272' 00"	70' 00"	21' 09"
Built: Davie Shipbuilding Co., Lauzon, QC (fueled by liquid natural gas)								
Grue-des-Iles	8011732	PA/CF	1981	D	447*	155' 10"	41' 01"	12' 06"
Built: Bateaux Tur-Bec Ltd., Ste-Catherine, QC								
Ivan-Quinn	9554028	PA/CF	2008	D	241*	83' 07"	26' 09"	11' 03"
Built: Meridien Maritime Reparation Inc., Matane, QC								
Jos-Deschenes	391571	PA/CF	1980	D	1,287*	203' 07"	72' 00"	18' 04"
Built: Marine Industries Ltd., Sorel, QC								
Joseph-Savard	8409343	PA/CF	1985	D	1,445*	206' 00"	71' 10"	18' 10"
Built: Davie Shipbuilding Co., Lauzon, QC								
Lomer-Gouin	7109221	PA/CF	1971	D	1,741*	214' 00"	71' 06"	20' 00"
Built: Davie Shipbuilding Co., Lauzon, QC								
Lucien-L.	6721981	PA/CF	1967	D	867*	220' 10"	61' 06"	15' 05"
Built: Marine Industries Ltd., Sorel, QC								
Peter-Fraser		PA/CF	2012	DE	292*	110' 02"	39' 03"	7' 03"
Built: Chantier Naval Forillon, Gaspé, QC								
Radisson {1}		PA/CF	1954	D	1,037*	164' 03"	72' 00"	10' 06"
Built: Davie Shipbuilding Co., Lauzon, QC								

Algosteel turning in the Detroit River to unload at Windsor, Ont. (Matt Miner)

Fleet Name Vessel Name	Vessel IMO #	Vessel Type	Year Built	Engine Type	Cargo Cap. or Gross*	Overall Length	Vessel Breadth	Vessel Depth
SOO LOCKS BOAT TOURS, SAULT STE. MARIE, MI *(soolocks.com)*								
Bide-A-Wee {3}		ES	1955	D	99*	64' 07"	23' 00"	7' 11"
Built: Blount Marine Corp., Warren, RI								
Hiawatha {2}		ES	1959	D	99*	64' 07"	23' 00"	7' 11"
Built: Blount Marine Corp., Warren, RI								
Holiday		ES	1957	D	99*	64' 07"	23' 00"	7' 11"
Built: Blount Marine Corp., Warren, RI								
Le Voyageur		ES	1959	D	70*	65' 00"	25' 00"	7' 00"
Built: Sturgeon Bay Shipbuilding & Dry Dock Co., Sturgeon Bay, WI								
Nokomis		ES	1959	D	70*	65' 00"	25' 00"	7' 00"
Built: Sturgeon Bay Shipbuilding & Dry Dock Co., Sturgeon Bay, WI								
SOO MARINE SUPPLY INC., SAULT STE. MARIE, MI *(soomarine.com)*								
Ojibway		SB	1945	D	53*	53' 00"	28' 00"	7' 00"
Built: Great Lakes Engineering Works, Ashtabula, OH								
SOO PILOT LLC, SAULT STE. MARIE, MI								
Soo Pilot		PB	1976	D	22*	41' 03"	13' 06"	5' 09"
Provides pilot service at Sault Ste. Marie, MI								
SOUTH SHORE DREDGE & DOCK INC., LORAIN, OHIO								
Cojak		TB	1954	D	11*	31' 04"	10' 09"	5' 06"
SPIRIT CRUISES LLC, CHICAGO, IL *(spiritcruises.com/chicago)*								
Spirit of Chicago		ES	1988	D	92*	156' 00"	35' 00"	7' 01"
SPIRIT OF THE SOUND SCHOONER CO. LTD., PARRY SOUND, ON *(spiritofthesound.ca)*								
Chippewa III		PA	1954	D	47*	65' 00"	16' 00"	6' 06"
Built: Russel-Hipwell Engines Ltd., Owen Sound, ON (Maid of the Mist III '54-'56, Maid of the Mist '56-'92)								

Fleet Name / Vessel Name	Vessel IMO #	Vessel Type	Year Built	Engine Type	Cargo Cap. or Gross*	Overall Length	Vessel Breadth	Vessel Depth
ST. JAMES MARINE CO. & FOGG TOWING & MARINE, BEAVER ISLAND, MI *(stjamesmarine.com)*								
American Girl		TB	1922	D	63*	62' 00"	14' 00"	6' 05"
Built: Defoe Shipbuilding Co., Bay City, MI								
Wendy Anne		TB	1955	D	89*	71' 00"	20' 00"	8' 05"
Built: Smith Basin Drydock, Port Everglades, FL (ST-2199)								
ST. LAWRENCE CRUISE LINES INC., KINGSTON, ON *(stlawrencecruiselines.com)*								
Canadian Empress		PA	1981	D	463*	108' 00"	30' 00"	8' 00"
Built: Algan Shipyards Ltd., Gananoque, ON								
ST. LAWRENCE SEAWAY DEVELOPMENT CORP., MASSENA, NY *(www.seaway.dot.gov)*								
Grasse River		GL	1958	GL		150' 00"	65' 08"	5' 06"
Performance		TB	1997	D		50' 00"	16' 06"	7' 05"
Built: Marine Builders Inc., Utica, IN								
Robinson Bay		TB	1958	DE	213*	103' 00"	26' 10"	14' 06"
Built: Christy Corp., Sturgeon Bay, WI								
ST. LAWRENCE SEAWAY MANAGEMENT CORP., CORNWALL, ON *(greatlakes-seaway.com)*								
VM/S Hercules		GL	1962	D	2,107*	200' 00"	75' 00"	18' 08"
VM/S St. Lambert		TB	1974	D	20*	30' 08"	13' 01"	6' 05"
ST. MARYS CEMENT INC., TORONTO, ON *(stmaryscement.com)*								
THE FOLLOWING VESSELS OPERATED BY FETTES SHIPPING, BURLINGTON, ON								
Sea Eagle II	7631860	ATB	1979	D	560*	132' 00"	35' 00"	19' 00"
Built: Modern Marine Power Co., Houma, LA; paired with barge St. Marys Cement II (Sea Eagle '79-'81, Canmar Sea Eagle '81-'91)								
St. Marys Cement	8972077	CC	1986	B	9,400	360' 00"	60' 00"	23' 03"
Built: Merce Industries East, Cleveland, OH								
St. Marys Cement II	8879914	CC	1978	B	19,513	496' 00"	76' 00"	35' 00"
Built: Galveston Shipbuilding Co., Galveston, TX (Velasco '78-'81, Canmar Shuttle '81-'90)								
THE FOLLOWING VESSEL CHARTERED BY ST. MARYS CEMENT GROUP FROM GREAT LAKES & INTERNATIONAL TOWING & SALVAGE CO., BURLINGTON, ON								
Petite Forte	6826119	TB	1969	D	368*	127' 00"	32' 00"	14' 06"
Built: Cochrane and Sons Ltd., Selby, Yorkshire, England; paired with barge St. Marys Cement								
STAR LINE MACKINAC ISLAND FERRY, ST. IGNACE, MI *(mackinacferry.com)*								
Algomah		PF/PK	1961	D	81*	93' 00"	29' 08"	5' 02"
Built: Paasch Marine Services Inc., Erie, PA								
Anna May		ES	1947	D	94*	64' 10"	30' 00"	7' 03"
(West Shore '47-'12)								
Cadillac {5}		PF	1990	D	73*	64' 07"	20' 00"	7' 07"
Chippewa {6}		PF/PK	1962	D	81*	93' 00"	29' 08"	5' 02"
Built: Paasch Marine Services Inc., Erie, PA								
Good Fortune		PA	2015	D	57*	65' 00"	19' 00"	7' 00"
Huron {5}		PF/PK	1955	D	99*	91' 06"	25' 00"	7' 00"
Built: Paasch Marine Services Inc., Erie, PA								
Joliet {3}		PF	1993	D	83*	64' 08"	22' 00"	8' 03"
LaSalle {4}		PF	1983	D	55*	65' 00"	20' 00"	7' 05"
Mackinac Islander		CF	1947	D	99*	84' 00"	30' 00"	8' 02"
Built: Sturgeon Bay Shipbuilding, Sturgeon Bay, WI (Drummond Islander '47-'02)								
Marquette II {2}		PF	2005	D	65*	74' 00"	23' 06"	8' 00"
Ottawa {2}		PF/PK	1959	D	81*	93' 00"	29' 08"	5' 02"
Built: Paasch Marine Services Inc., Erie, PA								
Radisson {2}		PF	1988	D	97*	80' 00"	23' 06"	7' 00"
Straits Express		PF/CA	1995	D	99*	101' 00"	28' 08"	10' 00"
Built: Marinette Marine Corp., Marinette, WI								
Straits of Mackinac II		PF/PK	1969	D	89*	90' 00"	27' 06"	8' 08"
Built: Blount Marine Corp., Warren, RI								
STERLING FUELS LTD., HAMILTON, ON *(sterlingfuels.ca)*								
Sterling Energy	9277058	RT	2002	D	749*	226' 03"	32' 10"	14' 09"
Built: Selahattin Alsan Shipyard, Istanbul Turkey; refueling tanker serves vessels in the vicinity of Hamilton and Toronto, ON, and the Welland Canal (Melisa D '02-'13)								

T

Fleet Name / Vessel Name	Vessel IMO #	Vessel Type	Year Built	Engine Type	Cargo Cap. or Gross*	Overall Length	Vessel Breadth	Vessel Depth
TALL SHIP WINDY, CHICAGO, IL *(tallshipwindy.com)*								
Windy		ES/4S	1996	W	75*	148' 00"	25' 00"	8' 00"
Built: Detyens Shipyards Inc., North Charleston, SC								

Fleet Name / Vessel Name	Vessel IMO #	Vessel Type	Year Built	Engine Type	Cargo Cap. or Gross*	Overall Length	Vessel Breadth	Vessel Depth

TALL SHIP RED WITCH LLC, KENOSHA, WI (redwitch.com)

Red Witch		ES/2S	1986	W	41*	77' 00"	17' 06"	6' 05"

Built: Nathaniel Zirlott, Bayou La Batre, AL

TGL MARINE HOLDINGS ULC, TORONTO, ON

Jane Ann IV	7802809	ATB	1978	D	954*	150' 11"	42' 08"	21' 04"

Built: Mitsui Engineering & Shipbuilding Co., Tokyo, Japan; paired with barge Sarah Spencer; in long-term lay-up at Toledo, OH (Ouro Fino '78-'81, Bomare '81-'93, Tignish Sea '93-'98)

Sarah Spencer	5002223	SU	1959	B	21,844	693' 10"	72' 00"	40' 00"

Built: Manitowoc Shipbuilding Co., Manitowoc, WI; engine removed, converted to a self-unloading barge by Halifax Dartmouth Industries, Halifax, NS, in '89; in long-term lay-up at Toledo, OH (Adam E. Cornelius {3} '59-'89, Capt. Edward V. Smith '89-'91, Sea Barge One '91-'96)

THOUSAND ISLAND MARINE CONSTRUCTION LTD., GANANOQUE, ON (timarineconstruction.com)

Steelhead		TB	1944	D	36*	56' 00"	20' 00"	5' 03"

Built: W.F. Kolbe & Co. Ltd., Port Dover, ON

THOUSAND ISLANDS & SEAWAY CRUISES, BROCKVILLE, ON (1000islandscruises.com)

General Brock III		ES	1977	D	56*	56' 05"	15' 04"	5' 02"
Lady of the Isles		ES	1986	D	105*	65' 00"	20' 00"	6' 08"
Sea Fox II		ES	1988	D	55*	39' 08"	20' 00"	2' 00"

THUNDER BAY TUG SERVICES LTD., THUNDER BAY, ON (thunderbaytugservices.ca)

Glenada		TB	1943	D	107*	80' 06"	25' 00"	10' 01"

Built: Russel Brothers Ltd., Owen Sound, ON (HMCS Glenada [W-30] '43-'45)

Miseford		TB	1915	D	116*	85' 00"	20' 00"	9' 06"

Built: M. Beatty & Sons Ltd., Welland, ON

Point Valour		TB	1958	D	246*	97' 08"	28' 02"	13' 10"

Built: Davie Shipbuilding Co., Lauzon, QC (Foundation Valour '58-'83)

Robert W.		TB	1949	D	48*	60' 00"	16' 00"	8' 06"

Built: Russel Brothers Ltd., Owen Sound, ON

Rosalee D.		TB	1943	D	22*	55' 00"	12' 07"	4' 11"

Built: Northern Shipbuilding & Repair Co., Bronte, ON

TORONTO BOAT CRUISES, TORONTO, ON (torontoboatcruises.com)

Aurora Borealis		ES	1983	D	277*	108' 00"	24' 00"	6' 00"

Built: Ralph Hurley, Port Burwell, ON

TORONTO BRIGANTINE INC., TORONTO, ON (torontobrigantine.org)

Pathfinder		TV	1963	D/W	32*	59' 08"	15' 00"	8' 00"

Built: Canadian Shipbuilding & Engineering Co., Collingwood, ON

Playfair		TV	1973	D/W	33*	59' 08"	15' 00"	8' 00"

Built: Canadian Dredge & Co., Kingston, ON

TORONTO DRYDOCK LTD., TORONTO, ON (torontodrydock.com)

Coastal Titan	7700477	HL	1978	B	3,000*	300' 00"	55' 00"	27' 00"

Built: Peterson Builders, Sturgeon Bay, WI; converted to a barge in '09 at Port Colborne, ON (John Henry, Marinelink Explorer, Chaulk Lifter 15)

Menier Consol		FD	1962					

Built: Davie Shipbuilding Co., Lauzon, QC; former pulpwood carrier was converted to a floating drydock in 1984

M.R. Kane		TB	1945	D	51*	60' 06"	16' 05"	6' 07"

Built: Central Bridge Co. Ltd., Trenton, ON (Tanac V-276 '45-'47)

Radium Yellowknife	5288956	TB	1948	D	235*	120' 00"	28' 00"	6' 06"

Built: Yarrows Ltd., Esquimalt, BC

Salvage Monarch	5308275	TB	1959	D	219*	97' 09"	29' 00"	13' 06"

Built: P.K. Harris Ltd., Appledore, England

TORONTO FIRE SERVICES, TORONTO, ON (toronto.ca/fire)

William Thornton		FB	1982	D	55*	70' 10"	18' 00"	8' 09"

Built: Breton Industrial & Marine Ltd., Port Hawkesbury, NS (Cape Hurd '82-'14)

Wm. Lyon Mackenzie	6400575	FB	1964	D	102*	81' 01"	20' 00"	10' 00"

Built: Russel Brothers Ltd., Owen Sound, ON

TORONTO ISLANDS TRANSIT SERVICES INC., TORONTO ON

Dartmouth III	7801776	PA	1978	D	255*	78' 08"	31' 00"	8' 04"

Built: Ferguson Industries, Pictou, NS

TORONTO PORT AUTHORITY, TORONTO, ON (torontoport.com)

Brutus I		TB	1992	D	10*	36' 01"	11' 09"	4' 04"

Built: Mariner Jack Inc., Michigan City, IN

David Hornell VC		PA/CF	2006	D	219*	95' 10"	37' 07"	7' 05"

Built: Hike Metal Products, Wheatley, ON (TCCA 2 '09-'10)

Fleet Name / Vessel Name	Vessel IMO #	Vessel Type	Year Built	Engine Type	Cargo Cap. or Gross+	Overall Length	Vessel Breadth	Vessel Depth
Iron Guppy		TB	2016	D	65*	66' 96"	21' 00"	10' 24"
Built: Hike Metal Products, Wheatley, ON								
Maple City		PA/CF	1951	D	135*	70' 06"	36' 04"	5' 11"
Built: Muir Brothers Dry Dock Co. Ltd., Port Dalhousie, ON; in long-term lay-up								
Marilyn Bell I		PA/CF	2009	D	270*	95' 10"	37' 07"	7' 05"
Built: Hike Metal Products, Wheatley, ON (TCCA 2 '09-'10)								
Windmill Point		PA/CF	1954	D	118*	65' 00"	36' 00"	10' 00"
Built: Kingston Shipyards Ltd., Kingston, ON; in long-term lay-up								

TORONTO HARBOUR TOURS INC., TORONTO, ON (harbourtourstoronto.ca)

Miss Kim Simpson		ES	1960	D	33*	90' 02"	13' 04"	3' 09"
New Beginnings		ES	1961	D	28*	41' 09"	13' 01"	4' 09"
Shipsands		ES	1972	D	23*	58' 03"	12' 01"	4' 07"

TRAVERSE RIVIERE-DU-LOUP SAINT-SIMEON LTD., RIVIERE-DU-LOUP, QC (traverserdl.com)

Trans-St-Laurent	5409586	CF/PA	1963	D	2,173*	249' 06"	60' 01"	15' 04"
Built: Geo. T. Davie & Sons Ltd., Lauzon, QC								

TRAVERSE TALL SHIP CO., TRAVERSE CITY, MI (tallshipsailing.com)

Manitou {1}		ES/2S	1983	W	78*	114' 00"	21' 00"	9' 00"
Built: Steel Ship Corp., Portsmouth, NH								

30,000 ISLANDS CRUISE LINES INC., PARRY SOUND, ON (islandqueencruise.com)

Island Queen V		ES	1990	D	526*	130' 00"	35' 00"	6' 06"
Built: Herb Fraser & Associates, Port Colborne, ON								

TRIDENT MARINE CORP., CLEVELAND, OH (holidaycleveland.com)

Holiday		PA	1964	D	25*	60' 00"	16' 01"	5' 06"

U

UNCLE SAM BOAT TOURS, ALEXANDRIA BAY, NY (usboattours.com)

Alexandria Belle		ES	1988	D	92*	82' 00"	32' 00"	8' 00"
Island Duchess		ES	1988	D	73*	90' 03"	27' 08"	9' 00"
Island Wanderer		ES	1971	D	57*	62' 05"	22' 00"	7' 02"
Uncle Sam 7		ES	1976	D	55*	60' 04"	22' 00"	7' 01"

U.S. ARMY CORPS OF ENGINEERS – GREAT LAKES & OHIO RIVER DIV., CINCINNATI, OH (www.lre.usace.army.mil)

U.S. ARMY CORPS OF ENGINEERS – BUFFALO DISTRICT

Cheraw		TB	1970	D	356*	109' 00"	30' 06"	16' 03"
Built: Southern Shipbuilding Corp., Slidell, LA (USS Cheraw [YTB-802] '70-'96)								
McCauley		CS	1948	B		112' 00"	52' 00"	4' 25"
Mike Donlon		TB	1999	TB	64*	53' 00"	19' 02"	7' 07"
Built: Marine Builders Inc., Utica, Ind.								
Simonsen		CS	1954	B		142' 00"	58' 00"	5' 00"

U.S. ARMY CORPS OF ENGINEERS – DETROIT DISTRICT, LAKE MICHIGAN AREA OFFICE, KEWAUNEE SUB-OFFICE

Kenosha		TB	1954	D	82*	70' 00"	20' 00"	9' 08"
Built: Missouri Valley Bridge & Iron Works, Leavenworth, KS (U. S. Army ST-2011 '54-'65)								
Manitowoc		CS	1976	B		132' 00"	44' 00"	8' 00"
Racine		TB	1931	D	61*	66' 03"	18' 05"	7' 08"
Built: Marine Iron & Shipbuilding Co., Duluth MN								

U.S. ARMY CORPS OF ENGINEERS – DETROIT DISTRICT, DETROIT AREA OFFICE

Demolen		TB	1974	D	356*	109' 00"	30' 06"	16' 03"
Built: Marinette Marine Corp., Marinette, WI (USS Metacom [YTB-829] '74-'01, Metacom '01-'02)								
Veler		CS	1991	B	613*	150' 00"	46' 00"	10' 06"

U.S. ARMY CORPS OF ENGINEERS – DETROIT DISTRICT, DULUTH AREA OFFICE

D. L. Billmaier		TB	1968	D	356*	109' 00"	30' 06"	16' 03"
Built: Southern Shipbuilding Corp., Slidell, LA (USS Natchitoches [YTB-799] '68-'95)								
Hammond Bay		TB	1953	D	23*	45' 00"	13' 00"	7' 00"
Built: Roamer Boat Co., Holland, MI								
H. J. Schwartz		DB	1995	B		150' 00"	48' 00"	11' 00"

U.S. ARMY CORPS OF ENGINEERS – DETROIT DISTRICT, SOO AREA OFFICE

Harvey		DB	1961	B		120' 00"	40' 00"	8' 00"
Nicolet		DB	1971	B		120' 00"	40' 00"	8' 00"
Owen M. Frederick		TB	1942	D	56*	65' 00"	17' 00"	7' 06"
Built: Sturgeon Bay Shipbuilding Co., Sturgeon Bay, WI								
Paul Bunyan		GL	1945	B		150' 00"	65' 00"	12' 06"
Built: Wiley Equipment Co., Port Deposit, MD								

Fleet Name / Vessel Name	Vessel IMO #	Vessel Type	Year Built	Engine Type	Cargo Cap. or Gross*	Overall Length	Vessel Breadth	Vessel Depth
Whitefish Bay		TB	1953	D	23*	45' 00"	13' 00"	7' 00"
Built: National Steel & Shipbuilding Co., San Diego, CA								

U.S. COAST GUARD 9TH COAST GUARD DISTRICT, CLEVELAND, OH *(uscg.mil/d9)*

Alder [WLB-216]	9271145	BT	2004	D	2,000*	225' 09"	46' 00"	19' 08"
Built: Marinette Marine Corp., Marinette, WI; stationed at Duluth, MN								
Biscayne Bay [WTGB-104]	8635148	IB	1979	D	662*	140' 00"	37' 06"	12' 00"
Built: Tacoma Boatbuilding Co., Tacoma, WA; stationed at St. Ignace, MI								
Bristol Bay [WTGB-102]	8635150	IB	1979	D	662*	140' 00"	37' 06"	12' 00"
Built: Tacoma Boatbuilding Co., Tacoma, WA; stationed at Detroit, MI								
Buckthorn [WLI-642]		BT	1963	D	200*	100' 00"	24' 00"	4' 08"
Built: Mobile Ship Repair Inc., Mobile, AL; stationed at Sault Ste. Marie, MI								
CGB-12001		BT	1991	B	700*	120' 00"	50' 00"	6' 00"
CGB-12002		BT	1992	B	700*	120' 00"	50' 00"	6' 00"
Hollyhock [WLB-214]	9271133	BT	2003	D	2,000*	225' 09"	46' 00"	19' 08"
Built: Marinette Marine Corp., Marinette, WI; stationed at Port Huron, MI								
Katmai Bay [WTGB-101]		IB	1978	D	662*	140' 00"	37' 06"	12' 00"
Built: Tacoma Boatbuilding Co., Tacoma, WA; stationed at Sault Ste. Marie, MI								
Mackinaw [WLBB-30]	9271054	IB	2005	D	3,407*	240' 00"	58' 00"	15' 05"
Built: Marinette Marine Corp., Marinette, WI; stationed at Cheboygan, MI								
Mobile Bay [WTGB-103]	8635162	IB	1979	D	662*	140' 00"	37' 06"	12' 00"
Built: Tacoma Boatbuilding Co., Tacoma, WA; stationed at Sturgeon Bay, WI								
Morro Bay [WTGB-106]	8635215	IB	1979	D	662*	140' 00"	37' 06"	12' 00"
Built: Tacoma Boatbuilding Co., Tacoma, WA; stationed at Cleveland, OH								
Neah Bay [WTGB-105]	8635174	IB	1980	D	662*	140' 00"	37' 06"	12' 00"
Built: Tacoma Boatbuilding Co., Tacoma, WA; stationed at Cleveland, OH								

U.S. ENVIRONMENTAL PROTECTION AGENCY, CHICAGO, IL *(epa.gov)*

Lake Explorer II		RV	1966	D	150*	86' 09"	22' 00"	7' 02"
Built: Jackobson Shipyard, Oyster Bay, NY (NOAA Rude '66-'08)								
Lake Guardian	8030609	RV	1981	D	959*	180' 00"	40' 00"	14' 00"
Built: Halter Marine Inc., Moss Point MS (Marsea Fourteen '81-'90)								

U.S. FISH & WILDLIFE SERVICE, ALPENA, MI

Spencer F. Baird	9404326	RV	2006	D	256*	95' 00"	30' 00"	9' 05"
Built: Conrad Industries Inc., Morgan City, LA								
Stanford H. Smith		RV	2018	D	37*	57' 00"	16' 00"	N/A
Built: Moran Ironworks, Onaway, MI								

U.S. NATIONAL PARK SERVICE - ISLE ROYALE NATIONAL PARK, HOUGHTON, MI *(nps.gov)*

Greenstone II		TK	2003	B	114*	70' 01"	24' 01"	8' 00"
Built: Fraser Shipyards, Superior, WI								
Ranger III	7618234	PK	1958	D	648*	152' 08"	34' 00"	13' 00"
Built: Christy Corp., Sturgeon Bay, WI								

U.S. NAVAL SEA CADET CORPS, GREAT LAKES DIVISION, MOUNT CLEMENS, MI *(prideofmichigan.org)*

Pride of Michigan [YP-673]		TV	1977	D	70*	80' 06"	17' 08"	5' 03"
Built: Peterson Builders Inc., Sturgeon Bay, WI; based at Mount Clemens, MI (USS YP-673 '77-'89)								

U.S. OIL, A DIVISION OF U.S. VENTURE INC., APPLETON, WI *(usoil.com)*
MANAGED BY BETTER WAY LOGISTICS LLC, MUSKEGON, MI

Great Lakes {2}		TK	1982	B	5,024*	414' 00"	60' 00"	30' 00"
Built: Bay Shipbuilding Co., Sturgeon Bay, WI (Amoco Great Lakes '82-'85)								
Michigan {10}	8121795	AT	1982	D	292*	107' 08"	34' 00"	16' 00"
Built: Bay Shipbuilding Co., Sturgeon Bay, WI (Amoco Michigan '82-'85)								

UNIVERSITY OF MINNESOTA LARGE LAKES OBSERVATORY, DULUTH, MN *(scse.d.umn.edu/blue-heron)*

Blue Heron		RV	1985	D	175*	87' 00"	23' 00"	11' 00"
Built: Goudy and Stevens, East Boothbay, ME (Fairtry '85-'97)								

UNIVERSITY OF WISCONSIN SCHOOL OF FRESHWATER SCIENCES, MILWAUKEE, WI *(glwi.uwm.edu)*

Neeskay		RV	1952	D	75*	71' 00"	17' 06"	7' 06"
Built: Higgins Industries, New Orleans, LA (T-494)								

URGENCE MARINE INC., MONTREAL, QC *(urgencemarine.com)*

Simon Cote		TB	1953	D	14*	38' 02"	11' 05"	4' 00"

USS GREAT LAKES LLC, NEW YORK, NY

Robert F. Deegan		TK	1968	B	2,424*	225' 08"	60' 00"	18' 00"
Built: Wyatt Industries, Houston, TX; paired with tug Zeus								

V-W

VANENKEVORT TUG & BARGE INC., ESCANABA MI *(vtbarge.com)*

Clyde S. VanEnkevort		ATB	2011	D	1,179*	135' 04"	50' 00"	26' 00"

    Built: Donjon Shipbuilding & Repair, Erie, PA; paired with the barge Erie Trader (Ken Boothe Sr. '11-'17)

Erie Trader		SU	2012	B	37,600	740' 04"	78' 00"	30' 00"

    Built: Donjon Shipbuilding & Repair, Erie, PA (Lakes Contender '12-'17)

Great Lakes Trader	8635966	SU	2000	B	39,600	740' 00"	78' 00"	45' 00"

    Built: Halter Marine, Pearlington, MS; paired with tug Joyce L. VanEnkevort

Joseph H. Thompson		SU	1944	B	21,200	706' 06"	71' 06"	38' 06"

    Built: Sun Shipbuilding & Drydock Co., Chester, PA; converted from a saltwater vessel to a Great Lakes bulk carrier by Maryland Dry Dock, Baltimore, MD, and American Shipbuilding Co., South Chicago, IL, in '52; converted to a self-unloading barge by the owners in '91 (USNS Marine Robin '44-'52)

Joseph H. Thompson Jr.	5175745	ATB	1990	D	841*	146' 06"	38' 00"	30' 00"

    Built at Marinette, WI, from steel left over from the conversion of Joseph H. Thompson (above)

Joyce L. VanEnkevort	8973033	AT	1998	D	1,179*	135' 04"	50' 00"	26' 00"

    Built: Bay Shipbuilding Co., Sturgeon Bay, WI; paired with barge Great Lakes Trader

VICTORIAN PRINCESS CRUISE LINES, ERIE, PA *(victorianprincess.com)*

Victorian Princess		ES	1985	D	46*	67' 00"	24' 00"	4' 05"

VISTA FLEET, DULUTH, MN *(vistafleet.com)*

Vista Queen		ES	1987	D	97*	64' 00"	16' 00"	6' 02"

    Built: Mid-City Steel Fabricating Inc., La Crosse, WI (Queen of Excelsior)

Vista Star		ES	1987	D	95*	91' 00"	24' 09"	5' 02"

    Built: Freeport Shipbuilding Inc., Freeport, FL (Island Empress '87-'88)

VOIGHT'S MARINE SERVICES LTD., ELLISON BAY & GILLS ROCK, WI *(islandclipper.com)*

Island Clipper {2}		ES	1987	D	71*	65' 00"	20' 00"	8' 00"
Yankee Clipper		ES	1971	D	41*	46' 06"	17' 00"	6' 00"

WALPOLE-ALGONAC FERRY LINE, PORT LAMBTON, ON *(walpoleislandferry.ca)*

City of Algonac		CF	1990	D	82*	62' 06"	27' 09"	5' 09"

    Built: Duratug Shipyard & Fabricating Ltd., Port Dover, ON

Walpole Islander		CF	1986	D	72*	54' 05"	27' 09"	6' 03"

    Built: Hike Metal Products, Wheatley, ON

WALSTROM MARINE, HARBOR SPRINGS, MI *(walstrom.com)*

Elizabeth		TB	1945	D	21*	42' 02"	12' 01"	5' 05"

    Built: Burger Boat Co., Manitowoc, WI (ST-912 '45-'48, Ashland '48-'72, Charles F. Liscomb '72-'94 and '94-'01, Lydie Rae '01-'03)

Drone's-eye view of Edwin H. Gott on the lower St. Marys River. *(Dan Vaught)*

Cold air makes *James R. Barker's* steam plume stand out. *(Marc Dease)*

A new age of steam?
Exhaust gas scrubbers clean engine emissions

Lee A. Tregurtha trailing her signature steam stream. *(Peter Groh)*

A scrubber unit being installed. *(Chris Winters)*

No, Great Lakes fleets aren't returning to age of steam, even though that can look to be the case as more and more vessels are equipped with exhaust gas scrubbers that send an eco-friendly plume of steam out the smokestack.

Here's how the system works. Exhaust gas from the engine is sent through a series of absorption sprays that wash and remove impurities, specifically sulfur and particulate matter. That washed exhaust gas then travels through a droplet separator before a signature clean plume of white steam is discharged into the atmosphere.

Specifically, the scrubber units, which are attached to the exhaust system of each of a ship's engines, rely on an injection of sodium hydroxide to neutralize and remove sulfur from the exhaust gas. This chemical has to be delivered to the vessel about twice a month. The result is a reduction of emissions to a level that meets or exceeds North American Emissions Control Area requirements.

Interlake Steamship Co. has been a leader in adopting this technology. It was the first U.S.-flagged fleet to test freshwater scrubbers on the Great Lakes, in April 2015 on the motor vessel *Hon. James L. Oberstar*. Five Interlake vessels – including the longest ship on the Great Lakes, *Paul R. Tregurtha* – were to be outfitted with these types of scrubbers by 2018.

Fleet Name Vessel Name	Vessel IMO #	Vessel Type	Year Built	Engine Type	Cargo Cap. or Gross*	Overall Length	Vessel Breadth	Vessel Depth
WARNER PETROLEUM CORP., CLARE, MI *(warnerpetroleum.com)*								
Coloma L. Warner	7337892	TB	1955	D	134*	86' 00"	24' 00"	10' 00"

Built: Sturgeon Bay Shipbuilding, Sturgeon Bay, WI; paired with the barge Warner Provider (Harbor Ace '55-'61, Gopher State '61-'71, Betty Gale '71-'93, Hannah D. Hannah '93-'10)

Marysville		TK	1973	B	1,136*	200' 00"	50' 00"	12' 06"

Built: St. Louis Shipbuilding, St. Louis, MO (N.M.S. No. 102 '73-'81)

Warner Provider	8641185	RT	1962	B	1,698*	264' 00"	52' 05"	12' 00"

Built: Port Houston Iron Works, Houston, TX (Hannah 2903); in use as a fueling barge at south Lake Michigan ports

William L. Warner	7322055	RT	1973	D	492*	120' 00"	40' 00"	14' 00"

Built: Halter Marine, New Orleans, LA (Jos. F. Bigane '73-'04); in use as a vessel fueling barge at Detroit, MI

WASHINGTON ISLAND FERRY LINE, WASHINGTON ISLAND, WI *(wisferry.com)*								
Arni J. Richter		PA/CF	2003	D	92*	104' 00"	38' 06"	10' 11"

Built: Bay Shipbuilding Co., Sturgeon Bay, WI

Eyrarbakki		PA/CF	1970	D	95*	87' 00"	36' 00"	7' 06"

Built: Bay Shipbuilding Co., Sturgeon Bay, WI

Karfi		PA/CF	1967	D	23*	36' 00"	16' 00"	4' 08"

Built: T.D. Vinette Co., Escanaba, MI

Robert Noble		PA/CF	1979	D	97*	90' 04"	36' 00"	8' 03"

Built: Peterson Builders Inc., Sturgeon Bay, WI

Washington {2}		PA/CF	1989	D	97*	100' 00"	37' 00"	9' 00"

Built: Peterson Builders Inc., Sturgeon Bay, WI

WENDELLA SIGHTSEEING CO. INC., CHICAGO, IL *(wendellaboats.com)*								
Linnea		ES	2010	D	77*	85' 05"	30' 00"	7' 01"
Lucia		ES	2015	D	80*	85' 05"	30' 00"	7' 01"
Ouilmette		ES	2001	D	43*	65' 00"	22' 04"	4' 05"
Wendella		ES	2007	D	77*	85' 05"	30' 00"	7' 01"
Wendella LTD		ES	1992	D	66*	68' 00"	20' 00"	4' 09"
WHITE LAKE DOCK & DREDGE INC., MONTAGUE, MI *(wlddi.com)*								
Captain George		TB	1929	D	61*	60' 09"	16' 07"	7' 07"

Built: Charles Ward Engine Works, Charleston, WV (Captain George '29-'73, Kurt R. Luedtke '73-'91)

J-Krab		TW	2010	D	14*	25' 05"	14' 00"	5' 07"
Lauren A		TB	1980	D	68*	51' 05"	21' 00"	6' 00"

Built: Melancon Fabricators Inc., Lockport, LA (Janine Alicia '80-'89)

WILLY'S CONTRACTING CO., SOUTHAMPTON, ON *(willyscontracting.com)*								
Howard W. Fitzpatrick		TB	1971	D	97*	78' 00"	20' 05"	4' 09"

Built: Grafton Boat Co. Inc., Grafton, IL (Fireboat No. 1)

Misty Jean		TB	1947	D	34*	54' 00"	22' 00"	4' 11"

Built: Erieau Shipbuilding & Dry Dock Co., Erieau, ON (W.D. Candice)

Pride		TB	1957	D	47*	52' 06"	29' 08"	5' 01"

Built: Strege Fisheries Inc., Racine, WI

WINDSOR RIVER CRUISES LTD., WINDSOR, ON *(windsorrivercruises.com)*								
Macassa Bay	8624709	ES	1986	D	210*	93' 07"	29' 07"	10' 04"

Built: Boiler Pump & Marine Works Ltd., Hamilton, ON

WOHLLEB-SOCIE CO., TOLEDO, OH								
Bessie B		TB	1947	D	30*	52' 03"	13' 09"	5' 05"
WISCONSIN DEPARTMENT OF NATURAL RESOURCES, BAYFIELD & STURGEON BAY, WI *(dnr.wi.gov)*								
Coregonus		RV	2011	D	37*	60' 00"	16' 00"	5' 09"
Gaylord Nelson		RV	1992	D	12*	45' 09"	16' 00"	5' 05"
Hack Noyes		RV	1947	D	50*	56' 00"	14' 05"	4' 00"
1089856 ONTARIO LTD., THUNDER BAY, ON								
W. N. Twolan	5384360	TB	1962	D	299*	106' 00"	29' 05"	15' 00"

Built: George T. Davie & Sons, Lauzon, QC

NACC Quebec carries product for NovaAlgoma Cement Carriers Ltd. (*J. Brian Way*)

Mississagi motors into the MacArthur Lock at Sault Ste. Marie, Mich. (*Roger LeLievre*)

Veteran motor vessel Saginaw meets the Great Lakes-built Freedom-class littoral combat ship Little Rock on the St. Lawrence Seaway Dec. 22, 1017. (Ron Beaupre)

Grain carrier Ojibway fitting out at Sarnia, Ont. *(Bill Bird)*

Walter J. McCarthy Jr. departs Duluth, Minn., on a stormy day. (Paul Scinocca)

LAKER LONGEVITY

1906: St. Marys Challenger *(re: '67, '14)* **1936**: J.A.W. Iglehart *(re: '65)** **1937**: St. Marys Conquest *(re: '87)*

1941: Pere Marquette 41 *(re: '97)* **1942**: Alpena *(re: '91)*, American Victory *(re: '61, '82)*** Lee A. Tregurtha *(re: '61)* **1943**: Cuyahoga *(re: '74)*, Manistee *(re: '64)***, Mississagi *(re: '67)* **1944**: Joseph H. Thompson *(re '52, '91)*, McKee Sons *(re: '53, '91**)* **1949**: Wilfred Sykes

1952: Arthur M. Anderson *(re: '75, '82)*, Kaye E. Barker *(re: '76, '81)*, Cason J. Callaway *(re: '74, '82)*, Philip R. Clarke *(re: '74, '82)*, Menominee *(re: '06)*, Michipicoten *(re: '57, '80)*, Ojibway, John G. Munson **1953**: American Valor *(re: '74, '82)***, Badger, James L. Kuber *(re: '07)*, Pathfinder *(re: '98)*, Saginaw **1958**: John Sherwin** **1959**: Cedarglen *(re: '77)*, Hon. James L. Oberstar *(re: '72, '81)*, Herbert C. Jackson *(re: '75)*, Sarah Spencer *(re: '89)***

1960: Edward L. Ryerson** **1961**: English River *(re: '74)* **1965**: Stephen B. Roman *(re: '83)* **1966**: Algosteel *(re: '89)* **1967**: Tim S. Dool *(re: '96)*, John D. Leitch *(re: '02)*, Manitoba **1968**: Algorail, Frontenac *(re: '73)* **1969**: CSL Tadoussac *(re: '01)*

1972: Algoway, Roger Blough, CSL Niagara *(re: '99)*, Stewart J. Cort **1973**: Adam L., Calumet, Manitowoc, John J. Boland, Rt. Hon. Paul J. Martin *(re: '00)*, Presque Isle, Tecumseh **1974**: H. Lee White, Robert S. Pierson **1975**: Sam Laud **1976**: James R. Barker, Joseph L. Block, Algoma Olympic, St. Clair **1977**: Algolake, CSL Assiniboine *(re: '05)*, CSL Laurentien *(re: '01)*, Walter J. McCarthy Jr., Mesabi Miner **1978**: Radcliffe R. Latimer *(re: '09)*, American Integrity, American Spirit, Algoma Buffalo

1979: American Courage, Algoma Enterprise, Algoma Transport, Edwin H. Gott, Indiana Harbor

1980: American Mariner, Burns Harbor, Salarium, Edgar B. Speer, Oakglen **1981**: Algowood *(re: '00)*, American Century, Great Republic, Capt. Henry Jackman *(re: '96)*, Paul R. Tregurtha **1982**: Michigan, Ashtabula **1983**: Spruceglen, Kaministiqua **1984**: Atlantic Huron *(re: '89, '03)* **1986**: Algoma Spirit **1987**: Algoma Discovery, Algoma Guardian

1991: Manitoulin *(re: '15)* **1992**: Dara Desgagnés, Esta Desgagnés **1993**: Jana Desgagnés **1996**: Integrity **1998**: Algosea **1999**: Maria Desgagnés

2000: Great Lakes Trader **2001**: Norman McLeod **2003**: NACC Toronto **2004**: Algoscotia, Lake Express **2006**: Innovation **2007**: Rosaire A. Desgagnés, Argentia Desgagnés, Taiga Desgagnés, Evans Spirit, McKeil Spirit **2008**: Algocanada, Algonova, John J. Carrick, Zélada Desgagnés **2009**: Sedna Desgagnés

2011: Algoma Mariner, Claude A. Desgagnés , NACC Quebec **2012**: Erie Trader, Bella Desgagnés, Baie St. Paul **2013**: Algoma Equinox, Thunder Bay, Whitefish Bay, Baie Comeau, Acadia Desgagnés **2014**: Algoma Harvester, G3 Marquis, CSL Welland, CSL St-Laurent **2016**: Mia Desgagnés, Damia Desgagnés **2017**: Algoma Strongfield, Algoma Niagara **2018**: Paul A. Desgagnés, Argentia Desgagnés, Algoma Innovator, Algoma Sault, Algoma Conveyor, Algoma Endurance

(re = major rebuild; * = storage barge; ** means in long-term lay-up)

There are four birthday milestones to mark in 2018: Mississagi and Algorail turn 75, John Sherwin turns 60, and Frontenac turns 50. The latter is shown loading at Two Harbors, Minn. (Chris Mazzella)

87

ENGINES – Major Great Lakes & Seaway Vessels

Vessel Name	Engine Manufacturer & Model #	Engine Type	Total Engines	Total Cylinders	Rated HP	Total Props	Speed MPH
Acadia Desgagnés	MaK - 8M32C	Diesel	1	8	5,362 bhp	1	13.8
Adam L.	GM EMD - 20-645-E7B	Diesel	2	20	7,200 bhp	1 cpp	16.1
Alder (USCG)	Caterpillar - 3608TA	Diesel	2	6	3,100 bhp	1 cpp	
Algocanada	MaK - 9M32C	Diesel	1	9	6,118 bhp	1 cpp	16.1
Algolake	Pielstick - 10PC2-2V-400	Diesel	2	10	9,000 bhp	1 cpp	17.3
Algoma Buffalo	GM EMD - 20-645-E7	Diesel	2	20	7,200 bhp	1 cpp	16.1
Algoma Conveyor	Sulzer - 7RTA48T-B	Diesel	1	7	11,140 bhp	1	16.1
Algoma Dartmouth	MAN-B&W - 6L23/30A	Diesel	2	6	2,310 bhp	2 cpp	13.3
Algoma Discovery	Sulzer - 6RTA62	Diesel	1	6	15,499 bhp	1 cpp	16.4
Algoma Endurance	Wartsila 5RT-flex50-D	Diesel	1	5	11,863 bhp	1 cpp	16.1
Algoma Enterprise	MAN - 7L40/45	Diesel	2	7	8,804 bhp	1 cpp	13.8
Algoma Equinox	Wartsila 5RT-flex50-D	Diesel	1	5	11,863 bhp	1 cpp	16.1
Algoma Guardian	Sulzer - 6RTA62	Diesel	1	6	15,499 bhp	1 cpp	16.4
Algoma Hansa	Wartsila - 6L46A	Diesel	1	6	6,525 bhp	1	15.8
Algoma Harvester	Wartsila 5RT-flex50-D	Diesel	1	5	11,863 bhp	1 cpp	16.1
Algoma Innovator	Details unavailable						
Algoma Integrity	Sulzer - 6RT-FLEX-58T-B	Diesel	1	6	14,895 bhp	1	
Algoma Mariner	MAN-B&W - 6L48/60CR	Diesel	1	6	9,792 bhp	1 cpp	
Algoma Niagara	Sulzer - 7RTA48T-B	Diesel	1	7	11,140 bhp	1	16.1
Algoma Olympic	MAN - 8L40/54A	Diesel	2	8	10,000 bhp	1 cpp	15.0
Algoma Sault	Sulzer - 7RTA48T-B	Diesel	1	7	11,140 bhp	1	16.1
Algoma Spirit	Sulzer - 6RTA62	Diesel	1	6	11,284 bhp	1 cpp	16.4
Algoma Strongfield	Sulzer - 7RTA48T-B	Diesel	1	7	11,140 bhp	1	16.1
Algoma Transport	MAN - 8L40/45	Diesel	2	8	10,000 bhp	1 cpp	13.8
Algonova	MaK - 9M32C	Diesel	1	9	6,118 bhp	1 cpp	16.1
Algoscotia	Wartsila - 6L46C	Diesel	1	6	8,445 bhp	1 cpp	16.0
Algosea	Wartsila - 6L46A	Diesel	1	6	6,434 bhp	1 cpp	15.0
Algosteel	Sulzer - 6RND76	Diesel	1	6	9,599 bhp	1	17.0
Algowood	MaK - 6M552AK	Diesel	2	6	10,200 bhp	1 cpp	13.8
Alpena	De Laval Steam Turbine Co.	Turbine	1	**	4,400 shp	1	14.1
American Century	GM - EMD - 20-645-E7B	Diesel	4	20	14,400 bhp	2 cpp	17.3
American Courage	GM - EMD - 20-645-E7	Diesel	2	20	7,200 bhp	1 cpp	16.1
American Integrity	GM EMD - 20-645-E7	Diesel	4	20	14,400 bhp	2 cpp	18.4
American Mariner	GM EMD - 20-645-E7	Diesel	2	20	7,200 bhp	1 cpp	15.0
American Spirit	Pielstick - 16PC2-2V-400	Diesel	2	16	16,000 bhp	2 cpp	17.3
American Valor	Westinghouse Elec. Corp.	Turbine	1	**	7,700 shp	1	16.1
American Victory	Bethlehem Steel Corp.	Turbine	1	**	7,700 shp	1	19.0
Amundsen (CCG)	Alco - 16V251F	Diesel	6	16	17,700 bhp	2	18.6
Anglian Lady *	Deutz - SBA12M528	Diesel	2	12	3,480 bhp	2 cpp	15.5
Arctic	MAN - 14V52/55A	Diesel	1	14	14,770 bhp	1	17.8
Argentia Desgagnés	Wartsila C - W6L32B3	Diesel	1	6	5,362 bhp	1	15.6
Arthur M. Anderson	Westinghouse Elec. Corp.	Turbine	1	**	7,700 shp	1	16.1
Atlantic Huron	Sulzer - 6RLB66	Diesel	1	6	11,094 bhp	1 cpp	17.3
Avenger IV *	British Polar	Diesel	1	9	2,700 bhp	1 cpp	12.0
Badger **	Skinner Engine Co. - Steeple Compound Uniflow	Steam	2	8	3,500 ihp	2	18.4
Baie Comeau	MAN B&W - 6S50ME-B9	Diesel	1	6	11,897 bhp	1	15.5
Baie St. Paul	MAN B&W - 6S50ME-B9	Diesel	1	6	11,897 bhp	1	15.5
Barbara Andrie *	GM EMD 16-645-EF	Diesel	1	16	2,000 bhp	1	
Bella Desgagnés	Wartsila - 9L20CR	Diesel	4	9	8,320 bhp	2 azimuth	17.3
Beverly M 1 *	Niigata - 6L28HX	Diesel	2	6	1,971 bhp	2	16.0
Biscayne Bay (USCG)	Fairbanks Morse - 10-38D8-1/8	Diesel	2	10	2,500 bhp	1	13.8
Bradshaw McKee *	GM EMD - 12-645-E5	Diesel	2	12	4,320 bhp	2	11.5
Bristol Bay (USCG)	Fairbanks Morse - 10-38D8-1/8	Diesel	2	10	2,500 bhp	1	13.8
Burns Harbor	GM EMD - 20-645-E7	Diesel	4	20	14,400 bhp	2 cpp	18.4

* = tug   ** = ferry

bhp: brake horsepower, a measure of diesel engine output measured at the crankshaft before entering gearbox or any other power take-out device

ihp: indicated horsepower, based on an internal measurement of mean cylinder pressure, piston area, piston stroke and engine speed; used for reciprocating engines

shp: shaft horsepower, a measure of engine output at the propeller shaft at the output of the reduction gearbox; used for steam and diesel-electric engines

cpp: controllable pitch propeller

Vessel Name	Engine Manufacturer & Model #	Engine Type	Total Engines	Total Cylinders	Rated HP	Total Props	Speed MPH
Calumet	Alco - 16V251E	Diesel	2	16	5,600 bhp	1	16.1
Calusa Coast *	GM EMD 12-645-E2	Diesel	2	12	3,400 bhp	2	
Capt. Henry Jackman	MaK - 6M552AK	Diesel	2	6	9,465 bhp	1 cpp	17.3
Cason J. Callaway	Westinghouse Elec. Corp.	Turbine	1	**	7,700 shp	1	16.1
Cedarglen	B&W - 7-74VTBF-160	Diesel	1	7	8,750 bhp	1 cpp	15.5
Chi-Cheemaun **	Caterpillar - C280-6	Diesel	4	6	9,280 bhp	2	
Claude A. Desgagnés	MaK/Caterpillar - 6M43C	Diesel	1	6	7,342 bhp	1 cpp	17.8
Clyde S. VanEnkevort *	Cat-MaK - 8M32C	Diesel	2	8	10,876 bhp	2 cpp	18.4
CSL Assiniboine	MaK/Caterpillar - 6M32C	Diesel	2	6	8,060 bhp	1 cpp	
CSL Laurentien	MaK/Caterpillar - 6M32C	Diesel	2	6	8,060 bhp	1 cpp	
CSL Niagara	MaK/Caterpillar - 6M32C	Diesel	2	6	8,060 bhp	1 cpp	
CSL St-Laurent	MAN B&W 6S50ME-B	Diesel	1	6	11,897 bhp	1 cpp	15.5
CSL Tadoussac	Sulzer - 6RND76	Diesel	1	6	9,600 bhp	1	17.0
CSL Welland	MAN B&W 6S50ME-B	Diesel	1	6	11,897 bhp	1 cpp	15.5
Cuyahoga	Caterpillar - 3608	Diesel	1	8	3,000 bhp	1 cpp	12.6
Damia Desgagnés	Wärtsilä 5RT-flex 50DF	Diesel/LNG	1	5	7,305 bhp	1 cpp	15
Dara Desgagnés	B&W - 6L35MC	Diesel	1	6	5,030 bhp	1 cpp	14.4
Defiance *	GM EMD - 20-645-E7	Diesel	2	20	7,200 bhp	2	15.0
Des Groseilliers (CCG)	Alco - 16V251F	Diesel	6	16	17,700 bhp	2	18.6
Donny S *	GM -12-278A	Diesel	2	12	1,850 bhp	2	
Dorothy Ann *	GM EMD - 20-645-E7B	Diesel	2	20	7,200 bhp	2 Z-drive cpp	16.1
Ecosse *	GM Detroit - 16V92 N	Diesel	2	16	1,800 bhp	2	13.8
Edgar B. Speer	Pielstick - 18PC2-3V-400	Diesel	2	18	19,260 bhp	2 cpp	17.0
Edward L. Ryerson	General Electric Co.	Turbine	1	**	9,900 shp	1	19.0
Edwin H. Gott	MaK - 8M43C	Diesel	2	8	19,578 bhp	2 ccp	16.7
English River	Werkspoor - TMAB-390	Diesel	1	8	1,850 bhp	1 cpp	13.8
Espada Desgagnés	B&W - 6S60MC-C	Diesel	1	5	18,605 bhp	1 cpp	18.4
Esta Desgagnés	B&W - 6L35MC	Diesel	1	6	5,030 bhp	1 cpp	14.4
Evans McKeil *	GM EMD - 16-645C	Diesel	1	16	2,150 bhp	1	11.5
Evans Spirit	Wartsila - 6L38B	Diesel	1	6	5,831 bhp	1 cpp	16.1
Everlast *	Daihatsu - 8DSM-32	Diesel	2	8	6,000 bhp	2	16.5
Federal Asahi	B&W - 6S46MC-C	Diesel	1	6	10,710 bhp	1	16.1
Federal Baltic	B&W - 6S46MC-C	Diesel	1	5	10,710 bhp	1	16.1
Federal Barents	B&W - 6S46MC-C	Diesel	1	6	10,710 bhp	1	16.1
Federal Beaufort	B&W - 6S46MC-C	Diesel	1	6	10,710 bhp	1	16.1
Federal Bering	B&W - 6S46MC-C	Diesel	1	6	10,710 bhp	1	16.1
Federal Biscay	B&W - 6S46MC-C	Diesel	1	6	10,710 bhp	1	16.1
Federal Bristol	B&W - 6S46MC-C	Diesel	1	6	10,710 bhp	1	16.1
Federal Caribou	B&W - 6S46MC-C	Diesel	1	6	10,710 bhp	1	16.1
Federal Cedar	B&W - 6S46MC-C	Diesel	1	6	10,710 bhp	1	16.1
Federal Champlain	B&W - 6S46MC-C	Diesel	1	6	10,710 bhp	1	16.1
Federal Churchill	B&W - 6S46MC-C	Diesel	1	6	10,710 bhp	1	16.1
Federal Clyde	B&W - 6S46MC-C	Diesel	1	6	10,710 bhp	1	16.1
Federal Columbia	B&W - 6S46MC-C	Diesel	1	6	10,710 bhp	1	16.1
Federal Danube	B&W - 6S46MC-C	Diesel	1	6	10,686 bhp	1	16.1
Federal Elbe	B&W - 6S46MC-C	Diesel	1	6	10,686 bhp	1	16.1
Federal Ems	B&W - 6S46MC-C	Diesel	1	6	10,686 bhp	1	16.1
Federal Hudson	B&W - 6S46MC-C	Diesel	1	6	10,710 bhp	1	15.5
Federal Hunter	B&W - 6S46MC-C	Diesel	1	6	10,710 bhp	1	15.5
Federal Katsura	Mitsubishi (Tokyo) - 6UEC52LA	Diesel	1	6	9,490 bhp	1	19.2
Federal Kivalina	B&W - 6S46MC-C	Diesel	1	6	10,710 bhp	1	16.1
Federal Kumano	B&W - 6S46MC-C	Diesel	1	6	10,710 bhp	1	16.1
Federal Kushiro	Mitsubishi - 6UEC52LA	Diesel	1	6	9,626 bhp	1	16.6
Federal Leda	B&W - 6S46MC-C	Diesel	1	6	10,686 bhp	1	16.1
Federal Maas	B&W - 6S50MC	Diesel	1	6	11,640 bhp	1	16.1
Federal Mackinac	B&W - 6S46MC-C	Diesel	1	6	10,540 bhp	1	16.1
Federal Margaree	B&W - 6S46MC-C	Diesel	1	6	10,686 bhp	1	16.1
Federal Mayumi	MAN B&W - 6S46MC-C	Diesel	1	6	10,686 bhp	1	16.1
Federal Nakagawa	B&W - 6S46MC-C	Diesel	1	6	10,710 bhp	1	16.1
Federal Oshima	B&W - 6S46MC-C	Diesel	1	6	10,710 bhp	1	16.1
Federal Rhine	B&W - 6S50MC	Diesel	1	6	11,640 bhp	1	16.1
Federal Rideau	B&W - 6S46MC-C	Diesel	1	6	10,710 bhp	1	16.1
Federal Saguenay	B&W - 6S50MC	Diesel	1	6	11,665 bhp	1	16.1
Federal Satsuki	B&W - 6S46MC-C	Diesel	1	6	9,235 bhp	1	16.1
Federal Schelde	B&W - 6S50MC	Diesel	1	6	11,640 bhp	1	16.1
Federal Seto	MAN B&W - 6S46MC-C	Diesel	1	6	10,711 bhp	1	16.7

Vessel Name	Engine Manufacturer & Model #	Engine Type	Total Engines	Total Cylinders	Rated HP	Total Props	Speed MPH
Federal Shimanto	Mitsubishi - 6UEC52LA	Diesel	1	6	9,600 bhp	1	16.6
Federal Welland	B&W - 6S46MC-C	Diesel	1	6	10,710 bhp	1	16.1
Federal Weser	B&W - 6S46MC-C	Diesel	1	6	10,686 bhp	1	18.0
Federal Yukina	B&W - 6S46MC-C	Diesel	1	6	8,833 bhp	1	16.1
Federal Yoshino	Mitsubishi - 6UEC52LA	Diesel	1	6	9,600 bhp	1	16.6
Federal Yukon	B&W - 6S46MC-C	Diesel	1	6	10,710 bhp	1	15.5
Ferbec	MAN B&W - 6S50MC	Diesel	1	6	9,222 bhp	1	16.7
Florence M. *	Fairbanks Morse - 8-28D8-1/4	Diesel	2	8	1,450 bhp	2	
Florence Spirit	Wartsila C - 6L38B	Diesel	1	6	5,831 bhp	1	15.5
Frontenac	Sulzer - 6RND76	Diesel	1	6	9,600 bhp	1 cpp	17.0
G3 Marquis	Wartsila 5RT-flex50-D	Diesel	1	5	11,863 bhp	1 cpp	16.1
G.L. Ostrander *	Caterpillar - 3608-DITA	Diesel	2	8	6,008 bhp	2	17.3
Great Republic	GM EMD - 20-645-E7	Diesel	2	20	7,200 bhp	2 cpp	15.0
Griffon (CCG)	Fairbanks Morse - 8-38D8-1/8	Diesel	4	8	5,332 bhp	2	13.0
H. Lee White	GM EMD - 20-645-E7B	Diesel	2	20	7,200 bhp	1 cpp	15.0
Herbert C. Jackson	MaK - 6M32E	Diesel	2	6	6,250 bhp	1 cpp	
Hollyhock (USCG)	Caterpillar - 3608TA	Diesel	2	6	3,100 bhp	1 cpp	
Hon. James L. Oberstar	Rolls-Royce Bergen - B32:40L6P	Diesel	2	6	8,160 shp	1 ccp	17.0
Indiana Harbor	GM EMD - 20-645-E7	Diesel	4	20	14,400 bhp	2 cpp	16.1
Invincible *	GM EMD - 16-645-E7B	Diesel	2	16	5,750 bhp	2	13.8
J. S. St. John	GM EMD - 8-567	Diesel	1	8	850 bhp	1	
James R. Barker	Pielstick - 16PC2-2V-400	Diesel	2	16	16,000 bhp	2 cpp	15.5
Jana Desgagnés	B&W - 6L35MC	Diesel	1	6	5,030 bhp	1 cpp	14.4
Jiimaan **	Ruston Paxman Diesels Ltd. - 6RK215	Diesel	2	6	2,839 bhp	2 cpp	15.0
John D. Leitch	B&W - 5-74VT2BF-160	Diesel	1	5	7,500 bhp	1 cpp	16.1
John G. Munson	MaK - 6M46C	Diesel	1	6	7,000 bhp	1 cpp	16.1
John J. Boland	GM EMD - 20-645-E7B	Diesel	2	20	7,200 bhp	1 cpp	15.0
Joseph H. Thompson Jr. *	Caterpillar	Diesel	2			1	
Joseph L. Block	GM EMD - 20-645-E7	Diesel	2	20	7,200 bhp	1 cpp	17.3
Joyce L. VanEnkevort *	Caterpillar - 3612	Diesel	2	12	10,200 bhp	2 cpp	
Kaministiqua	Sulzer - 4RLB76	Diesel	4	4	10,880 bhp	1cpp	15.5
Karen Andrie *	GM EMD - 8-710G7C	Diesel	2	8	4,000 bhp	2	19.0
Katmai Bay (USCG)	Fairbanks Morse - 10-38D8-1/8	Diesel	2	10	2,500 bhp	1	13.8
Kaye E. Barker	Rolls-Royce Bergen - B32:40L6P	Diesel	2	6	8,160 shp	1 ccp	17.0
Lake Express **	MTU 16V4000M70	Diesel	4	16	12,616 bhp	4 water jet	40.0
Laurentia Desgagnés	GM-S60MC-C	Diesel	1	5	18,605 bhp	1 cpp	18.4
Lee A. Tregurtha	Rolls-Royce Bergen B32:40L6P	Diesel	2	6	8,160 shp	1 ccp	17.0
Leo A. McArthur *	MaK - 6M25	Diesel	2	6	5,384 bhp	2 cpp	12.1
Leonard M	Ruston P - 6RK270M	Diesel	2	6	2,097 bhp	2	13.8
Mackinaw (USCG)	Caterpillar - 3612	Diesel	3	12	9,119 bhp	2 Azipod	17.3
Manistee	GM EMD - 20-645-E6	Diesel	2	20	2,950 bhp	1	
Manitoulin	B&W - 5L50MC	Diesel	1	5	8,113 bhp	1 cpp	16.5
Manitowoc	Alco - 16V251E	Diesel	2	16	5,600 bhp	1	16.1
Maria Desgagnés	B&W - 6S42MC	Diesel	1	6	8,361 bhp	1 cpp	16.1
Martha L. Black (CCG)	Alco - 16V251F	Diesel	3	16	8,973 bhp	2	13.8
Mary E. Hannah *	GM EMD - 16-567C	Diesel	2	16	3,200 bhp	2	15.0
McKeil Spirit	Wartsila-C	Diesel	1	6	5,831 bhp	1 cpp	16.1
Mesabi Miner	Pielstick - 16PC2-2V-400	Diesel	2	16	16,000 bhp	2 cpp	15.5
Mia Desgagnés	Wärtsilä 5RT-flex 50DF	Diesel/LNG	1	5	7,305 bhp	1 cpp	15.0
Michigan *	GM EMD - 20-645-E6	Diesel	2	16	3,900 bhp	2	13.2
Michipicoten	MaK - 6M32C	Diesel	2	6	8,160 bhp	1 cpp	14.0
Mississagi	Caterpillar - 3612-TA	Diesel	1	12	4,500 bhp	1 cpp	13.8
Mobile Bay (USCG)	Fairbanks Morse - 10-38D8-1/8	Diesel	2	10	2,500 bhp	1	13.8
Morro Bay (USCG)	Fairbanks Morse - 10-38D8-1/8	Diesel	2	10	2,500 bhp	1	13.8
Neah Bay (USCG)	Fairbanks Morse - 10-38D8-1/8	Diesel	2	10	2,500 bhp	1	13.8
NACC Quebec	Wartsila - 6L38B	Diesel	1	6	5,831 bhp	1 cpp	15
Nordik Express	GM EMD - 20-645-E7	Diesel	2	20	7,200 bhp	2 ccp	16.0
Nunalik	Caterpillar MaK - 6M43C	Diesel	1	6	7,238 bhp	1 cpp	17.3
Nunavik	MAN-B&W 7S70ME-C	Diesel	1	7	29,623 bhp	1 cpp	15.5
Nordika Desgagnés	B&W - 6S46MC-C	Diesel/LNG	1	6	8,955 bhp	1	17.3
Oakglen	B&W - 6K67GF	Diesel	1	6	11,600 bhp	1	15.5
Ojibway	GE - 7FDM EFI	Diesel	1	16	4,100 bhp	1 cpp	
Olive L. Moore *	Alco - 16V251	Diesel	2	16	5,830 bhp	1	
Paul A. Desgagnés	Sulzer - 5RT-fles 50 DF	LNG	1	5	7,305 bhp	1	15
Paul R. Tregurtha	MaK - 6M43C	Diesel	2	6	17,120 bhp	2 cpp	15.5
Pearl Mist	Caterpillar - 3516C-DITA	Diesel	2	16	3,386 bhp	2	

Vessel Name	Engine Manufacturer & Model #	Engine Type	Total Engines	Total Cylinders	Rated HP	Total Props	Speed MPH
Pelee Islander **	Caterpillar - 3408	Diesel	2	8	910 bhp	2	
Petite Forte *	Ruston - 8ATC	Diesel	2	8	4,200 bhp	2	15.5
Philip R. Clarke	Westinghouse Elec. Corp.	Turbine	1	**	7,700 shp	1	16.1
Pierre Radisson (CCG)	Alco - 16V251F	Diesel	6	16	17,700 bhp	2	18.4
Prentiss Brown *	GM EMD - 12-645-E2	Diesel	2	12	3,900 bhp	1	
Presque Isle *	Mirrlees Blackstone Ltd. - KVMR-16	Diesel	2	16	14,840 bhp	2 cpp	
Quinte Loyalist **	Caterpillar - 3196	Diesel	2	6	770 bhp		
Radcliffe R. Latimer	MaK - 8M32C	Diesel	2	8	10,442 bhp	1 cpp	
Rebecca Lynn *	GM EMD - 16-567-BC	Diesel	2	16	3,600 bhp	2	
Reliance *	A.B. Nohab - SVI 16VS-F	Diesel	2	16	5,600 bhp	1 cpp	17.6
Robert S. Pierson	Alco - 16V251E	Diesel	2	16	5,600 bhp	1	17.8
Roger Blough	Pielstick - 16PC2V-400	Diesel	2	16	14,200 bhp	1 cpp	16.7
Rosaire A. Desgagnés	MaK/Caterpillar - 6M43	Diesel	1	6	7,344 bhp	1 cpp	17.8
Rt. Hon. Paul J. Martin	MaK/Caterpillar - 6M32C	Diesel	2	6	8,060 bhp (est)	1 cpp	
Saginaw	MaK - 6M43C	Diesel	1	6	8,160 bhp	1 cpp	16.1
Salarium	Pielstick - 10PC2-2V-400	Diesel	2	10	10,700 bhp	1 cpp	13.8
Salvor *	GM EMD - 16-645-E7	Diesel	2	16	5,750 bhp	2	13.8
Sam Laud	GM EMD - 20-645-E7	Diesel	2	20	7,200 bhp	1 cpp	16.1
Samuel de Champlain *	GM EMD - 20-645-E5	Diesel	2	20	7,200 bhp	2 cpp	17.3
Samuel Risley (CCG)	Wartsila - VASA 12V22HF	Diesel	4	12	8,836 bhp	2 cpp	17.3
Sarah Desgagnés	MaK - 7M43	Diesel	1	7	9,517 bhp	1 cpp	15.0
Sea Eagle II *	GM EMD - 20-645-E7	Diesel	2	20	7,200 bhp	2	13.8
Sedna Desgagnés	MaK/Caterpillar - 6M43	Diesel	1	6	7,344 bhp	1 cpp	17.8
Sharon M 1 *	Niigata - 6L38HX	Diesel	2	6	1,934 bhp	2	16.0
Spruceglen	Sulzer - 4RLB76	Diesel	1	4	10,880 bhp	1 cpp	13.8
St. Clair	GM EMD - 20-645-E7	Diesel	3	20	10,800 bhp	1 cpp	16.7
Stephen B. Roman	Total	Diesel			5,996 bhp	1 cpp	18.4
(Center)	Fairbanks Morse - 10-38D8-1/8	Diesel	2	10	3,331 bhp		
(Wing)	Fairbanks Morse - 8-38D8-1/8	Diesel	2	8	2,665 bhp		
Sterling Energy	GUASCOR - F360TA-SP	Diesel	1	12	900 bhp	1	
Stewart J. Cort	GM EMD - 20-645-E7	Diesel	4	20	14,400 bhp	2 cpp	18.4
Tecumseh	Pielstick - 12PC-2V-400	Diesel	2	12	12,000 bhp	1 cpp	16.1
Taiga Desgagnés	B&W - 6S46MC-C	Diesel	1	6	9,482 bhp	1	17.3
Tim McKeil*	Niigata 6L38HX	Diesel	2	6	2,400 bhp	2	15.3
Tim S. Dool	MaK - 8M43C	Diesel	1	8	10,750 bhp	1 cpp	17.3
Tony MacKay *	Ruston - 12C-5VM	Diesel	1	12	2,800 bhp	1 cpp	15.0
Thunder Bay	MAN-B&W - 6S50ME-B9	Diesel	1	6	11,897 bhp	1	15.5
Umiak I	M.A.N.-B&W - 7S70ME-C	Diesel	1	7	29,598 bhp	1 cpp	16.5
Umiavut	Hanshin - 6LF58	Diesel	1	6	6,000 bhp	1 cpp	16.2
Undaunted *	Cummins K38-M	Diesel	2	12	2,000 bhp	2	
Victory *	MaK - 6MU551AK	Diesel	2	6	7,880 bhp	2	16.1
Victory I	Caterpillar 3516TA-B	Diesel	2	16	4,000 bhp	2	11.5
Victory II	Caterpillar 3516TA-B	Diesel	2	16	4,000 bhp	2	11.5
Walter J. McCarthy Jr.	GM EMD - 20-645-E7B	Diesel	4	20	14,400 bhp	2 cpp	16.1
Whitefish Bay	MAN-B&W - 6S50ME-B9	Diesel	1	6	11,897 bhp	1	15.5
Wilfred Sykes	Westinghouse Elec. Corp.	Turbine	1	**	7,700 shp	1	16.1
Wilf Seymour *	GM EMD - 16-645-E7	Diesel	2	16	5,750 bhp	2	13.8
Zélada Desgagnés	MaK/Caterpillar - 6M43	Diesel	1	6	7,344 bhp	1 cpp	17.8
Zeus *	Caterpillar - D399	Diesel	2	8	2,250 bhp	2	

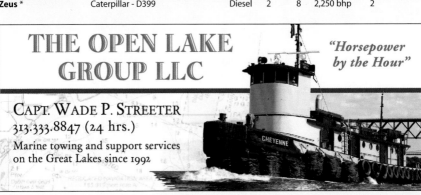

Saltwater Fleets

Federal Rideau in the Welland Canal. (Nathan Leindecker)

A

ABC MARITIME, NYON, SWITZERLAND *(abcmaritime.ch)*

Fleet Name / Vessel Name	Vessel IMO #	Vessel Type	Year Built	Engine Type	Cargo Cap. or Gross*	Overall Length	Vessel Breadth	Vessel Depth
Adfines Sea	9580962	TK	2011	D	19,118	530' 05"	75' 06"	40' 08"
(Osttank Norway '11-'12)								
Adfines Star	9580974	TK	2011	D	19,118	530' 05"	75' 06"	40' 08"
(Osttank Denmark '11-'11, Osttank Sweden '11-'11)								
Adfines Sun	9580998	TK	2011	D	19,118	530' 05"	75' 06"	40' 08"
(Osttank Denmark '11-'11, Osttank Sweden '11-'11)								

ACE TANKERS CV, AMSTERDAM, NETHERLANDS *(ace-tankers.com)*

Fleet Name / Vessel Name	Vessel IMO #	Vessel Type	Year Built	Engine Type	Cargo Cap. or Gross*	Overall Length	Vessel Breadth	Vessel Depth
Chem Hydra	9486180	TK	2009	D	17,055	475' 01"	75' 06"	40' 08"
Chem Norma	9486192	TK	2009	D	17,055	475' 11"	75' 06"	40' 08"
Chem Polaris	9416044	TK	2008	D	19,994	481' 00"	77' 09"	42' 08"
*(Braken '08-'10, **Maemi** '10-'15)*								

ALLIANCE TANKERS, HAMILTON, BERMUDA *(alliancemaritime.com)*

Fleet Name / Vessel Name	Vessel IMO #	Vessel Type	Year Built	Engine Type	Cargo Cap. or Gross*	Overall Length	Vessel Breadth	Vessel Depth
Askholmen	9436381	TK	2009	D	16,850	472' 05"	74' 02"	42' 00"
*(**Hellespont Charger** '09-'14)*								
Furuholmen	9553397	TK	2010	D	16,500	473' 02"	75' 06"	40' 08"
Golden Oak	9445655	TK	2008	D	13,226	419' 07"	67' 00"	37' 09"
(Sichem Berlin '08-'08, Marida Marguerite '08-'14)								
Kirkeholmen	9553402	TK	2010	D	16,730	473' 02"	75' 06"	40' 08"
(CF Sophia '10-'12)								
Larsholmen	9436410	TK	2009	D	16,850	472' 05"	74' 02"	42' 00"
*(**Hellespont Centurion** '10-'14)*								
Lokholmen	9433303	TK	2010	D	16,850	472' 05"	74' 02"	42' 00"
*(**Hellespont Crusader** '10-'14)*								

ARA GROUP, WERKENDAM, NETHERLANDS *(aragroup.nl)*

Fleet Name / Vessel Name	Vessel IMO #	Vessel Type	Year Built	Engine Type	Cargo Cap. or Gross*	Overall Length	Vessel Breadth	Vessel Depth
ARA Rotterdam	9240471	BC	2002	D	10,500	468' 02"	59' 10"	33' 04"
*(Sabrina '02-'02, MSC Rades '02-'04, Sabrina '04-'04, SCM Olympic '04-'05, **Sabrina** '05-'14)*								

ARMADOR GEMI ISLETMECILIGI TICARET LTD., ISTANBUL, TURKEY *(armadorshipping.com)*

Fleet Name / Vessel Name	Vessel IMO #	Vessel Type	Year Built	Engine Type	Cargo Cap. or Gross*	Overall Length	Vessel Breadth	Vessel Depth
Cornelia	9216597	BC	2001	D	16,807	574' 02"	75' 09"	44' 09"
(Pine '01-'04)								
Pochard S	9262534	BC	2003	D	37,384	655' 10"	77' 09"	50' 02"
*(**Pochard** '03-'14)*								

ATLANTSKA PLOVIDBA D.D., DUBROVNIK, CROATIA *(atlant.hr)*

Fleet Name / Vessel Name	Vessel IMO #	Vessel Type	Year Built	Engine Type	Cargo Cap. or Gross*	Overall Length	Vessel Breadth	Vessel Depth
Orsula	9110901	BC	1996	D	34,372	656' 02"	77' 01"	48' 10"
*(**Federal Calumet** {2} '96-'97)*								

B

BD-SHIPSNAVO GMBH & CO., HAREN-EMS, GERMANY *(shipsnavo.de)*

Fleet Name / Vessel Name	Vessel IMO #	Vessel Type	Year Built	Engine Type	Cargo Cap. or Gross*	Overall Length	Vessel Breadth	Vessel Depth
Active	9343821	BC	2008	D	12,523	378' 03"	64' 04"	37' 05"
(Antilles VII '08-'14)								

BERNHARD SCHULTE GROUP OF COMPANIES, HAMBURG, GERMANY *(schultegroup.com)*

Fleet Name / Vessel Name	Vessel IMO #	Vessel Type	Year Built	Engine Type	Cargo Cap. or Gross*	Overall Length	Vessel Breadth	Vessel Depth
Edzard Schulte	9439852	TK	2011	D	16,427	476' 02"	75' 06"	41' 01"
Elisabeth Schulte	9439840	TK	2010	D	16,427	476' 02"	75' 06"	41' 01"
Eva Schulte	9439826	TK	2010	D	16,427	476' 02"	75' 06"	41' 01"
Everhard Schulte	9439838	TK	2010	D	16,427	476' 02"	75' 06"	41' 01"

BIGLIFT SHIPPING BV, AMSTERDAM, NETHERLANDS *(bigliftshipping.com)*

Fleet Name / Vessel Name	Vessel IMO #	Vessel Type	Year Built	Engine Type	Cargo Cap. or Gross*	Overall Length	Vessel Breadth	Vessel Depth
Happy Ranger	9139311	HL	1998	D	15,593	452' 09"	74' 10"	42' 06"
Happy River	9139294	HL	1997	D	15,634	452' 09"	74' 10"	42' 06"
Happy Rover	9139309	HL	1997	D	15,593	452' 09"	74' 10"	42' 06"
Tracer	9204702	HL	2000	D	8,874	329' 09"	73' 06"	26' 11"

BLOUNT SMALL SHIP ADVENTURES, WARREN, RI *(blountsmallshipadventures.com)*

Fleet Name / Vessel Name	Vessel IMO #	Vessel Type	Year Built	Engine Type	Cargo Cap. or Gross*	Overall Length	Vessel Breadth	Vessel Depth
Grande Caribe	8978631	PA	1997	D	97*	182' 07"	39' 01"	9' 10"
Built: Blount Industries Inc., Warren, RI								
Grande Mariner	8978643	PA	1998	D	97*	182' 07"	39' 01"	9' 10"
Built: Blount Industries Inc., Warren, RI								

BLYSTAD GROUP, OSLO, NORWAY *(blystad.no)*
  FOLLOWING VESSELS UNDER CHARTER TO SONGA SHIPMANAGEMENT

Fleet Name / Vessel Name	Vessel IMO #	Vessel Type	Year Built	Engine Type	Cargo Cap. or Gross*	Overall Length	Vessel Breadth	Vessel Depth
Songa Challenge	9409510	TK	2009	D	17,596	472' 05"	74' 02"	41' 00"
Songa Emerald	9473937	TK	2009	D	17,596	472' 05"	74' 02"	41' 00"

Fleet Name Vessel Name	Vessel IMO #	Vessel Type	Year Built	Engine Type	Cargo Cap. or Gross*	Overall Length	Vessel Breadth	Vessel Depth
Songa Opal	9473913	TK	2009	D	17,596	472' 05"	74' 02"	41' 00"
Songa Peace	9409522	TK	2009	D	17,596	472' 05"	74' 02"	41' 00"
(Global Peace '09-'13)								
BRIESE SCHIFFAHRTS GMBH & CO. KG, LEER, GERMANY *(briese.de)*								
BBC Alberta	9468102	HL	2010	D	12,699	452' 11"	68' 11"	36' 01"
*(Beluga Maturity '10-'10, Beluga Firmament '10-'11, **BBC Celina** '11-'15)*								
BBC Austria	9433327	GC	2009	D	7,530	393' 00"	66' 03"	32' 02"
BBC Elbe	9347059	GC	2006	D	17,349	469' 07"	75' 11"	43' 08"
(Horumersiel '06-'06)								
BBC Europe	9266308	GC	2003	D	7,409	391' 09"	66' 03"	32' 02"
BBC Fuji	9508419	GC	2011	D	9,310	412' 09"	72' 02"	35' 05"
BBC Hudson	9435868	GC	2009	D	17,349	469' 07"	75' 11"	43' 08"
BBC Kibo	9508421	GC	2011	D	9,310	412' 09"	72' 02"	35' 05"
BBC Kwiatkowski	9436953	GC	2008	D	7,733	401' 09"	59' 09"	31' 02"
(Eugeniusz Kwiatkowski '08-'08)								
BBC Mississippi	9347061	GC	2006	D	17,349	469' 07"	75' 11"	43' 08"
(Greetsiel '06-'07)								
BBC Mont Blanc	9508433	GC	2011	D	9,310	412' 09"	72' 02"	35' 05"
BBC Olympus	9508457	GC	2012	D	9,310	412' 09"	72' 02"	35' 05"
BBC Rushmore	9508469	GC	2012	D	9,310	412' 09"	72' 02"	35' 05"
BBC Switzerland	9433315	GC	2008	D	7,530	393' 00"	66' 03"	32' 02"
BBC Volga	9436329	GC	2009	D	17,349	469' 07"	75' 11"	43' 08"
(Ocean Breeze '09-'09)								
BBC Vesuvius	9508471	GC	2012	D	9,310	412' 09"	72' 02"	35' 05"
BBC Weser	9347047	GC	2006	D	17,349	469' 07"	75' 11"	43' 08"
(Westerdamm '06-'06, BBC Weser '06-'10, STX Bright '10-'14)								
BBC Xingang	9508483	GC	2013	D	9,310	412' 09"	72' 02"	35' 05"
Kurt Paul	9435856	GC	2009	D	17,349	469' 07"	75' 11"	43' 08"
Peter Ronna	9198628	BC	2002	D	4,303	324' 03"	49' 10"	24' 03"
(Peter Ronna '02-'03, Svend '03-'05)								
Sjard	9303314	GC	2007	D	17,349	469' 07"	75' 11"	43' 08"
BROSTROM AB, COPENHAGEN, DENMARK *(brostrom.com)*								
Bro Agnes	9348302	TK	2008	D	16,979	472' 07"	75' 07"	40' 09"
Bro Alma	9356610	TK	2007	D	16,979	472' 07"	75' 06"	40' 08"
(Ganstar '07-'07)								
Bro Anna	9344435	TK	2008	D	16,949	472' 07"	75' 06"	40' 08"
(Gan Gesture '08-'08)								

C

Fleet Name Vessel Name	Vessel IMO #	Vessel Type	Year Built	Engine Type	Cargo Cap. or Gross*	Overall Length	Vessel Breadth	Vessel Depth
CANADA FEEDER LINES BV, GRONINGEN, NETHERLANDS *(cfl.nl)*								
Industrial More	9534482	GC	2013	D	10,049	381' 05"	58' 05"	34' 05"

CANFORNAV INC. (CANADIAN FOREST NAVIGATION INC.), MONTREAL, QUEBEC, CANADA *(canfornav.com)*
At press time, Canadian Forest Navigation Co. Ltd. had the following vessels under long or short-term charter. Please consult their respective fleets for details: **Andean, Barnacle, Blacky, Bluebill, Bluewing, Brant, Cape, Chestnut, Cinnamon, Eider, Greenwing, Labrador, Maccoa, Mandarin, Mottler, Puffin, Redhead, Ruddy, Shoveler, Sunda, Torrent, Tufty, Tundra, Whistler** and **Wigeon**.

Fleet Name Vessel Name	Vessel IMO #	Vessel Type	Year Built	Engine Type	Cargo Cap. or Gross*	Overall Length	Vessel Breadth	Vessel Depth
CARISBROOKE SHIPPING LTD., COWES, UNITED KINGDOM *(carisbrooke.co)*								
Charlotte C	9528706	BC	2009	D	13,517	447' 06"	69' 07"	37' 01"
Greta C	9528720	BC	2009	D	13,517	447' 06"	69' 07"	37' 01"
Heleen C	9331490	BC	2006	D	13,517	447' 06"	69' 07"	37' 01"

A Note About Saltwater Listings

Observers will likely spot saltwater vessels that are not included in this book. These may be newcomers to the Great Lakes/Seaway system, recent renames or new construction. This is not meant to be an exhaustive listing of every saltwater vessel that could potentially visit the Great Lakes and St. Lawrence Seaway. To attempt to do so, given the sheer number of world merchant ships, would be space and cost prohibitive. This list reflects vessels whose primary trade routes are on saltwater but which also regularly visit Great Lakes and St. Lawrence Seaway ports above Montreal. Fleets listed may operate other vessels worldwide than those included herein; additional vessels may be found on fleet websites, which have been included where available. Former names listed in **boldface** type indicate the vessel visited the Seaway under that name.

Fleet Name Vessel Name	Vessel IMO #	Vessel Type	Year Built	Engine Type	Cargo Cap. or Gross*	Overall Length	Vessel Breadth	Vessel Depth
Jacqueline C	9429754	BC	2009	D	12,914	453' 01"	68' 11"	36' 01"
Jasmine C	9463542	BC	2010	D	12,948	453' 01"	68' 11"	36' 01"
Johanna C	9430131	BC	2009	D	12,948	453' 01"	68' 11"	36' 01"
Michelle C	9452218	BC	2010	D	12,948	453' 01"	68' 11"	36' 01"
(Michelle-C '10-'10, Nirint Pioneer '10-'11)								
Sally Ann C	9338151	BC	2007	D	13,517	447' 06"	69' 07"	37' 01"

CANDLER SCHIFFFAHRT GMBH, BREMEN, GERMANY *(candler-schiffahrt.de)*

Pioneer	9488633	BC	2008	D	8,091	381' 04"	59' 01"	34' 01"
(FCC Pioneer '08-'08, BBC Tasmania '08-'10, Thorco Bronco '10-'15)								

CHEMBULK MARITIME LLC, SOUTHPORT, CT *(chembulktankers.com)*

Chembulk Kobe	9263136	TK	2002	D	19,992	477' 05"	77' 09"	43' 10"

CHEMFLEET SHIPPING LTD., ISTANBUL, TURKEY *(chemfleet.org)*

Mehmet A	9418822	TK	2011	D	20,000	530' 04"	73' 06"	34' 01"
(Aldemar '11-'11)								

CHEMIKALIEN SEETRANSPORT GMBH, HAMBURG, GERMANY *(cst-hamburg.de)*

Chemtrans Elbe	9439345	TK	2008	D	13,073	421' 11"	66' 11"	37' 09"

CLEARWATER GROUP, ROTTERDAM, NETHERLANDS *(clearwatergroup.nl)*

Rosy	9298387	TK	2008	D	20,610	539' 02"	75' 06"	42' 00"
(MCT Stockhorn '08-'15, SCT Stockhorn '15-'17)								

COASTAL SHIPPING LTD., GOOSE BAY, NEWFOUNDLAND, CANADA *(woodwards.nf.ca)*

Travestern	9053206	TK	1993	D	17,089	529' 01"	75' 06"	38' 05"

C.O.E. SHIPPING GMBH & CO., BUXTEHUDE, GERMANY *(coeshipping.com)*
FOLLOWING VESSELS UNDER CHARTER TO SPLIETHOFF

COE Leni	9453793	HL	2010	D	12,767	454' 05"	68' 11"	36' 01"
(Marselisborg '10-'12, Clipper Anne '12-'14, Marselisborg '14-'16)								

COSCO SOUTHERN ASPHALT SHIPPING CO. LTD, GUANGZHOU, CHINA

Zhuang Yuan Ao	9650339	TK	2012	D	12,000	479' 00"	72' 02"	35' 05"

D-E

DUZGIT GEMI INSA SANAYI, ISTANBUL, TURKEY *(duzgit.com)*

Duzgit Dignity	9581019	TK	2014	D	8,488	390' 09"	56' 05"	30' 02"
Duzgit Endeavour	9581007	TK	2013	D	16,004	509' 09"	71' 02"	36' 05"

***HR Constellation** on the Saginaw River. (Todd Shorkey)*

Fleet Name Vessel Name	Vessel IMO #	Vessel Type	Year Built	Engine Type	Cargo Cap. or Gross*	Overall Length	Vessel Breadth	Vessel Depth
EASTERN PACIFIC SHIPPING, SINGAPORE								
Ebony Ray	9363857	TK	2008	D	19,998	477' 05"	77' 09"	43' 10"
(*Millennium Park '08-'14*)								
ELBE SHIPPING GMBH, DROCHTERSEN, GERMANY (*reederei-elbe-shipping.de*)								
BBC Thames	9368340	HL	2008	D	17,323	469' 02"	70' 06"	43' 08"
(*Beluga Graduation '08-'09*)								
EMPIRE CHEMICAL TANKER HOLDINGS INC., PIRAEUS, GREECE								
Malmo	9373242	TK	2008	D	19,992	491' 11"	76' 01"	42' 10"

F-G

Fleet Name Vessel Name	Vessel IMO #	Vessel Type	Year Built	Engine Type	Cargo Cap. or Gross*	Overall Length	Vessel Breadth	Vessel Depth
FAIRFIELD CHEMICAL CARRIERS, WILTON, CONNECTICUT, USA (*fairfieldchemical.com*)								
Fairchem Charger	9367401	TK	2009	D	19,998	477' 05"	77' 09"	43' 10"
Fairchem Colt	9304344	TK	2005	D	19,998	477' 05"	77' 09"	43' 10"
Fairchem Friesian	9367413	TK	2005	D	19,998	477' 05"	77' 09"	43' 10"
Fairchem Steed	9311256	TK	2005	D	19,998	477' 05"	77' 09"	43' 10"
Fairchem Yuka	9477505	TK	2010	D	19,998	477' 05"	77' 09"	43' 10"
FEDNAV, MONTREAL, QUEBEC, CANADA (*fednav.com*)								
CANARCTIC SHIPPING CO. LTD. – DIVISION OF FEDNAV								
Arctic	7517507	BK	1978	D	26,440	727' 06"	75' 00"	50 00"
Built: Port Weller Dry Docks, Port Weller, ON								
Nunavik	9673850	BK	2014	D	24,997	619' 05"	87' 03"	51' 06"
Umiak I	9334715	BK	2006	D	31,992	619' 05"	87' 03"	51' 06"
FEDNAV INTERNATIONAL LTD. - DIVISION OF FEDNAV								
Federal Asahi {2}	9200419	BC	2000	D	36,563	656' 02"	77' 11"	48' 09"
Federal Baltic	9697806	BC	2015	D	34,564	656' 01"	77' 11"	48' 09"
Federal Barents	9697820	BC	2015	D	34,564	656' 01"	77' 11"	48' 09"
Federal Beaufort	9697818	BC	2015	D	34,564	656' 01"	77' 11"	48' 09"
Federal Bering	9697832	BC	2015	D	34,564	656' 01"	77' 11"	48' 09"
Federal Biscay	9697856	BC	2015	D	34,564	656' 01"	77' 11"	48' 09"
Federal Bristol	9697844	BC	2015	D	34,564	656' 01"	77' 11"	48' 09"
Federal Caribou	9671096	BC	2016	D	34,564	656' 01"	77' 11"	48' 09"
Federal Cedar	9671101	BC	2016	D	34,564	656' 01"	77' 11"	48' 09"
Federal Champlain	9671058	BC	2016	D	34,564	656' 01"	77' 11"	48' 09"
Federal Churchill	9671060	BC	2016	D	34,564	656' 01"	77' 11"	48' 09"
Federal Clyde	9671072	BC	2016	D	34,564	656' 01"	77' 11"	48' 09"

Florijngracht and HHL Amur offload at Duluth Port Authority. (*Matt Adamski*)

Fleet Name / Vessel Name	Vessel IMO #	Vessel Type	Year Built	Engine Type	Cargo Cap. or Gross*	Overall Length	Vessel Breadth	Vessel Depth
Federal Columbia	9671084	BC	2016	D	34,564	656' 01"	77' 11"	48' 09"
Federal Danube {2}	9271511	BC	2003	D	37,180	652' 11"	78' 05"	50' 02"
Federal Elbe	9230000	BC	2003	D	37,180	652' 11"	78' 05"	50' 02"
Federal Ems	9229984	BC	2002	D	37,180	652' 11"	78' 05"	50' 02"
Federal Hudson {3}	9205902	BC	2000	D	36,563	656' 02"	77' 11"	48' 09"
Federal Hunter {2}	9205938	BC	2001	D	36,563	656' 02"	77' 11"	48' 09"
Federal Kivalina	9205885	BC	2000	D	36,563	656' 02"	77' 11"	48' 09"
Federal Kumano	9244257	BC	2001	D	36,563	656' 02"	77' 11"	48' 09"
Federal Kushiro	9284702	BC	2003	D	32,594	624' 09"	77' 05"	49' 10"
Federal Leda	9229996	BC	2003	D	37,180	655' 10"	77' 09"	50' 02"
Federal Maas {2}	9118135	BC	1997	D	34,372	656' 02"	77' 01"	48' 10"
Federal Mackinac	9299460	BC	2004	D	27,783	607' 03"	77' 01"	46' 03"
Federal Margaree	9299472	BC	2005	D	27,783	607' 03"	77' 01"	46' 03"
Federal Mayumi	9529578	BC	2012	D	35,868	655' 06"	77' 11"	48' 09"
Federal Nakagawa	9278791	BC	2005	D	36,563	656' 02"	77' 11"	48' 09"
Federal Oshima	9200330	BC	1999	D	36,563	656' 02"	77' 11"	48' 09"
Federal Rhine {2}	9110925	BC	1997	D	34,372	656' 02"	77' 01"	48' 10"

Fleet Name Vessel Name	Vessel IMO #	Vessel Type	Year Built	Engine Type	Cargo Cap. or Gross*	Overall Length	Vessel Breadth	Vessel Depth
Federal Rideau	9200445	BC	2000	D	36,563	656' 02"	77' 11"	48' 09"
Federal Saguenay {2}	9110913	BC	1996	D	34,372	656' 02"	77' 01"	48' 10"
Federal Sakura	9288291	BC	2005	D	32,594	624' 09"	77' 05"	49' 10"
Federal Satsuki	9529578	BC	2012	D	35,868	655' 06"	77' 11"	48' 09"
Federal Schelde {3}	9118147	BC	1997	D	34,372	656' 02"	77' 01"	48' 10"
Federal Seto	9267209	BC	2004	D	36,563	656' 02"	77' 11"	48' 09"
Federal Shimanto	9218404	BC	2001	D	32,787	624' 09"	77' 05"	49' 10"
Federal Welland	9205926	BC	2000	D	36,563	656' 02"	77' 11"	48' 09"
Federal Weser	9229972	BC	2002	D	37,180	655' 10"	77' 09"	50' 02"
Federal Yoshino	9218416	BC	2001	D	32,787	624' 09"	77' 05"	49' 10"
Federal Yukon	9205897	BC	2000	D	36,563	656' 02"	77' 11"	48' 09"

At press time, Fednav also had the following vessels under charter. Please consult their respective fleets for details: **Federal Alster, Federal Mosel, Federal Ruhr** and **Federal Yukina**.

FORESTWAVE NAVIGATION, HEERENVEEN, NETHERLANDS (forestwave.nl)

FWN Bonafide	9321108	BC	2006	D	10,683	477' 09"	59' 10"	33' 10"

(UAL Antwerp '06-'12, UAL Nigeria '12-'15, Anna C '15-'15)

Fednav's Arctic unloads at Deception Bay, Que. This versatile vessel can carry either bulk cargo or petroleum products to the Canadian Arctic. (Shane Ruther)

Fleet Name Vessel Name	Vessel IMO #	Vessel Type	Year Built	Engine Type	Cargo Cap. or Gross*	Overall Length	Vessel Breadth	Vessel Depth
FRANCO COMPANIA NAVIERA SA, ATHENS, GREECE *(franco.gr)*								
Helena G.	9358369	BC	2007	D	37,238	655'10"	77'09"	50'02"
(*Garganey* '07-'17)								
Maria G.	9358383	BC	2007	D	37,238	655'10"	77'09"	50'02"
(*Gadwall* '07-'17)								
FREESE SHIPPING, STADE, GERMANY *(freeseship.com)*								
BBC Kansas	9349291	HL	2006	D	12,711	453'00"	68'11"	36'01"
(*Beluga Foundation* '06-'11, *Opal Gallant* '11-'11, *Freya Scan* '11-'13, *Thorco Denmark* '13-'15, **Amber** '15-'16)								
Lisanna	9283954	HL	2004	D	12,700	453'00"	68'11"	36'01"
(*Beluga Efficiency* '04-'06, *BBC Carolina* '06-'07, **Beluga Efficiency** '07-'11, *Lilia* '11-'11, *Freese Scan* '11-'12								
BBC Washington '12-'15)								
Pacific Huron	9546796	BC	2010	D	30,206	623'04"	77'11"	47'11"
(*Seven Islands* '10-'10)								
Three Rivers	9546784	BC	2010	D	30,206	623'04"	77'11"	47'11"
GEBRUDER AHRENS REEDEREI, GRUNENDEICH, GERMANY								
Alina	9468085	HL	2010	D	12,669	452'11"	68'11"	36'01"
(*Beluga Modification* '10-'10, *Beluga Faith* '10-'11)								

H

Fleet Name Vessel Name	Vessel IMO #	Vessel Type	Year Built	Engine Type	Cargo Cap. or Gross*	Overall Length	Vessel Breadth	Vessel Depth
HAMMONIA REEDEREI GMBH & CO., HAMBURG, GERMANY *(hammonia-reederei.de)*								
HR Constellation	9273806	HL	2006	D	12,765	514'04"	70'06"	30'06"
(*Beluga Constellation* '06-'11)								
HANSA HEAVY LIFT GMBH, BREMEN, GERMANY *(hansaheavylift.com)*								
HHL Amur	9435753	HL	2007	D	12,669	452'11"	68'11"	36'01"
(*Beluga Fidelity* '07-'11)								
HHL Congo	9467005	HL	2011	D	12,700	453'00"	68'11"	36'01"
(*Beluga Fealty* '11-'11)								
HHL Elbe	9433262	HL	2008	D	12,840	454'05"	68'11"	36'01"
(**BBC Alaska** '08-'13, *Elbe* '13-'14)								
HHL Mississippi	9435765	HL	2009	D	12,744	452'11"	68'11"	36'01"
(*Beluga Fantasy* '09-'11, *OXL Fantasy* '11-'11)								
HHL Rhine	9467017	HL	2011	D	12,837	453'00"	68'11"	36'01"
(*Beluga Feasibility* '11-'11)								
HHL Tyne	9433274	HL	2009	D	12,782	454'05"	68'11"	36'01"
(*BBC Montana* '09-'13, *Tyne* '13-'14)								
HARREN & PARTNER SCHIFFAHRTS GMBH, BREMEN, GERMANY *(harren-partner.de)*								
Patras	9348297	TK	2007	D	16,979	472'07"	75'06"	40'08"
FOLLOWING VESSELS UNDER CHARTER TO COMBI LIFT								
Palabora	9501875	HL	2010	D	10,052	436'04"	75'06"	37'05"
Palau	9501899	HL	2010	D	10,052	436'04"	75'06"	37'05"
Palmerton	9501863	HL	2009	D	10,052	436'04"	75'06"	37'05"
Pantanal	9316579	HL	2004	D	7,837	393'00"	66'03"	32'02"
HARTMAN SEATRADE, URK, NETHERLANDS *(hartmanseatrade.com)*								
Pacific Dawn	9558464	BC	2010	D	3,750	343'10"	52'06"	24'03"
HERMANN BUSS GMBH, LEER, GERMANY								
BBC Carolina	9402043	HL	2007	D	12,744	452'11"	68'11"	36'01"
(*Beluga Fantastic* '07-'11)								
BBC Manitoba	9384320	HL	2007	D	12,837	453'00"	68'11"	36'01"
(**Beluga Formation** '07-'12, *Formation* '12-'14, *Thorco Diamond* '14-'15)								
BBC Quebec	9402031	HL	2007	D	12,700	453'00"	68'11"	36'01"
(*Beluga Fiction* '07-'11, *Fiction* '11-'11)								
HERNING SHIPPING AS, HERNING, DENMARK *(herning-shipping.com)*								
Charlotte Theresa	9400708	TK	2008	D	11,383	424'10"	63'00"	36'01"
Jette Theresa	9406582	TK	2009	D	11,383	424'10"	63'00"	36'01"
Tina Theresa	9478298	TK	2009	D	7,902	332'08"	62'06"	34'05"
HS SCHIFFAHRT GMBH & CO, HAREN-EMS, GERMANY *(hs-schiffahrt.de)*								
BBC Brazil	9535618	GC	2011	D	10,872	477'10"	59'10"	33'10"
(*Thorco Copenhagen* '11-'16)								
BBC Haren	9511636	GC	2010	D	11,121	477'09"	59'10"	33'10"
(*Beluga Loyalty* '10-'12, *BBC Haren* '12-'15, *Haren* '15-'15)								
Onego Rotterdam	9631345	GC	2013	D	8,096	387'07"	52'02"	28'10"

Fleet Name Vessel Name	Vessel IMO #	Vessel Type	Year Built	Engine Type	Cargo Cap. or Gross*	Overall Length	Vessel Breadth	Vessel Depth
HUARONG HUIYIN LTD., HONG KONG, CHINA								
Chemical Aquarius	9576820	TK	2012	D	18,044	467' 06"	75' 06"	41' 04"

I-J-K

Fleet Name Vessel Name	Vessel IMO #	Vessel Type	Year Built	Engine Type	Cargo Cap. or Gross*	Overall Length	Vessel Breadth	Vessel Depth
ICDAS CELIK ENERJI TERSANE VE ULASIM SANAYII A.S., ISTANBUL, TURKEY *(icdas.com.tr)*								
Icdas-09	9421219	TK	2010	D	19,998	491' 11"	75' 06"	42' 10"
INTERMARINE, HOUSTON, TEXAS, USA *(intermarineusa.com)*								
Industrial Charger	9213959	GC	2000	D	8,040	393' 01"	65' 07"	37' 01"
(Virgo J '00-'00, Industrial Charger '00-'09, Ocean Charger '09-'15)								
Industrial Eagle	9407574	GC	2008	D	10,340	456' 00"	65' 07"	27' 03"
Ocean Crescent	9258193	GC	2002	D	8,097	393' 01"	65' 07"	37' 01"
(Pollux J. '02-'02, Industrial Crescent '02-'10)								
INTERSHIP NAVIGATION CO. LTD., LIMASSOL, CYPRUS *(intership-cyprus.com)*								
FOLLOWING VESSELS UNDER CHARTER TO FEDNAV LTD.								
Federal Alster	9766164	BC	2016	D	36,583	655' 10"	77' 09"	50' 03"
Federal Katsura	9293923	BC	2005	D	32,787	624' 08"	77' 05"	49' 10"
Federal Mosel	9766188	BC	2017	D	36,583	655' 10"	77' 09"	50' 03"
Federal Ruhr	9766176	BC	2017	D	36,583	655' 10"	77' 09"	50' 03"
INTREPID SHIPPING LLC., STAMFORD, CONNECTICUT, USA *(intrepidshipping.com)*								
Intrepid Republic	9466752	TK	2011	D	16,427	476' 02"	75' 06"	41' 00"
JO TANKERS BV, SPIJKENISSE, NETHERLANDS								
Jo Spirit	9140841	TK	1998	D	6,248	352' 02"	52' 02"	30' 02"
JOHANN M. K. BLUMENTHAL GMBH & CO., HAMBURG, GERMANY *(bluships.com)*								
Ida	9109536	BC	1995	D	18,796	486' 03"	74' 10"	40' 00"
Lita	9117416	BC	1995	D	18,796	486' 03"	74' 10"	40' 00"
JOHS THODE GMBH & CO., HAMBURG, GERMANY *(johs-thode.de)*								
Hanse Gate	9283540	BC	2004	D	27,783	607' 03"	77' 01"	46' 03"
*(**Federal Matane** '04-'11, **CL Hanse Gate** '11-'15)*								
JUMBO SHIPPING CO. SA, ROTTERDAM, NETHERLANDS *(jumbomaritime.nl)*								
Fairlane	9153654	HL	2000	D	7,123	362' 06"	67' 03"	44' 03"
Fairlift	8806905	HL	1990	D	7,780	330' 08"	68' 10"	43' 08"
JUNGERHANS MARITIME SERVICES GMBH & CO., HAREN EMS, GERMANY *(juengerhans.de)*								
BBC Kimberley	9407586	HL	2009	D	10,340	456' 00"	65' 07"	37' 01"
(Bellatrix J '09-'09, Industrial Egret '09-'12)								
BBC Lena	9147693	HL	1998	D	9,928	497' 05"	66' 11"	34' 05"
*(Lena '98-'15, **Lena J** '15-'15)*								
KALLIANIS BROS SHIPPING, ATHENS, GREECE *(kallianisbros.gr)*								
Dimitrios K	9216602	BC	2001	D	24,765	576' 03"	75' 09"	44' 09"
*(**Cedar** '01-'03, **Atlantic Castle** '03-'07, Ladytramp '07-'13)*								
KREY SCHIFFFAHRTS GMBH & COMPANY KG, LEER, GERMANY *(krey-schiffahrt.de)*								
FOLLOWING VESSELS UNDER CHARTER TO SPLIETHOFF								
Erik	9435105	HL	2008	D	12,837	453' 00"	68' 11"	36' 01"
*(**BBC Louisiana** '08-'17)*								
Frieda	9435117	HL	2008	D	12,837	453' 00"	68' 11"	36' 01"
*(**BBC Colorado** '08-'17)*								
Pia	9384318	HL	2007	D	12,837	453' 00"	68' 11"	36' 01"
*(**BBC Alabama** '07-'17)*								

L-M

Fleet Name Vessel Name	Vessel IMO #	Vessel Type	Year Built	Engine Type	Cargo Cap. or Gross*	Overall Length	Vessel Breadth	Vessel Depth
LAURANNE SHIPPING BV, GHENT, NETHERLANDS *(lauranne-shipping.com)*								
LS Evanne	9519614	TK	2010	D	7,003	390' 09"	55' 05"	27' 07"
(Kormel '10-'12)								
LONGSHIP BV, GRONINGEN, NETHERLANDS *(longship.com)*								
Pride	9480277	BC	2008	D	16,987	497' 00"	68' 11"	39' 08"
(Qin Feng165 '08-'08, Avenue Pride '08-'13, Polaris Pride '13-'16)								
Silda	9515280	GC	2009	D	16,622	484' 01"	75' 06"	38' 09"
(Alaya '09-'16)								
Star II	9476068	BC	2008	D	16,987	497' 00"	68' 11"	39' 08"
(Avenue Star '08-'10, Polaris Star '10-'16)								

Fleet Name / Vessel Name	Vessel IMO #	Vessel Type	Year Built	Engine Type	Cargo Cap. or Gross*	Overall Length	Vessel Breadth	Vessel Depth
LUBECA MARINE GERMANY GMBH & CO., LUBECK, GERMANY (lubeca-marine.de)								
Gotland	9480136	BC	2011	D	17,409	471' 11"	74' 10"	43' 10"
(Rickmers Tianjin '11-'15)								
MASSOEL LTD., GENEVA, SWITZERLAND (massoel.com)								
Lugano	9244087	BC	2002	D	20,035	509' 00"	77' 09"	42' 08"
(DS Regent '02-'06)								
Martigny	9229867	BC	2002	D	20,035	509' 00"	77' 09"	42' 08"
(VOC Regal '02-'03, Clipper Regal '03-'06)								
MED MARITIME LTD., LONDON, ENGLAND								
Med Arctic	9410545	TK	2009	D	8,239	403' 10"	56' 05"	30' 02"
(Nordic Harmony '09-'09, Med Arctic '09-'15, Sea Dolphin '15-'15)								
MINERALIEN SCHIFFAHRT, SCHNAITTENBACH, GERMANY (minship.com)								
Harriett	9239458	BC	2002	D	25,565	590' 05"	75' 09"	45' 09"
Lady Doris	9459955	BC	2011	D	30,898	606' 11"	77' 09"	47' 11"
(Merganser '11-'11)								
Trudy	9415246	BC	2009	D	30,898	606' 11"	77' 09"	47' 11"
(Cresty '09-'09)								
Yulia	9459967	BC	2011	D	30,898	606' 11"	77' 09"	47' 11"
(Harlequin '11-'11)								
MTM SHIP MANAGEMENT LTD., SINGAPORE (mtmshipmanagement.com)								
MTM Southport	9416032	TK	2008	D	20,216	481' 00"	77' 09"	42' 08"
(Golten '08-'10)								

N-O

Fleet Name / Vessel Name	Vessel IMO #	Vessel Type	Year Built	Engine Type	Cargo Cap. or Gross*	Overall Length	Vessel Breadth	Vessel Depth
NAVARONE SA MARINE ENTERPRISES, LIMASSOL, CYPRUS								
FOLLOWING VESSELS UNDER CHARTER TO CANFORNAV								
Andean	9413925	BC	2009	D	30,898	606' 11"	77' 09"	47' 11"
Barnacle	9409742	BC	2009	D	30,898	607' 04"	77' 09"	47' 11"
Blacky	9393149	BC	2008	D	30,802	607' 04"	77' 09"	47' 11"
Bluebill	9263306	BC	2004	D	37,332	655' 10"	77' 09"	50' 02"
Brant	9393151	BC	2008	D	30,802	607' 04"	77' 09"	47' 11"
Chestnut	9477866	BC	2009	D	30,802	607' 04"	77' 09"	47' 11"
Labrador	9415222	BC	2010	D	30,898	606' 11"	77' 09"	47' 11"
Maccoa	9413913	BC	2009	D	30,898	606' 11"	77' 09"	47' 11"
Mottler	9477828	BC	2009	D	30,802	607' 04"	77' 09"	47' 11"
Ruddy	9459981	BC	2009	D	30,898	606' 11"	77' 09"	47' 11"
Shoveler	9459979	BC	2009	D	30,930	606' 11"	77' 09"	47' 11"

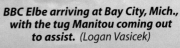

BBC Elbe arriving at Bay City, Mich., with the tug Manitou coming out to assist. (Logan Vasicek)

Fleet Name Vessel Name	Vessel IMO #	Vessel Type	Year Built	Engine Type	Cargo Cap. or Gross*	Overall Length	Vessel Breadth	Vessel Depth
Torrent	9415210	BC	2010	D	30,930	606' 11"	77' 09"	47' 11"
Tufty	9393163	BC	2009	D	30,802	607' 04"	77' 09"	47' 11"
Tundra	9415208	BC	2009	D	30,898	606' 11"	77' 09"	47' 11"

NAVIGATION MARITIME BULGARE LTD., VARNA, BULGARIA *(navbul.com)*

Belasitza	9498262	BC	2011	D	30,688	610' 03"	77' 09"	48' 01"
Kom	9132480	BC	1997	D	13,960	466' 04"	72' 10"	36' 07"
Ludogorets	9415155	BC	2010	D	29,724	622' 02"	77' 04"	47' 11"
(Fritz '10-'15, MarBacan '15-'16)								
Lyulin	9498248	BC	2011	D	30,688	610' 03"	77' 09"	48' 01"
Oborishte	9415167	BC	2010	D	29,724	622' 02"	77' 04"	47' 11"
(Luebbert '10-'15, MarBioko '15-'16)								
Osogovo	9498250	BC	2010	D	30,688	610' 03"	77' 09"	47' 11"
Rodopi	9498274	BC	2012	D	30,688	610' 03"	77' 09"	48' 01"
Strandja	9564140	BC	2010	D	30,688	610' 03"	77' 09"	47' 11"
(Eastwind York '10-'10, Federal Yangtze '10-'10)								
Vitosha	9564138	BC	2010	D	30,688	610' 03"	77' 11"	47' 11"
(Eastwind Yates '10-'10, Federal Pearl '10-'10)								

NGM ENERGY S.A., PIRAEUS, GREECE

El Zorro	9344801	TK	2007	D	13,073	451' 11"	66' 11"	37' 09"

NORBULK SHIPPING CO. LTD., HAMILTON, BERMUDA *(www.norbulkshipping.com)*

Anuket Ruby	9393668	TK	2008	D	7,315	332' 08"	62' 06"	34' 05"

NOMADIC SHORT SEA SHIPPING, BERGEN, NORWAY *(nomadic.no)*

Nomadic Hjellestad	9452220	BC	2010	D	12,914	453' 01"	68' 11"	36' 01"
Nomadic Milde	9463554	BC	2011	D	12,914	453' 01"	68' 11"	36' 01"

NORDIC TANKERS MARINE A/S, COPENHAGEN, DENMARK *(nordictankers.com)*

Njord Clear	9230012	TK	2001	D	16,875	453' 01"	75' 06"	40' 02"
(Jo Chiara D '01-'04, Chiara '04-'06, Nora '06-'09, Harbour Clear '09-'15)								
Njord Cloud	9291066	TK	2004	D	16,875	453' 01"	75' 06"	40' 02"
(Phase D '04-'04, Phase '04-'09, Harbour Cloud '09-'15)								
Nordic Mari	9422677	TK	2009	D	19,822	481' 00"	77' 10"	42' 08"
(Clipper Mari '09-'14)								

OCEAN CHALLENGE LTD., NICOSIA, CYPRUS
FOLLOWING VESSELS UNDER CHARTER TO CANFORNAV

Bluewing	9230919	BC	2002	D	26,737	611' 08"	77' 09"	46' 07"
Cinnamon	9239800	BC	2002	D	26,737	611' 08"	77' 09"	46' 07"
Greenwing	9230921	BC	2002	D	26,737	611' 08"	77' 09"	46' 07"
Mandarin	9239812	BC	2003	D	26,737	611' 08"	77' 09"	46' 07"

Cornelia under the Aerial Lift Bridge at Duluth, Minn., with tug Arkansas. (Matt Adamski)

Fleet Name / Vessel Name	Vessel IMO #	Vessel Type	Year Built	Engine Type	Cargo Cap. or Gross*	Overall Length	Vessel Breadth	Vessel Depth
OCEANEX INC., MONTREAL, QUEBEC, CANADA *(oceanex.com)*								
Oceanex Avalon	9315044	CO	2005	D	14,747	481' 11"	85' 00"	45' 11"
Oceanex Connaigra	9649718	CO	2013	D	19,460	689' 00"	97' 01"	56' 01"
Oceanex Sanderling	7603502	RR	1977	D	15,195	364' 01"	88' 05"	57' 07
(Rauenfels '77-'80, Essen '80-'81, Kongsfjord '81-'83, Onno '83-'87, ASL Sanderling '87-'08)								

P

Fleet Name / Vessel Name	Vessel IMO #	Vessel Type	Year Built	Engine Type	Cargo Cap. or Gross*	Overall Length	Vessel Breadth	Vessel Depth
PARAKOU SHIPPING LTD., HONG KONG, CHINA *(parakougroup.com)*								
FOLLOWING VESSELS UNDER CHARTER TO CANFORNAV								
Eider	9285938	BC	2004	D	37,238	655' 10"	77' 09"	50' 02"
Redhead	9285940	BC	2005	D	37,238	655' 10"	77' 09"	50' 02"
Whistler	9358371	BC	2007	D	37,238	655' 10"	77' 09"	50' 02"
Wigeon	9358395	BC	2007	D	37,238	655' 10"	77' 09"	50' 02"
PEARL SEAS CRUISES LLC., GUILFORD, CT *(pearlseascruises.com)*								
Pearl Mist	9412701	PA	2009	D	5,109*	325' 00"	52' 00"	15' 07"
PETER DOHLE SCHIFFAHRTS, HAMBURG, GERMANY *(doehle.de)*								
Diana	9370082	BC	2007	D	13,450	453' 00"	68' 11"	36' 01"
Foresight	9388912	HL	2008	D	12,782	453' 00"	70' 01"	36' 01"
(Beluga Foresight '08-'11)								
Fortune	9402067	HL	2008	D	12,782	453' 00"	70' 01"	36' 01"
(Beluga Fortune '08-'11)								
PHOENIX SHIPPING & TRADING SA, PIRAEAUS, GREECE *(phoenix-shipping.ro)*								
Fearless	9228265	BC	2001	D	30,778	606' 11"	77' 05"	48' 11"
(Bright Laker '01-'13)								
POLSTEAM (POLISH STEAMSHIP CO.), SZCZECIN, POLAND *(polsteam.com)*								
Drawsko	9393450	BC	2010	D	30,206	623' 04"	77' 11"	47' 11"
Gardno	9767704	BC	2017	D	36,500	656' 02"	77' 09"	50' 02"
Ina	9521875	BC	2012	D	17,096	492' 00"	77' 05"	41' 00"
Irma	9180396	BC	2000	D	34,946	655' 10"	77' 05"	50' 02"
Iryda	9180384	BC	1999	D	34,946	655' 10"	77' 05"	50' 02"
Isa	9180358	BC	1999	D	34,946	655' 10"	77' 05"	50' 02"
Isadora	9180372	BC	1999	D	34,946	655' 10"	77' 05"	50' 02"
Isolda	9180360	BC	1999	D	34,946	655' 10"	77' 05"	50' 02"
Juno	9422378	BC	2011	D	30,206	623' 04"	77' 11"	47' 11"
Lubie	9441984	BC	2011	D	30,206	623' 04"	77' 11"	47' 11"
Mamry	9496264	BC	2012	D	30,206	623' 04"	77' 11"	47' 11"
Miedwie	9393448	BC	2010	D	30,206	623' 04"	77' 11"	47' 11"
Narew	9521813	BC	2012	D	17,096	492' 00"	77' 05"	41' 00"
Olza	9521837	BC	2012	D	17,096	492' 00"	77' 05"	41' 00"
Prosna	9521849	BC	2012	D	17,096	492' 00"	77' 05"	41' 00"
Raba	9521825	BC	2012	D	17,096	492' 00"	77' 05"	41' 00"
Regalica	9521758	BC	2011	D	17,096	492' 00"	77' 05"	41' 00"
Resko	9393462	BC	2010	D	30,206	623' 04"	77' 11"	47' 11"
San	9521851	BC	2012	D	17,096	492' 00"	77' 05"	41' 00"
Skawa	9521863	BC	2012	D	17,096	492' 00"	77' 05"	41' 00"
Solina	9496252	BC	2012	D	30,206	623' 04"	77' 11"	47' 11"
Wicko	9393474	BC	2010	D	30,206	623' 04"	77' 11"	47' 11"
POT SCHEEPVAART BV, DELFZIJL, NETHERLANDS *(pot-scheepvaart.nl)*								
FOLLOWING VESSELS UNDER CHARTER TO WAGENBORG SHIPPING								
Kwintebank	9234288	GC	2002	D	9,822	433' 09"	52' 01"	36' 07"
Varnebank	9213739	GC	2000	D	9,822	433' 09"	52' 01"	36' 07"
Vikingbank	9604184	GC	2012	D	11,850	468' 00"	52' 01"	37' 09"
PRINCIPAL MARITIME MANAGEMENT LLC, SOUTHPORT, CONNECTICUT, USA *(princimar.com)*								
Princimar Equinox	9486245	TK	2012	D	19,900	530' 10"	75' 06"	40' 08"
(Chem Vela '12-'12, Xinle No 25 '12-'12, Angel No. 12 '12-'14)								

R

Fleet Name / Vessel Name	Vessel IMO #	Vessel Type	Year Built	Engine Type	Cargo Cap. or Gross*	Overall Length	Vessel Breadth	Vessel Depth
REDERI AB DONSOTANK, DONSO, SWEDEN *(donsotank.se)*								
Solando	9428073	TK	2009	D	19,992	491' 11"	75' 06"	42' 10"
(Messinia '09-'09, Soley-1 '09-'13)								

Fleet Name Vessel Name	Vessel IMO #	Vessel Type	Year Built	Engine Type	Cargo Cap. or Gross*	Overall Length	Vessel Breadth	Vessel Depth
REDERIET STENERSEN AS, BERGEN, NORWAY *(stenersen.com)*								
Sten Arnold	9371610	TK	2007	D	16,635	472' 07"	75' 06"	40' 08"
Sten Baltic	9307671	TK	2005	D	16,635	472' 07"	75' 06"	40' 08"
Sten Bergen	9407988	TK	2009	D	16,635	472' 07"	75' 06"	40' 08"
Sten Hidra	9358931	TK	2002	D	16,635	472' 07"	75' 06"	40' 08"
Sten Idun	9261102	TK	2002	D	16,635	472' 07"	75' 06"	40' 08"
Sten Moster	9341184	TK	2006	D	16,635	472' 07"	75' 06"	40' 08"
REEDEREI H. SCHULDT GMBH & CO., HAMBURG, GERMANY *(norddeutsche-reederei.de)*								
Ocean Castle	9315537	BC	2005	D	27,783	607' 03"	77' 01"	46' 03"
(Federal Mattawa '05-'15)								
REEDEREI HEINO WINTER, HAMBURG, GERMANY *(reederei-winter.de)*								
Jule	9357999	HL	2005	D	12,711	453' 00"	68' 11"	36' 01"
(Beluga Expectation '05-'11, Jule '11-'13, OXL Avatar '13-'13, Clipper Anita '13-'15, Thorco Dolphin '15-'15)								
REEDEREI HEINZ CORLEIS KG, STADE, GERMANY								
Stade	9535620	BC	2011	D	10,872	477' 10"	59' 10"	33' 10"
REEDEREI NORD GMBH, HAMBURG, GERMANY *(reederei-nord.com)*								
Nordisle	9457828	TK	2009	D	12,810	393' 08"	66' 11"	39' 00")
(Rio Daintree '09-'09)								
RIGEL SCHIFFAHRTS GMBH, BREMEN, GERMANY *(rigel-hb.com)*								
Amur Star	9480368	TK	2010	D	13,076	421' 11"	66' 11"	37' 09"
Colorado Star	9527609	TK	2010	D	13,076	421' 11"	66' 11"	37' 09"
Ganges Star	9496692	TK	2010	D	13,076	421' 11"	66' 11"	37' 09"
Shannon Star	9503926	TK	2010	D	13,076	421' 11"	66' 11"	37' 09"

S

Fleet Name Vessel Name	Vessel IMO #	Vessel Type	Year Built	Engine Type	Cargo Cap. or Gross*	Overall Length	Vessel Breadth	Vessel Depth
SEAFARERS SHIPPING INC., MANILA, PHILIPPINES								
AS Omaria	9363819	TK	2008	D	19,992	447' 05"	77' 09"	43' 10"
(Bow Omaria '08-'11)								
SEASTAR SHIPMANAGEMENT LTD., ATHENS, GREECE								
Cape	9498224	BC	2010	D	30,688	610' 03"	77' 09"	47' 11"
(Heloise '10-'15)								
Sunda	9498236	BC	2010	D	30,688	610' 03"	77' 09"	47' 11"
(Emilie '10-'15)								
SLOMAN NEPTUN SHIFFAHRTS, BREMEN, GERMANY *(sloman-neptun.com)*								
Sloman Helios	9466740	TK	2011	D	16,427	476' 02"	75' 06"	41' 01"
(Intrepid Canada '10-'17)								
Sloman Herakles	9466726	TK	2012	D	16,427	476' 02"	75' 06"	41' 01"
Sloman Hermes	9466738	TK	2012	D	16,427	476' 02"	75' 06"	41' 01"
SOUTH END TANKER MANAGEMENT, BARENDRECHT, NETHERLANDS *(se-tm.com)*								
Selasse	9405320	TK	2008	D	11,796	426' 11"	64' 04"	35' 09"
(Selay-S '08-'17)								
SPLIETHOFF, AMSTERDAM, THE NETHERLANDS *(spliethoff.com)*								
Fagelgracht	9428425	HL	2011	D	12,178	447' 10"	62' 00"	38' 03"
Flevogracht	9509956	HL	2011	D	12,178	447' 10"	62' 00"	38' 03"
Floragracht	9509968	HL	2011	D	12,178	447' 10"	62' 00"	38' 03"
Floretgracht	9507611	HL	2012	D	12,178	447' 10"	62' 00"	38' 03"
Florijngracht	9428413	HL	2010	D	12,178	447' 10"	62' 00"	38' 03"
Fortunagracht	9507609	HL	2012	D	12,178	447' 10"	62' 00"	38' 03"
Heemskerkgracht	9443669	HL	2009	D	12,700	453' 00"	68' 11"	36' 01"
(Beluga Faculty '09-'11, HHL Nile '11-'16)								
Marsgracht	9571507	HL	2007	D	11,759	464' 11"	62' 00"	38' 03"
Merwedegracht	9571519	HL	2011	D	11,759	464' 11"	62' 00"	38' 03"
Minervagracht	9571521	HL	2011	D	11,759	464' 11"	62' 00"	38' 03"
Muntgracht	9571545	HL	2012	D	11,759	464' 11"	62' 00"	38' 03"

At press time, Spliethoff also had the following vessels under charter. Please consult their respective fleets for details: **COE Leni, Erik, Frieda** and **Pia**.

Fleet Name Vessel Name	Vessel IMO #	Vessel Type	Year Built	Engine Type	Cargo Cap. or Gross*	Overall Length	Vessel Breadth	Vessel Depth
SUNSHIP SCHIFFAHRTSKONTOR KG, EMDEN, GERMANY *(sunship.de)*								
Lake Ontario	9283538	BC	2004	D	27,783	607' 03"	77' 01"	46' 03"
(Federal Manitou '04-'11)								

Fleet Name / Vessel Name	Vessel IMO #	Vessel Type	Year Built	Engine Type	Cargo Cap. or Gross*	Overall Length	Vessel Breadth	Vessel Depth
Lake St. Clair	9315549	BC	2004	D	27,783	607' 03"	77' 01"	46' 03"
(Federal Miramichi '04-'16)								

T-V

TARBIT TANKERS B.V., DORDRECHT, NETHERLANDS *(tarbittankers.nl)*

Stella Polaris	9187057	TK	1999	D	8,000	387' 02"	55' 09"	34' 05"

TB MARINE SHIPMANAGEMENT GMBH & CO., HAMBURG GERMANY *(tbmarine.de)*

Harbour Fashion	9473080	TK	2011	D	16,909	473' 02"	75' 06"	40' 08"
Harbour Feature	9473092	TK	2011	D	16,909	473' 02"	75' 06"	40' 08"
(Nordtank Lerner '11-'11)								
Harbour First	9473119	TK	2011	D	16,909	473' 02"	75' 06"	40' 08"
Harbour Fountain	9473107	TK	2011	D	16,909	473' 02"	75' 06"	40' 08"
Harbour Pioneer	9572757	TK	2010	D	19,118	530' 05"	75' 06"	40' 09"
(Harbour Pioneer '10-'10, Nordtank Franklin '10-'10)								
Harbour Progress	9572745	TK	2010	D	19,118	530' 05"	75' 06"	40' 09"

TEAM TANKERS MANAGEMENT AS, HELLERUP, DENMARK *(teamtankers.com)*

Sichem Beijing	9397042	TK	2007	D	13,073	421' 11"	66' 11"	37' 09"
Sichem Challenge	9196448	TK	1998	D	17,485	382' 06"	62' 04"	33' 02"
*(Queen of Montreaux '98-'99, **North Challenge** '99-'06, Songa Challenge '06-'07)*								
Sichem Defiance	9244374	TK	2001	D	17,369	442' 11"	74' 10"	41' 00"
*(**North Defiance** '01-'06, **Songa Defiance** '06-'07)*								
Sichem Melbourne	9376921	TK	2007	D	12,936	417' 04"	67' 00"	37' 09"
Sichem Mumbai	9322085	TK	2006	D	13,141	421' 11"	66' 11"	37' 09"
Sichem New York	9337834	TK	2007	D	12,956	417' 04"	67' 00"	37' 09"

TERAS BBC OCEAN NAVIGATION ENTERPRISES, HOUSTON, TEXAS

Houston	9331593	GC	2005	D	7,530	393' 00"	66' 03"	32' 02"
*(**BBC Australia** '05-'05, Wesier Hiede '05-'05, **BBC Australia** '05-'10, **BBC Houston** '10-'14)*								

THORCO PROJECTS, COPENHAGEN, DENMARK *(thorcoprojects.com)*

America	9504114	GC	2010	D	11,048	434' 08"	52' 01"	35' 04"
(Flinter America '10-'17)								
Arctic	9504126	GC	2010	D	11,048	434' 08"	52' 01"	35' 04"
(Flinter Arctic '10-'17)								
Riga	9504140	GC	2011	D	11,048	434' 08"	52' 01"	35' 04"
(Flinter Aland '10-'16)								
Rotterdam	9504138	GC	2011	D	11,048	434' 08"	52' 01"	35' 04"
(Flinterafrica '11-'11, Flinter Atlantic '11-'16)								
Thorco Marjanne	9232462	GC	2001	D	17,539	465' 10"	70' 06"	43' 08"
*(**Magdalena Green** '01-'12, Clipper Magdalena '12-'16)*								

Federal Clyde at anchor on Lake Ontario. (Jeff Cameron)

Fleet Name / Vessel Name	Vessel IMO #	Vessel Type	Year Built	Engine Type	Cargo Cap. or Gross*	Overall Length	Vessel Breadth	Vessel Depth
TRADEWIND TANKERS, BARCELONA, SPAIN (tradewindtankers.com)								
Tradewind Adventure	9485590	TK	2008	D	13,000	467' 06"	72' 02"	39' 04"
UNI-TANKERS A/S, MIDDELFART, DENMARK (unitankers.com)								
Erria Swan	9347748	TK	2006	D	11,348	425' 08"	64' 04"	34' 01"
(Alaattin Bey '06-'07, Erria Helen '07-'12)								
Fionia Swan	9328974	TK	2005	D	15,602	485' 07"	70' 10"	37' 01"
Mona Swan	9371804	TK	2006	D	11,348	425' 08"	64' 04"	34' 01"
(M Can Bey '06-'08, Erria Ida '08-'12)								
Selandia Swan	9371787	TK	2008	D	17,998	438' 11"	73' 06"	41' 04"
Swan Baltic	9386249	TK	2007	D	11,530	426' 11"	64' 04"	35' 09"
(Ozay-5 '07-'14)								
Swan Biscay	9438444	TK	2008	D	11,530	426' 11"	64' 04"	35' 09"
(Ozay-6 '08-'14)								
UNICORN TANKERS INTERNATIONAL LTD., LONDON, UNITED KINGDOM								
Kowie	9382504	TK	2010	D	16,885	472' 05"	75' 06"	41' 00"
Umgeni	9382499	TK	2011	D	16,500	472' 05"	75' 06"	41' 00"
(Siyanda '11-'11, Umzimvubu '11-'11)								
UNISEA SHIPPING B.V., SNEEK, NETHERLANDS								
Beauforce	9526095	BC	2010	D	8,284	387' 07"	52' 02"	28' 10"
UTKILEN AS, BERGEN, NORWAY (utkilen.no)								
Susana S	9406714	TK	2009	D	12,862	539' 02"	76' 01"	42' 00"
VBG DENIZCILIK SANAYI VE TICARET AS, ISTANBUL, TURKEY (vbgshipping.com)								
Halit Bey	9410143	TK	2009	D	19,999	530' 04"	73' 06"	42' 00"
Nilufer Sultan	9410131	TK	2008	D	19,999	530' 04"	73' 06"	42' 00"
VICTORY CRUISE LINES, MIAMI, FL (victorycruiselines.com)								
Victory I	9213129	PA	2001	D	4,954*	300' 00"	50' 00"	20' 00"
Built: Atlantic Marine Inc., Jacksonville, FL (**Cape May Light** '01-'09, Sea Voyager '09-'14, **Saint Laurent** '14-'16)								
Victory II	9213131	PA	2004	D	4,954*	300' 00"	50' 00"	20' 00"
Built: Atlantic Marine Inc., Jacksonville, FL (**Cape Cod Light** '04-'07, Coastal Queen 2 '07-'08, **Clipper Discoverer** '08-'10, **Sea Discoverer** '10-'17)								

W-Z

Fleet Name / Vessel Name	Vessel IMO #	Vessel Type	Year Built	Engine Type	Cargo Cap. or Gross*	Overall Length	Vessel Breadth	Vessel Depth
W. BOCKSTIEGEL REEDEREI KG, EMDEN, GERMANY (reederei-bockstiegel.de)								
BBC Campana	9291963	HL	2003	D	12,837	453' 00"	68' 11"	36' 01"
BBC Florida	9433286	HL	2009	D	12,767	454' 05"	68' 11"	36' 01"

Pilot boat Huron Maid, BBC Elbe and Hon. James L. Oberstar at Detroit. (Christopher Dark)

Fleet Name / Vessel Name	IMO #	Vessel Type	Year Built	Engine Type	Cargo Cap. or Gross*	Overall Length	Breadth	Depth
BBC Maine	9357200	HL	2007	D	12,767	454' 05"	68' 11"	36' 01"
BBC Plata	9291975	HL	2005	D	12,837	453' 00"	68' 11"	36' 01"
(Asian Voyager '05-'05)								
BBC Zarate	9337236	HL	2007	D	12,767	454' 05"	68' 11"	36' 01"

WAGENBORG SHIPPING BV, DELFZIJL, NETHERLANDS *(wagenborg.com)*

Fleet Name / Vessel Name	IMO #	Vessel Type	Year Built	Engine Type	Cargo Cap. or Gross*	Overall Length	Breadth	Depth
Alamosborg	9466348	GC	2011	D	17,323	469' 02"	70' 06"	43' 08"
Alaskaborg	9466374	GC	2012	D	17,323	469' 02"	70' 06"	43' 08"
Albanyborg	9466300	GC	2010	D	17,323	469' 02"	70' 06"	43' 08"
Amazoneborg	9333541	GC	2007	D	17,323	469' 02"	70' 06"	43' 08"
Americaborg	9365659	GC	2007	D	17,323	469' 02"	70' 06"	43' 08"
Amstelborg	9333527	GC	2006	D	17,323	469' 02"	70' 06"	43' 08"
Amurborg	9466336	GC	2011	D	17,323	469' 02"	70' 06"	43' 08"
Andesborg	9466324	GC	2011	D	17,323	469' 02"	70' 06"	43' 08"
Arneborg	9333539	GC	2006	D	17,323	469' 02"	70' 06"	43' 08"
Arubaborg	9466295	GC	2010	D	17,323	469' 02"	70' 06"	43' 08"
Atlanticborg	9466350	GC	2012	D	17,323	469' 02"	70' 06"	43' 08"
Avonborg	9466362	GC	2012	D	17,323	469' 02"	70' 06"	43' 08"
Azoresborg	9466051	GC	2010	D	17,323	469' 02"	70' 06"	43' 08"
Beatrix	9419280	GC	2009	D	14,596	507' 03"	56' 05"	37' 09"
(Fivelborg '09-'09)								
Ebroborg	9463451	GC	2010	D	10,750	452' 03"	52' 01"	36' 01"
Edenborg	9463449	GC	2010	D	10,750	452' 03"	52' 01"	36' 01"
Eeborg	9568328	GC	2012	D	12,004	474' 03"	52' 01"	36' 07"
Eemsborg	9225586	GC	2009	D	10,750	452' 03"	52' 01"	36' 01"
Elbeborg	9568249	GC	2011	D	12,004	474' 03"	52' 01"	36' 07"
Erieborg	9463437	GC	2009	D	10,750	452' 03"	52' 01"	36' 01"
Exeborg	9650482	GC	2011	D	12,004	474' 03"	52' 01"	36' 07"
Finnborg	9419321	GC	2011	D	14,596	507' 03"	56' 05"	37' 09"
Fivelborg	9419307	GC	2010	D	14,596	507' 03"	56' 05"	37' 09"
Flevoborg	9419292	GC	2010	D	14,596	507' 03"	56' 05"	37' 09"
Fraserborg	9419319	GC	2011	D	14,596	507' 03"	56' 05"	37' 09"
Fuldaborg	9559092	GC	2012	D	14,596	507' 03"	56' 05"	37' 09"
Jan van Gent	9456721	GC	2010	D	12,000	469' 00"	62' 00"	35' 11"
(Jan van Gent '10-'14, Nordana Madeleine '14-'16)								
Mississippiborg	9207508	GC	2000	D	9,141	441' 05"	54' 02"	32' 02"
Nassauborg	9248564	GC	2006	D	16,740	467' 03"	72' 06"	42' 00"
Reestborg	9592563	GC	2013	D	23,249	556' 11"	66' 11"	37' 11"
Reggeborg	9592575	GC	2014	D	23,249	556' 11"	66' 11"	37' 11"
Roerborg	9592599	GC	2014	D	23,249	556' 11"	66' 11"	37' 11"

Nunalik near Montreal. (René Beauchamp)

Fleet Name / Vessel Name	Vessel IMO #	Vessel Type	Year Built	Engine Type	Cargo Cap. or Gross*	Overall Length	Vessel Breadth	Vessel Depth
Taagborg	9546461	GC	2013	D	21,338	565' 03"	70' 06"	43' 08"
Thamesborg	9546459	GC	2013	D	21,338	565' 03"	70' 06"	43' 08"
Trinityborg	9546485	GC	2013	D	21,338	565' 03"	70' 06"	43' 08"
Vaasaborg	9196242	GC	1999	D	8,664	433' 10"	52' 01"	31' 08"
*(**Vaasaborg** '00-'03, Normed Hamburg '03-'04)*								
Vancouverborg	9213741	GC	2001	D	9,857	433' 10"	52' 01"	31' 08"
Victoriaborg	9234276	GC	2001	D	9,857	433' 10"	52' 01"	31' 08"
Virginiaborg	9234290	GC	2001	D	9,857	433' 10"	52' 01"	31' 08"
Vlieborg	9554781	GC	2012	D	11,850	468' 00"	52' 01"	35' 04"
Volgaborg	9631072	GC	2013	D	11,850	468' 00"	51' 09"	35' 04"
Voorneborg	9179373	GC	1999	D	8,664	433' 10"	52' 01"	31' 08"

At press time, Wagenborg Shipping also had the following vessels under charter. Please consult their respective fleets for details: **Kwintebank, Morgenstond I, Morgenstond II, Varnebank** and **Vikingbank**.

WECO SHIPPING, RUNDSTED, DENMARK *(wecobulk.com)*

Fleet Name / Vessel Name	Vessel IMO #	Vessel Type	Year Built	Engine Type	Cargo Cap. or Gross*	Overall Length	Vessel Breadth	Vessel Depth
Billesborg	9488047	HL	2011	D	12,767	454' 05"	68' 11"	36' 01"
(Billesborg '11-'11, Clipper Angela '11-'12)								

WIJNNE BARENDS, DELFZIJL, NETHERLANDS *(wijnnebarends.com)*

Fleet Name / Vessel Name	Vessel IMO #	Vessel Type	Year Built	Engine Type	Cargo Cap. or Gross*	Overall Length	Vessel Breadth	Vessel Depth
Morgenstond I	9320506	BC	2006	D	12,000	469' 00"	62' 00"	35' 11"
*(Morgenstond I '06-'06, Beluga Locomotion '06-'08, Kent Locomotion '08-'08, Beluga Locomotion '08-'09, Morgenstond I '09-'10, **Kent Sunrise** '10-'12, Morgenstond I '12-'12, Clipper Athena '12-'14)*								
Morgenstond II	9367073	BC	2007	D	12,000	469' 00"	62' 00"	35' 11"
*(**Morgenstond II** '07-'07, Beluga Legislation '07-'07, Kent Legislation '07-'09, **Beluga Legislation** '09-'10, Kent Sunset '10-'13, **Morgenstond II** '13-'13, Clipper Aurora '13-'15)*								

YARDIMCI SHIPPING GROUP, ISTANBUL, TURKEY

Fleet Name / Vessel Name	Vessel IMO #	Vessel Type	Year Built	Engine Type	Cargo Cap. or Gross*	Overall Length	Vessel Breadth	Vessel Depth
Ayane	9395991	TK	2010	D	16,745	472' 07"	75' 06"	40' 08"
CT Dublin	9395989	TK	2008	D	16,745	472' 07"	75' 06"	40' 08"
Elevit	9466609	TK	2012	D	16,745	472' 07"	75' 06"	40' 08"

YAWATAHAMA KISEN Y. K., YAWATAHAMA, JAPAN
FOLLOWING VESSEL UNDER CHARTER TO FEDNAV

Fleet Name / Vessel Name	Vessel IMO #	Vessel Type	Year Built	Engine Type	Cargo Cap. or Gross*	Overall Length	Vessel Breadth	Vessel Depth
Federal Yukina	9476977		2010	D	35,868	655' 06"	77' 11"	48' 09"

YILMAR SHIPPING & TRADING LTD., ISTANBUL, TURKEY *(yilmar.com)*

Fleet Name / Vessel Name	Vessel IMO #	Vessel Type	Year Built	Engine Type	Cargo Cap. or Gross*	Overall Length	Vessel Breadth	Vessel Depth
YM Jupiter	9291597	TK	2007	D	16,000	485' 07"	70' 10"	37' 01"
YM Saturn	9362138	TK	2007	D	16,000	485' 07"	70' 10"	37' 01"

ZEALAND SHIPPING BV, ALMERE, NETHERLANDS *(zealand-shipping.nl)*

Fleet Name / Vessel Name	Vessel IMO #	Vessel Type	Year Built	Engine Type	Cargo Cap. or Gross*	Overall Length	Vessel Breadth	Vessel Depth
Zealand Beatrix	9507087	BC	2010	D	13,089	441' 11"	67' 03"	36' 01"
Zealand Delilah	9507075	BC	2011	D	13,089	441' 11"	67' 03"	36' 01"

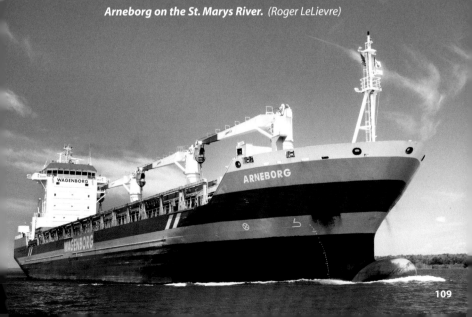

Arneborg on the St. Marys River. (Roger LeLievre)

Three Rivers on the Maumee River at Toledo, Ohio. (Jim Hoffman)

Silda anchored on Lake Ontario off Port Weller, Ont., conducting lifeboat drills. (Jeff Cameron)

Erik above the Soo Locks, December 2017. (Kari Eliason)

112

Marine Museums™

Independence Day fireworks over the stern of the museum ship Valley Camp at Sault Ste. Marie, Mich. (Matt Miner)

MUSEUMS AFLOAT

Museum Name Vessel Name	Vessel Type	Year Built	Engine Type	Cargo Cap. or Gross*	Overall Length	Breadth	Depth
BUFFALO AND ERIE COUNTY NAVAL & MILITARY PARK, BUFFALO, NY (buffalonavalpark.org)							
Croaker	MU	1944	D	1,526*	311'07"	27'02"	33'09"
Former U. S. Navy Gato class submarine IXSS-246; open to the public at Buffalo, NY							
Little Rock	MU	1945	T	10,670*	610'01"	66'04"	25'00"
Former U. S. Navy Cleveland / Little Rock class guided missile cruiser; open to the public at Buffalo, NY							
The Sullivans	MU	1943	T	2,500*	376'06"	39'08"	22'08"
Former U. S. Navy Fletcher class destroyer; open to the public at Buffalo, NY (Launched as USS Putnam)							
CITY OF KEWAUNEE, KEWAUNEE, WI							
Ludington	TB/MU	1943	D	249*	115'00"	26'00"	13'08"
Built: Jakobson Shipyard, Oyster Bay, NY; former U.S. Army Corps of Engineers tug is open to the public as a marine museum at Kewaunee, WI (Major Wilbur F. Browder [LT-4] '43-'47)							
DOOR COUNTY MARITIME MUSEUM & LIGHTHOUSE PRESERVATION SOCIETY INC., STURGEON BAY, WI (dcmm.org)							
John Purves	TB/MU	1919	D	436*	150'00"	27'06"	16'08"
Built: Bethlehem Steel Co., Elizabeth, NJ; former Roen/Andrie Inc. tug has been refurbished as a museum display at Sturgeon Bay, WI (Butterfield '19-'42, LT-145 '42-'57)							
DULUTH ENTERTAINMENT CONVENTION CENTER, DULUTH, MN (decc.org/william-a-irvin)							
William A. Irvin	BC/MU	1938	T	14,050	610'09"	60'00"	32'06"
Built: American Shipbuilding Co., Lorain, OH; former United States Steel Corp. bulk carrier last operated Dec. 16, 1978; open to the public at Duluth, MN							
ERIE MARITIME MUSEUM, ERIE, PA (flagshipniagara.org)							
Niagara	MU/2B	1988	W	295*	198'00"	32'00"	10'06"
Reconstruction of Oliver Hazard Perry's U. S. Navy brigantine from the War of 1812							
FRIENDS OF KEEWATIN, PORT McNICOLL, ON (sskeewatin.com)							
Keewatin {2}	PA/MU	1907	Q	3,856*	346'00"	43'08"	26'06"
Built: Fairfield Shipbuilding and Engineering Co. Ltd., Govan, Scotland; former Canadian Pacific Railway Co. passenger vessel last operated Nov. 29, 1965; now a marine museum at Port McNicoll, ON, but may be relocated							
GREAT LAKES NAVAL MEMORIAL & MUSEUM, MUSKEGON, MI (silversidesmuseum.org)							
McLane	MU	1927	D	289*	125'00"	24'00"	12'06"
Built: American Brown Boveri Electric Co., Camden, NJ; former U.S. Coast Guard Buck & A Quarter class medium endurance cutter; on display at Muskegon, MI (USCGC McLane '27-'70, Manatra II '70-'93)							
Silversides	MU	1941	D/V	1,526*	311'08"	27'03"	33'09"
Built: Mare Island Naval Yard, Vallejo, CA; former U.S. Navy Albacore (Gato) class submarine AGSS-236; open to the public at Muskegon, MI							
GREAT LAKES SCIENCE CENTER, CLEVELAND, OH (greatscience.com)							
William G. Mather {2}	BC/MU	1925	T	13,950	618'00"	62'00"	32'00"
Built: Great Lakes Engineering Works, Ecorse, MI; former Cleveland-Cliffs Steamship Co. bulk carrier last operated Dec. 21, 1980; open to the public at Cleveland, OH							
HMCS HAIDA NATIONAL HISTORICAL SITE, HAMILTON, ON (hmcshaida.com)							
Haida	MU	1943	T	2,744*	377'00"	37'06"	15'02"
Former Royal Canadian Navy Tribal class destroyer G-63 / DDE-215; open to the public at Hamilton, ON							
ICEBREAKER MACKINAW MARITIME MUSEUM INC., MACKINAW CITY, MI (themackinaw.org)							
Mackinaw [WAGB-83]	IB/MU	1944	D	5,252*	290'00"	74'00"	29'00"
Built: Toledo Shipbuilding Co., Toledo, OH; former U.S. Coast Guard icebreaker was decommissioned in 2006; open to the public at Mackinaw City, MI (Launched as USCGC Manitowoc [WAG-83])							
LAKE COUNTY HISTORICAL SOCIETY, TWO HARBORS, MN (lakecountyhistoricalsociety.org)							
Edna G.	TB/MU	1896	R	154*	102'00"	23'00"	14'06"
Built: Cleveland Shipbuilding Co., Cleveland, OH; former Duluth, Missabe & Iron Range Railroad tug last operated in 1981; open to the public at Two Harbors, MN							
LAKEHEAD TRANSPORTATION MUSEUM SOCIETY, THUNDER BAY, ON (ltms.ca)							
Alexander Henry	IB/MU	1959	D	1,674*	210'00"	44'00"	17'09"
Built: Port Arthur Shipbuilding Co., Port Arthur, ON; former Canadian Coast Guard icebreaker was retired in 1985; formerly at Kingston, ON, now open to the public at Thunder Bay, ON							
LE SAULT DE SAINTE MARIE HISTORIC SITES INC., SAULT STE. MARIE, MI (saulthistoricsites.com)							
Valley Camp {2}	BC/MU	1917	R	12,000	550'00"	58'00"	31'00"
Built: American Shipbuilding Co., Lorain, OH; former Hanna Mining Co./Wilson Marine Transit Co./Republic Steel Corp. bulk carrier last operated in 1966; open to the public at Sault Ste. Marie, MI (Louis W. Hill '17-'55)							

84% of the continent's *fresh water...* and a *different story* in every *drop.*

NATIONAL MUSEUM *of the* GREAT LAKES

Voted as Ohio's 2nd Best Attraction by readers of USA Today!

USA TODAY 10BEST READERS' CHOICE 2017

COL. JAMES M. SCHOONMAKER

1701 Front Street, Toledo, OH 43605 • inlandseas.org • 419.214.5000

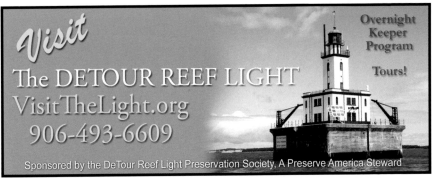

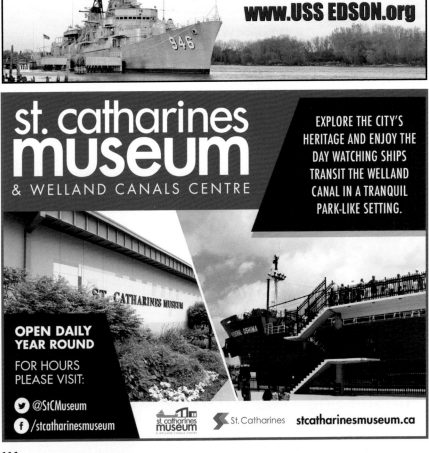

Museum Name / Vessel Name	Vessel Type	Year Built	Engine Type	Cargo Cap. or Gross*	Overall Length	Breadth	Depth

NATIONAL MUSEUM OF THE GREAT LAKES, TOLEDO, OH *(inlandseas.org)*

| Col. James M. Schoonmaker | BC/MU | 1911 | T | 15,000 | 617' 00" | 64' 00" | 33' 01" |

Built: Great Lakes Engineering Works, Ecorse, MI; former Shenango Furnace Co./Republic Steel Co./Cleveland-Cliffs Steamship Co. bulk carrier last operated in 1980; open to the public at Toledo, OH (Col. James M. Schoonmaker 1911-'69, Willis B. Boyer '69-'11)

| Ohio | TB/MU | 1903 | D | 194* | 101' 02" | 26' 00" | 13' 07" |

Built: Great Lakes Towing Co., Chicago, IL; veteran tug is the latest addition to the National Museum's growing collection (M.F.D. No. 15 '03-'52, Laurence C. Turner '52-'73)

PORT HURON MUSEUM, PORT HURON, MI *(phmuseum.org)*

| Huron | MU | 1920 | D | 392* | 96' 05" | 24' 00" | 10' 00" |

Built: Charles L. Seabury Co., Morris Heights, NY; former U.S. Coast Guard lightship WLV-526 was retired Aug. 20, 1970; open to the public at Port Huron, MI (Lightship 103 – Relief [WAL-526] '20-'36)

SAGINAW VALLEY NAVAL SHIP MUSEUM, BAY CITY, MI *(ussedson.org)*

| Edson [DD-946] | MU | 1958 | D | | 418' 03" | 45' 03" | |

Built: Bath Iron Works, Bath, ME; Forrest Sherman class destroyer was decommissioned in '88; from '89-'04 on display at the Intrepid Sea, Air & Space Museum, New York, N.Y. Declared a U.S. National Historic Landmark in '90; returned to U.S. Navy in '04; open to the public at Bay City, MI

S.S. CITY OF MILWAUKEE – NATIONAL HISTORIC LANDMARK, MANISTEE, MI *(carferry.com)*

| Acacia | BT/MU | 1944 | DE | 1,025* | 180' 00" | 37' 00" | 17' 04" |

Built: Marine Iron and Shipbuilding Corp., Duluth, MN; former U.S. Coast Guard buoy tender/icebreaker was decommissioned in '06 (Launched as USCGC Thistle [WAGL-406])

| City of Milwaukee | MU | 1931 | R | 26 cars | 360' 00" | 56' 03" | 21' 06" |

Built: Manitowoc Shipbuilding Co., Manitowoc, WI; train ferry sailed for the Grand Trunk Railroad '31-'78 and the Ann Arbor Railroad '78-'81; open to the public at Manistee, MI

S.S. COLUMBIA PROJECT, NEW YORK, NY *(sscolumbia.org)*

| Columbia {2} | PA/MU | 1902 | R | 968* | 216' 00" | 60' 00" | 13' 06" |

Built: Detroit Dry Dock Co, Wyandotte, MI; former Detroit to Bob-Lo Island passenger steamer last operated Sept. 2, 1991; moved to Buffalo, N.Y., Sept. 2, 2015, for further restoration and possible return to service

S.S. METEOR WHALEBACK SHIP MUSEUM, SUPERIOR, WI *(superiorpublicmuseums.org/s-s-meteor-2)*

| Meteor {2} | TK/MU | 1896 | R | 40,100 | 380' 00" | 45' 00" | 26' 00" |

Built: American Steel Barge Co., Superior, WI; former ore carrier/auto carrier/tanker is the last vessel of whaleback design surviving on the Great Lakes; Cleveland Tankers vessel last operated in 1969; open to the public at Superior, WI (Frank Rockefeller 1896-'28, South Park '1928-'43)

S.S. MILWAUKEE CLIPPER PRESERVATION INC., MUSKEGON, MI *(milwaukeeclipper.com)*

| Milwaukee Clipper | PA/MU | 1904 | Q | 4,272 | 361' 00" | 45' 00" | 28' 00" |

Built: American Shipbuilding Co., Cleveland, OH; rebuilt in '40 at Manitowoc Shipbuilding Co., Manitowoc, WI; former Wisconsin & Michigan Steamship Co. passenger/auto carrier last operated in 1970; undergoing restoration and open to the public at Muskegon, MI (Juniata '04-'41)

ST. MARYS RIVER MARINE CENTRE, SAULT STE. MARIE, ON *(norgoma.org)*

| Norgoma | PA/MU | 1950 | D | 1,477* | 188' 00" | 37' 06" | 22' 06" |

Built: Collingwood Shipyards, Collingwood, ON; former Ontario Northland Transportation Commission passenger vessel last operated in 1974; open to the public at Sault Ste. Marie, ON

USCG BRAMBLE, PORT HURON, MI *(uscgcbramble.com)*

| Bramble | BT/MU | 1944 | DE | 1,025* | 180' 00" | 37' 00" | 17' 04" |

Built: Zenith Dredge Co., Duluth, MN; former U.S. Coast Guard buoy tender/icebreaker was retired in 2003; open as an operational marine museum at Port Huron, MI (USCGC Bramble [WLB-392] '44-'03)

USS COD SUBMARINE MEMORIAL, CLEVELAND, OH *(usscod.org)*

| Cod | MU | 1943 | D/V | 1,525* | 311' 08" | 27' 02" | 33' 09" |

Built: Electric Boat Co., Groton, CT; former U.S. Navy Albacore (Gato) class submarine IXSS-224 open to the public at Cleveland, OH

USS LST 393 PRESERVATION ASSOCIATION, MUSKEGON, MI *(lst393.org)*

| LST-393 | MU | 1942 | D | 2,100 | 328' 00" | 50' 00" | 25' 00" |

Built: Newport News Shipbuilding and Dry Dock Co., Newport News, VA; former U.S. Navy/Wisconsin & Michigan Steamship Co. vessel last operated July 31, 1973; open to the public at Muskegon, MI (USS LST-393 '42-'47, Highway 16 '47-'99)

WISCONSIN MARITIME MUSEUM, MANITOWOC, WI *(wisconsinmaritime.com)*

| Cobia | MU | 1944 | D/V | 1,500* | 311' 09" | 27' 03" | 33' 09" |

Built: Electric Boat Co., Groton, CT; former U. S. Navy Gato class submarine AGSS-245 is open to the public at Manitowoc, WI

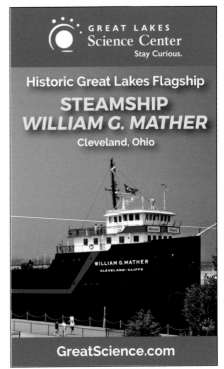
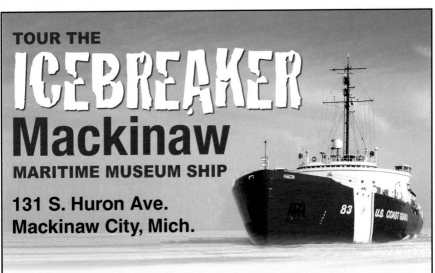
118

MUSEUMS ASHORE

Information can change without notice. Call ahead to verify location and hours.

ANTIQUE BOAT MUSEUM, 750 MARY ST., CLAYTON, NY – (315) 686-4104: A large collection of freshwater boats and engines. Annual show is the first weekend of August. Seasonal. (*abm.org*)

ASHTABULA MARITIME & SURFACE TRANSPORTATION MUSEUM, 1071 WALNUT BLVD., ASHTABULA, OH – (440) 964-6847: Housed in the 1876/1898-built former lighthouse keeper's residence, the museum includes models, paintings, artifacts, photos, the world's only working scale model of a Hullett ore unloading machine, a Titanic display, a display of the 1876 Ashtabula Train Bridge Disaster and the pilothouse from the steamer *Thomas Walters*. Seasonal.

BUFFALO HARBOR MUSEUM, 66 ERIE ST., BUFFALO, NY – (716) 849-0914: Exhibits explore local maritime history. Open all year, Thursday and Sunday only. (*llmhs.org*)

DOOR COUNTY MARITIME MUSEUM & LIGHTHOUSE PRESERVATION SOCIETY INC., 120 N. MADISON AVE., STURGEON BAY, WI – (920) 743-5958: Many excellent models help portray the role shipbuilding has played in the Door Peninsula. Open all year. (*dcmm.org*)

DOSSIN GREAT LAKES MUSEUM, 100 THE STRAND, BELLE ISLE, DETROIT, MI – (313) 833-5538: Models, interpretive displays, the smoking room from the 1912 passenger steamer *City of Detroit III*, an anchor from the *Edmund Fitzgerald* and the pilothouse from the steamer *William Clay Ford* are on display. (*detroithistorical.org/main/dossin*)

ELGIN MILITARY MUSEUM, 30 TALBOT ST., ST. THOMAS, ON – (519) 633-7641: *HMCS Ojibwa*, a Cold War Oberon-class submarine, is open to the public at Port Burwell, Ont. (*theelginmilitarymuseum.ca*)

ERIE MARITIME MUSEUM, 150 E. FRONT ST., ERIE, PA – (814) 452-2744: Displays depict the Battle of Lake Erie and more. Open all year. (*eriemaritimemuseum.org*)

FAIRPORT HARBOR LIGHTHOUSE & MARINE MUSEUM, 129 SECOND ST., FAIRPORT, OH – (440) 354-4825: Located in the Fairport Lighthouse, displays include the pilothouse from the *Frontenac* and the mainmast of the first *USS Michigan*. Seasonal. (*fairportharborlighthouse.org*)

GREAT LAKES LORE MARITIME MUSEUM, 367 N. THIRD ST., ROGERS CITY, MI – (989) 734-0706: The generations of men and women who sailed and made their livings on the Great Lakes are remembered here, as are their uniforms, personal possessions and navigational and other maritime tools. (*gllmm.com*)

GREAT LAKES SHIPWRECK MUSEUM, WHITEFISH POINT, MI – (906) 635-1742 or (800) 635-

Continued on Page 121

Museum Ship Stack Markings

Museum Ship City of Milwaukee
Manistee, MI

Museum Ship Col. James M. Schoonmaker
Toledo, OH

Museum Ship Keewatin
Port McNicoll, ON

Museum Ship Alexander Henry
Thunder Bay, ON

Museum Ship HMCS Haida
Hamilton, ON

Museum Ships USS Little Rock USS The Sullivans
Buffalo, N.Y.

Museum Ship Meteor
Superior, WI

Museum Ship Milwaukee Clipper
Muskegon, MI

Museum Ships Norgoma (Sault Ste. Marie, ON)
Norisle (Manitowaning, ON)

Museum Ship Valley Camp
Sault Ste. Marie, MI

Museum Ship William A. Irvin
Duluth, MN

Museum Ship William G. Mather
Cleveland, OH

Museum Ship USCG Mackinaw
Mackinaw City, MI

Museum Tug John Purves
Sturgeon Bay, WI

Museum Tug Edna G.
Two Harbors, MN

1742: Museum includes lighthouse and shipwreck artifacts, a shipwreck video theater, the restored lighthouse keeper's quarters and an *Edmund Fitzgerald* display that features the ship's bell. Seasonal. *(shipwreckmuseum.com)*

LAKE SUPERIOR MARITIME VISITOR CENTER, 600 CANAL PARK DRIVE, DULUTH, MN – (218) 720-5260: Museum provides displays, historic artifacts and programs that explain the roles of Duluth and Superior in Great Lakes shipping, as well as the job of the U.S. Army Corps of Engineers in maintaining the nation's waterways. Many excellent models and other artifacts are on display. Open all year. *(lsmma.com)*

LE SAULT DE SAINTE MARIE HISTORICAL SITES INC., 501 E. WATER ST., SAULT STE. MARIE, MI – (906) 632-3658: The 1917-built steamer *Valley Camp* is the centerpiece of this museum. The ship's three cargo holds house artifacts, models, aquariums, photos and other memorabilia, as well as a tribute to the *Edmund Fitzgerald* that includes the ill-fated vessel's lifeboats. Seasonal. *(saulthistoricsites.com)*

LUDINGTON MARITIME MUSEUM, 217 S. LAKESHORE DR., LUDINGTON, MI – (231) 843-4808): Diverse, interactive exhibits tell the stories of schooners, railroad carferries, the U.S. Coast Guard and the many other maritime activities of the region. *(ludingtonmaritimemuseum.org)*

MARINE CITY PRIDE & HERITAGE MUSEUM, 405 S. MAIN ST., MARINE CITY, MI – (810) 765-5446: Displays explore the ship and shipbuilding history of the area. Seasonal. *(marinecitymuseum.com)*

MARITIME MUSEUM OF SANDUSKY, 125 MEIGS ST., SANDUSKY, OHIO – (419) 624-0274: Exhibits explore local maritime history. Open all year. *(sanduskymaritime.org)*

MARQUETTE MARITIME MUSEUM, 300 N. LAKESHORE BLVD., MARQUETTE, MI – (906) 226-2006: Museum re-creates the offices of the first commercial fishing / passenger freight companies. Displays also include photos, models and maritime artifacts. Seasonal. *(mqtmaritimemuseum.com)*

MICHIGAN MARITIME MUSEUM, 260 DYCKMAN AVE., SOUTH HAVEN, MI – (269) 637-8078: Exhibits are dedicated to the U.S. Lifesaving Service / Coast Guard. The tall ship *Friends Good Will* operates during the summer. Open all year. *(michiganmaritimemuseum.org)*

Continued on Page 122

Victorian-era passenger steamer Keewatin at Port McNicoll, Ont. This beautifully-restored vessel is looking for a new home in 2018. (Drew Benke)

MUSKOKA BOAT AND HERITAGE CENTRE, 275 STEAMSHIP BAY RD., GRAVENHURST, ON – (705) 687-2115: Visiting this museum, which includes many models of the early steamships to serve the area, is the perfect complement to a trip on the *RMS Segwun*, moored adjacent. *(realmuskoka.com/discovery-centre)*

PORT COLBORNE HISTORICAL & MARINE MUSEUM, 280 KING ST., PORT COLBORNE, ON – (905) 834-7604: Wheelhouse from the tug *Yvonne Dupre Jr.* is among the museum's displays. Seasonal. *(portcolborne.com/page/museum)*

RUDY NAUTICAL MUSEUM, 23650 VAN DYKE, CENTERLINE, MI – (586) 206-2791: Exhibits include a collection of nautical artifacts, models, paintings and research summaries. *(rudynauticalmuseum.com)*

SOMBRA MUSEUM, 3470 ST. CLAIR PARKWAY, SOMBRA, ON – (519) 892-3982: Marine room includes nautical equipment, Great Lakes and St. Clair River photos, and the Alan Mann Collection. *(sombramuseum.webs.com)*

STRAITS OF MACKINAC SHIPWRECK MUSEUM, OLD MACKINAC POINT LIGHT, MACKINAC CITY, MI – (231) 436-4100: Houses artifacts recovered from the sunken *Cedarville* as well as others that tell the story of the many shipwrecks that dot the Straits of Mackinac. Seasonal. *(mackinacparks.com)*

U.S. ARMY CORPS OF ENGINEERS MUSEUM, SOO LOCKS VISITOR CENTER, SAULT STE. MARIE, MI – (906) 632-7020: Exhibits include a working model of the Soo Locks, historic photos and a 25-minute film. Free; open Mother's Day weekend through mid-October. Check at the Visitor Center information desk for a list of vessels expected at the locks.

WELLAND CANALS CENTRE & ST. CATHARINES MUSEUM, THOROLD, ON – (905) 984-8880: Museum at Lock 3 traces the development of the Welland Canal. Museum and adjacent gift shop open year-round. Observation deck open during the navigation season. Check at the information desk for vessels expected at Lock 3. *(infoniagara.com)*

WILLIAM PURVIS MARINE CENTRE, 40 WATER ST., GORE BAY, ON – (705-282-0190): This marine museum and archive is open Victoria Day-Thanksgiving Day (Canadian). *(gorebaymuseum.com/marine-museum)*

WISCONSIN MARITIME MUSEUM, 75 MARITIME DRIVE, MANITOWOC, WI – (866) 724-2356: Displays explore the history of area shipbuilding and also honor submariners and submarines built in Manitowoc. One of the engines of the Straits of Mackinac trainferry *Chief Wawatam* is on display. The World War II sub *Cobia* is adjacent to the museum and open for tours. Open all year. *(wisconsinmaritime.org)*

Former ore carrier Willam A. Irvin is open to the public at Duluth, Minn. (Matt Adamski)

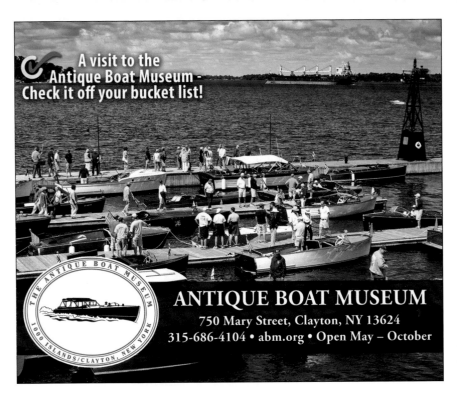

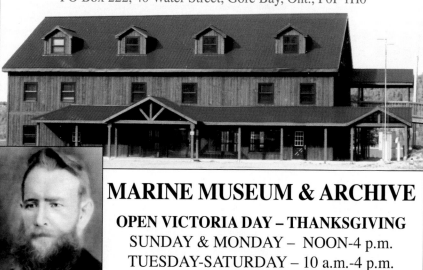

Stacks
and
Flags

Interlake Steamship Co. stack on Hon. James L. Oberstar. (Roger LeLievre)

COLORS OF THE GREAT LAKES

Abaco Marine Towing
Clayton, NY

Algoma Central Corp.
St. Catharines, ON

American Steamship Co.
Williamsville, NY

Andrie Inc.
Muskegon, MI

Andrie Specialized
Norton Shores, MI

Ashton Marine Co.
North Muskegon, MI

Bay City Boat Lines
Bay City, MI

Bay Shipbuilding Co.
Fincantieri Marine Group
Sturgeon, Bay, WI

Beaver Island Boat Co.
Charlevoix, MI

Blue Heron Co.
Tobermory, ON

Buffalo Dept. of Public Works
Buffalo, N.Y.

Busch Marine Inc.
Carrollton, MI

Calumet River Fleeting
Chicago, IL

Canada Steamship Lines Div. CSL Group
Montreal, QC

Canada Steamship Lines Div. CSL Group
Montreal, QC

Canadian Coast Guard
Ottawa, ON

Carmeuse North America (Erie Sand & Gravel)
Erie, PA

Causley Marine Contracting LLC
Bay City, MI

Central Marine Logistics Inc. Operator for ArcelorMittal
Griffith, IN

Chicago Fire Dept.
Chicago, IL

Cleveland Fire Dept.
Cleveland, OH

Cooper Marine Ltd.
Selkirk, OH

Croisières AML Inc.
Québec City, QC

Dann Marine Towing
Chesapeake City, MD

Dean Construction Co.
Windsor, ON

Detroit City Fire Dept.
Detroit, MI

Diamond Jack's River Tours
Detroit, MI

Duc D'Orleans Cruise Boat
Corunna, ON

Durocher Marine
Cheboygan, MI

Eastern Upper Peninsula Transportation Authority
Sault Ste. Marie, MI

Essroc Canada Inc.
Picton, ON

Fraser Shipyards Inc.
Superior, WI

G3 Canada Ltd. Algoma Central – Mgr
Winnipeg, MB

Gaelic Tugboat Co.
Detroit, MI

Gananoque Boat Line
Gananoque, ON

Genesis Energy
Houston, TX

Geo. Gradel Co.
Toledo, OH

Goodtime Cruise Line
Cleveland, OH

Grand Portage / Isle Royale Trans. Lines
Grand Portage, MN

Gravel & Lake Services
Thunder Bay, ON

Great Lakes Dock & Materials
Muskegon, MI

Great Lakes Fleet Inc. Key Lakes Inc.– Mgr.
Duluth, MN

Great Lakes & International Towing & Salvage
Burlington, ON

Great Lakes Maritime Academy
Traverse City, MI

Great Lakes Science Center
Ann Arbor, MI

Great Lakes Towing Co.
Cleveland, OH

Groupe C.T.M.A.
Cap-aux-Meules, QC

Groupe Desgagnés Inc.
Québec City, QC

AND SEAWAY SMOKESTACKS

Groupe Desgagnés Inc.
Québec City, QC

Groupe Desgagnés Inc.
Québec City, QC

Groupe Océan Inc.
Québec City, QC

Hamilton Port Authority
Hamilton, ON

Heritage Marine
Knife River, MN

Inland Lakes Management
Alpena, MI

Inland Tug & Barge
Brockville, ON

Interlake Steamship Co.
Middleburg Heights, OH

J.W. Westcott Co.
Detroit, MI

Kindra Lake Towing
Chicago, IL

The King Company
Holland, MI

Lafarge Canada Inc.
Mississauga, ON

Lafarge North America Inc.
Southfield, MI

Lake Erie Island Cruises
Sandusky, OH

Lakehead Tugboats Inc.
Thunder Bay, ON

Lake Michigan Carferry
Ludington, MI

**Lower Lakes Towing
Lower Lakes Transportation**
Port Dover, ON / Williamsville, NY

Luedtke Engineering
Frankfort, MI

MCM Marine Inc.
Sault Ste. Marie, MI

MacDonald Marine Ltd.
Goderich, ON

**Madeline Island
Ferry Line Inc.**
LaPointe, WI

Malcolm Marine
St. Clair, MI

Manitou Island Transit
Leland, MI

Marine Tech LLC
Duluth, MN

Mariposa Cruises
Toronto, ON

**McAsphalt Marine
Transportation**
Toronto, ON

McKeil Marine Ltd.
Burlington, ON

McKeil Marine Ltd.
Burlington, ON

McNally International
Hamilton, ON

Midwest Maritime Corp.
Franklin, WI

Miller Boat Line
Put-in-Bay, OH

Ministry of Transportation
Downsview, ON

Montreal Port Authority
Montreal, QC

**Muskoka Steamships
& Discovery Centre**
Gravenhurst, ON

Nadro Marine Services
Port Dover, ON

**New York State Marine
Highway Transportation**
Troy, NY

**North Shore Marine
Terminal and Logistics**
Escanaba, MI

**NovaAlgoma Cement
Carriers Ltd.**
St. Catharines, ON

Open Lake Group LLC.
Detroit, MI

**Owen Sound
Transportation Co. Ltd.**
Owen Sound, ON

Pere Marquette Shipping
Ludington, MI

**Port City Steamship
Port City Tug Inc.**
Muskegon, MI

Purvis Marine Ltd.
Sault Ste. Marie, ON

Roen Salvage Co.
Sturgeon Bay, WI

Ryba Marine Construction
Cheboygan, MI

Sea Service LLC
Superior, WI

Selvick Marine Towing Corp.
Sturgeon Bay, WI

Shoreline Sightseeing Co.
Chicago, IL

Société des Traversiers Du Québec
Québec City, QC

Soo Locks Boat Tours
Sault Ste. Marie, MI

St. James Marine Co.
Beaver Island, MI

St. Lawrence Cruise Lines Inc.
Kingston, ON

St. Lawrence Seaway Development Corp.
Massena, NY

St. Lawrence Seaway Management Corp.
Cornwall, ON

St. Marys Cement Inc.
Toronto, ON

Sterling Fuels Ltd.
Hamilton, ON

Thousand Islands & Seaway Cruises
Brockville, ON

Thunder Bay Tug Services Ltd.
Thunder Bay, ON

Toronto Drydock Ltd.
Toronto, ON

Toronto Fire Services
Toronto, ON

Toronto Port Authority
Toronto, ON

United States Army Corps of Engineers
Cincinnati, OH

United States Coast Guard 9th Coast Guard District
Cleveland, OH

United States Fish & Wildlife Service
Alpena, MI

U.S. Oil Div. U.S. Venture Inc.
Appleton, WI

VanEnkevort Tug & Barge
Escanaba, MI

SALTWATER FLEETS ON THE SEAWAY

ABC Maritime
Nyon, Switzerland

Ace Tankers CV
Amsterdam, Netherlands

Alliance Tankers
Hamilton, Bermuda

Ardmore Shipping Ltd.
Cork, Ireland

Armador Gemi Isletmeciligi Ticaret Ltd.
Istanbul, Turkey

ARA Group
Werkendam, Netherlands

Atlantska Plovidba
Dubrovnik, Croatia

Bernhard Schulte Group
Hamburg, Germany

BigLift Shipping
Amsterdam, Netherlands

Blystad Group
Oslo, Norway

Briese Schiffahrts GMBH & Co. KG
Leer, Germany

Brostrom AB
Copenhagen, Denmark

Canfornav Inc.
Montreal, QC, Canada

Carisbrooke Shipping Ltd.
Cowes, United Kingdom

Chemfleet Shipping
Istanbul, Turkey

Chemikalien Seetransport
Hamburg, Germany

Clipper Group AS
Copenhagen, Denmark

Coastal Shipping Ltd. (Div. Woodward Group)
Goose Bay, NL, Canada

C.O.E. Shipping GMBH & Co.
Buxtehude, Germany

Columbia Shipmanagement
Hamburg, Germany

Cosco Southern Asphalt Shipping Co.
Guangzhou, China

Danser Van Gent
Delfzijl, Netherlands

Duzgit Gemi Insa Sanayi
Istanbul, Turkey

Eastern Pacific Shipping
Singapore

Elbe Shipping GMBH
Drochtersen, Germany

Empire Chemical Tankers
Piraeus, Greece

Enzian Ship Management
Zürich, Switzerland

Fairfield Chemical Carriers
Wilton, CT, USA

Fednav
Montreal, QC, Canada

Fednav
Montreal, QC, Canada

Franco Compania Naviera SA
Athens, Greece

Freese Shipping
Stade, Germany

Hansa Heavy Lift GMBH
Bremen, Germany

Harren & Partner Schiffahrts GMBH
Bremen, Germany

Hermann Buss GMBH
Leer, Germany

Herning Shipping AS
Herning, Denmark

HS Schiffahrt
Haren-Ems, Germany

Icdas Celik Enerji Tersane
Istanbul, Turkey

Intership Navigation Co.
Limassol, Cyprus

Jo Tankers
Spijkenisse, Netherlands

Johann M.K. Blumenthal GMBH & Co.
Hamburg, Germany

Johs Thode & Company
Hamburg, Germany

Jumbo Shipping Co. SA
Rotterdam, Netherlands

Kallianis Bros Shipping
Athens, Greece

Krey Schiffahrts GMBH & Co.
Leer, Germany

Lauranne Shipping BV
Ghent, Netherlands

Longship BV
Groningen, Netherlands

Marconsult Schiffahrt GMBH & Co. KG
Hamburg, Germany

Mineralien Schiffahrt Spedition
Schnaittenbach, Germany

Navigation Maritime Bulgare Ltd.
Varna, Bulgaria

Neste Shipping OY
Espoo, Finland

Nordana Shipping Co.
Copenhagen, Denmark

Nordic Tankers Marine A/S
Copenhagen, Denmark

Oceanex Inc.
Montreal, QC, Canada

OSM Group AS
Kristiansand, Norway

Parakou Shipping Ltd.
Hong Kong, China

Pearl Seas Cruises LLC.
Guilford, CT, USA

Peter Dohle Schiffahrts
Hamburg, Germany

Phoenix Shipping and Trading SA
Piraeus, Greece

**Polsteam
(Polish Steamship Co.)**
Szczecin, Poland

Pot Scheepvaart BV
Delfzijl, Netherlands

Principal Maritime Management LLC
Southport, CT, USA

Rederi AB Donsotank
Donso, Sweden

Rederiet Stenersen AS
Bergen, Norway

Reederei H. Schuldt GMBH & Co. KG
Hamburg, Germany

Reederei Nord GMBH
Hamburg, Germany

Rigel Schiffahrts GMBH
Bremen, Germany

Sloman Neptun Shiffahrts
Bremen, Germany

Spliethoff
Amsterdam, Netherlands

Sunship Schiffahrtskontor KG
Emden, Germany

Tarbit Tankers B.V.
Dordrecht, Netherlands

TB Marine Shipmanagement GMBH & Co.
Hamburg, Germany

Team Tankers Management AS
Hellerup, Denmark

Thorco Projects
Copenhagen, Denmark

Tradewind Tankers
Barcelona, Spain

Uni-Tankers A/S
Middelfart, Denmark

Unicorn Tankers International Ltd.
London, United Kingdom

VBG Denizcilik Sanaya VE Ticaret AS
Istanbul, Turkey

Victory Cruise Lines
Miami, FL

W. Bockstiegel Reederei KG
Emden, Germany

Wagenborg Shipping
Delfzijl, Netherlands

Yardimci Shipping Group
Istanbul, Turkey

Yilmar Shipping & Trading Ltd.
Istanbul, Turkey

Zealand Shipping BV
Almere, Netherlands

TRANSLATIONS: The terms **REEDERI** and **SCHIFFFAHRT** mean shipping in German. **SCHEEPVAART** means shipping in Dutch. The acronym **GmbH** designates a company as a private, or limited liability company in Germany. **TICKARET** is Arabic for commerce or trade.

FLAGS OF REGISTRY

Bahamas

Barbados

Belgium

Bermuda

Bulgaria

Canada

China

Croatia

Cyprus

Denmark

Finland

France

Germany

Greece

Hong Kong

India

Ireland

Israel

Italy

Japan

Liberia

Lithuania

Malta

Monaco

Netherlands

Norway

Panama

Philippines

Poland

Russia

Singapore

Spain

St.Vincent and The Grenadines

Sweden

Switzerland

Taiwan

Turkey

Ukraine

United Kingdom

United States

Vanuatu

Yugoslavia

FLEET HOUSEFLAGS

Algoma Central Corp.
St. Catharines, ON

American Steamship Co.
Williamsville, NY

Andrie Inc.
Muskegon, MI

**ArcelorMittal
Central Marine Logistics**
Griffith, IN

Beaver Island Boat Co.
Charlevoix, MI

**Canada Steamship
Lines Inc. Group**
Montreal, QC

**Canadian Coast
Guard**
Ottawa, ON

Canfornav Inc.
Montreal, QC

Fednav
Montreal, QC

**G3 Canada Ltd.
Algoma Central – Mgr**
Winnipeg, MB

**Gaelic Tugboat Co.
Diamond Jack's River Tours**
Detroit, MI

**Great Lakes Fleet Inc.
Key Lakes Inc. - Mgr.**
Duluth, MN

**Great Lakes
Maritime Academy**
Traverse City, MI

Great Lakes Towing Co.
Cleveland, OH

Groupe Desgagnés Inc.
Québec City, QC

Groupe Océan Inc.
Québec City, QC

**Inland Lakes
Management Inc.**
Alpena, MI

Interlake Steamship Co
Middleburg Heights, OH

J.W. Westcott Co.
Detroit, MI

**Key Lakes Inc.
Mgr.-Great Lakes Fleet**
Duluth, MN

LafargeHolcim
Mississauga, ON
Southfield, MI

**Lake Michigan
Carferry**
Ludington, MI

**Lower Lakes Towing Ltd.
Lower Lakes Transportation Co.**
Port Dover, ON / Williamsville, NY

**McAsphalt Marine
Transportation Ltd.**
Toronto, ON

McKeil Marine Ltd.
Burlington, ON

**Pere Marquette
Shipping Co.**
Ludington, MI

**Polsteam
(Polish Steamship Co.)**
Szczecin, Poland

Purvis Marine Ltd.
Sault Ste. Marie, ON

Spliethoff
Amsterdam, Netherlands

**St.Lawrence Seaway
Development Corp.**
Massena, NY

**St.Lawrence Seaway
Management Corp.**
Cornwall, ON

St. Marys Cement Inc.
Toronto, ON

**U.S. Army Corps
of Engineers**
Cincinnati, OH

**U.S. Coast
Guard**
Cleveland, OH

Wagenborg Shipping
Delfzijl, Netherlands

**VanEnkevort
Tug & Barge**
Escanaba, MI

Victory Cruise Lines
Miami, FL

Other Flags of Note

Dangerous Cargo
On Board

Pilot On Board

Diver Down

Extra Tonnage

Ports • Cargoes
Locks • Canals

Paul R. Tregurtha unloading coal at the DTE Energy plant in Monroe, Mich. (Paul C. LaMarre III)

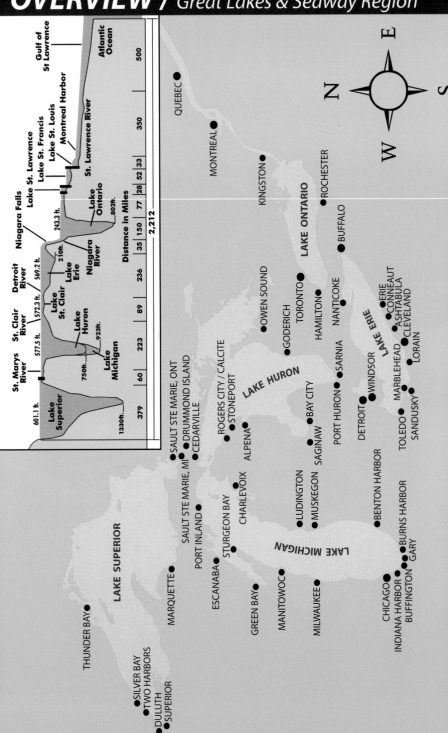

Compass: N, E, S, W

Elevation/Distance profile (Distance in Miles):

- Gulf of St Lawrence
- Atlantic Ocean — 500
- Montreal Harbor
- Lake St. Lawrence
- Lake St. Francis
- Lake St. Louis
- St. Lawrence River — 350
- Niagara Falls
- 243.3 ft.
- Lake Ontario — 802ft. — 52 | 33
- 77
- 150
- 35
- Niagara River
- Detroit River — 569.2 ft. — 210ft. — 236
- Lake Erie
- St. Clair River — 572.3 ft. — Lake St. Clair — 89
- St. Marys River — 577.5 ft. — Lake Huron — 923ft. — 223
- 750ft. — Lake Michigan — 60
- 601.1 ft. — Lake Superior — 1330ft. — 379
- **2,212**

Map labels:

- QUEBEC
- MONTREAL
- KINGSTON
- ROCHESTER
- BUFFALO
- LAKE ONTARIO
- OWEN SOUND
- TORONTO
- HAMILTON
- NANTICOKE
- GODERICH
- SARNIA
- ERIE
- CONNEAUT
- ASHTABULA
- CLEVELAND
- MARBLEHEAD
- LORAIN
- WINDSOR
- LAKE ERIE
- SANDUSKY
- TOLEDO
- DETROIT
- PORT HURON
- SAGINAW
- BAY CITY
- LAKE HURON
- SAULT STE MARIE, ONT
- SAULT STE MARIE, MI
- DRUMMOND ISLAND
- CEDARVILLE
- ROGERS CITY / CALCITE
- STONEPORT
- ALPENA
- CHARLEVOIX
- LUDINGTON
- MUSKEGON
- BENTON HARBOR
- PORT INLAND
- STURGEON BAY
- LAKE MICHIGAN
- MARQUETTE
- ESCANABA
- GREEN BAY
- MANITOWOC
- MILWAUKEE
- CHICAGO
- INDIANA HARBOR
- BUFFINGTON
- BURNS HARBOR
- GARY
- THUNDER BAY
- LAKE SUPERIOR
- SILVER BAY
- TWO HARBORS
- DULUTH
- SUPERIOR

PORTS / Loading & Unloading

Taconite ore is loaded for delivery to lower lakes steel mills at Duluth, Two Harbors, Taconite Harbor and Silver Bay, Minn., as well as Superior, Wis., and Marquette, Mich. Limestone-loading ports are Port Inland, Cedarville, Drummond Island, Calcite, Rogers City and Stoneport, Mich., and Marblehead, Ohio. Coal ports are Superior, Wis., S. Chicago, Ill., and the Ohio ports of Toledo, Sandusky, Ashtabula and Conneaut. Petroleum is loaded aboard vessels at Sarnia, Ont., and E. Chicago, Ind. Grain export ports include Duluth, Minn.; Milwaukee and Superior, Wis.; and the Ontario ports of Thunder Bay, Sarnia and Owen Sound.

The primary U.S. iron ore and limestone receiving ports are Cleveland and Chicago, along with Gary, Burns Harbor and Indiana Harbor, Ind.; Detroit, Mich; and Toledo, Lorain, Ashtabula and Conneaut, Ohio. In Canada, Nanticoke, Hamilton, and Sault Ste. Marie, Ont., are major ore-receiving ports. Coal is carried by self-unloaders to power plants in the United States and Canada. Most grain loaded on the lakes is destined for export via the St. Lawrence Seaway, although some is carried to Toledo, Ohio, and Buffalo, N.Y. Cement from Alpena and Charlevoix, Mich., is delivered to terminals from Lake Superior to Lake Ontario. Tankers bring petroleum products to cities as diverse in size as Cleveland, Ohio, Green Bay, Wis., and Cheboygan and Detroit, Mich. Self-unloaders carry limestone, coal, road salt and sand to cities throughout the region.

TREMENDOUS TONNAGE

Thanks to higher water levels, cargo records were smashed at the Soo Locks in 2017. On Sept. 24, the 1,000-foot-long *American Integrity* broke the all-time record for the largest load through the locks by carrying 75,095 tons of iron ore pellets, beating the record held for just two weeks by another 1,000-footer, the *Edwin H. Gott. American Integrity* was loaded to a draft of 29 feet, 7 inches on her way to Indiana Harbor, Ind. Her cargo added up to 150,190,000 pounds. Assuming each taconite pellet weighed 0.1 oz. (per info provided by the U.S. Army Corps of Engineers) that's more than 24 billion taconite pellets.

AVERAGE RUNNING TIMES

Times listed are for downbound passages. Reverse for upbound times. Times vary with speed / weather / traffic.

LAKE SUPERIOR
Duluth/Superior – Soo Locks .... 24 hrs
Marquette or Thunder Bay – Soo Locks .... 12 hrs

ST. MARYS RIVER
Soo Locks – DeTour, Mich. .... 6 hrs
DeTour – Port Huron .... 19 hrs

LAKE HURON
DeTour – Mackinac Bridge .... 2 hrs
DeTour – Port Huron .... 19 hrs
Harbor Beach – Port Huron .... 4 hrs

LAKE MICHIGAN
Gray's Reef Light – Gary, Ind. .... 22 hrs

LAKE ERIE
Detroit River Light – Toledo .... 1.75 hrs
Detroit River Light – Southeast Shoal .... 3 hrs
Southeast Shoal – Long Point .... 9 hrs
Long Point – CIP 15 (Welland Canal) .... 7 hrs
Detroit River Light – Port Colborne piers
(Welland Canal).. 19 hrs

LAKE ONTARIO
Welland Canal (Port Weller) – Hamilton .... 2 hrs
Welland Canal (Port Weller) – Cape Vincent, N.Y.
(call-in points at Newcastle, mid-lake and
Sodus Point) .... 12 hrs

Cuyahoga unloads salt at Owen Sound, Ont. The color means it is coated with chemicals that make it adhere better to roads, work at lower temperatures and reduce corrosiveness. (Mark Harris)

AGRICULTURAL PRODUCTS – Wheat, grain, soybeans, canola, flax and oats are shipped on the Great Lakes. Some is used domestically, but most is shipped to international markets overseas.

BUNKER C – A special grade of heavy fuel oil, also known as No. 6 fuel.

CEMENT CLINKER – A material, made by heating ground limestone and clay, that is ground up to a fine powder to produce cement.

CLINKER – The incombustible residue that remains after the combustion of coal.

COAL – Both eastern (high sulfur, used in industry) and western (low sulfur, burned at power plants) coal are shipped aboard Great Lakes vessels.

COKE – A byproduct of blended coals baked in ovens until mostly pure carbon is left. Coke is used to generate the high heat necessary to make steel in blast furnaces.

COKE BREEZE – Byproduct of coke production.

DOLOMITE – Rock similar to limestone but somewhat harder and heavier.

FLUXSTONE – Taconite pellets premixed with limestone, so no limestone needs to be added in a blast furnace.

IRON FINES – Fines (ore less than 6mm in diameter) are created as a result of mining, crushing and processing the larger pieces of ore. See **SINTER**.

LIMESTONE – Common sedimentary rock consisting mostly of calcium carbonate used as a building stone and in the manufacture of lime, carbon dioxide and cement.

MILL SCALE – Byproduct of the shaping of iron and steel.

PETROLEUM COKE – Petroleum coke (petcoke) is the bottom end of oil refining – the parts of crude oil that will not vaporize in the refining process. It is mostly used as fuel (often blended with coal) in power plants.

PIG IRON – Crude iron that is the direct product of the blast furnace and is refined to produce steel, wrought iron or ingot iron.

POTASH – A compound used for fertilizer.

SALT – Most salt shipped on the Great Lakes is used on roads and highways during the winter to melt ice.

SINTER – Broken taconite pellets, a.k.a. taconite pellet chips and fines. Small, but still useful in the blast furnace.

SLAG – Byproduct of the steelmaking process is used in the production of concrete and as seal coat cover, a base for paving, septic drain fields and railroad ballast.

TACONITE – A low-grade iron ore, containing about 27 percent iron and 51 percent silica, found as a hard rock formation in the Lake Superior region. It is pelletized for shipment to steel mills (see below).

TRAP ROCK – Rock, usually ground fairly fine, for use as foundations and roads or walkways. It is mined near Bruce Mines, Ont., and loaded there.

Why taconite pellets?

The high-grade iron ore (around 60 percent pure) that was mined on the ranges around Lake Superior was mostly exhausted in the tremendous mining efforts of World War II and in the early 1950s. There was still plenty of iron ore in the ground, but it was only about 20-30 percent iron. To mine and ship that ore in its natural form would have been expensive, so engineers developed the taconite pelletization process to increase the iron content of the product coming off the ranges headed for the steel mills.

Pellets have a number of positive attributes. Their iron content (and the content of other elements) can be precisely controlled, so the steel mills know exactly what they are getting. Pellets are relatively moisture free compared with raw iron ore, so they are less prone to freeze in rail cars, storage piles or dock pockets. This means the pellets can be shipped for a much longer season than natural iron ore, so companies need fewer rail cars and ships to carry the same amount of pellets, thus saving money on labor and infrastructure. Pellets are also uniform in size, shape and mass, making them very easy to handle on conveyor belt systems, which makes for speedy, precise ship loading and unloading using a shipboard self-unloading system, again cutting down on costs.

A self-unloader's system of belts carries the cargo from the hold, across the boom and onto the dock.

Vessels transiting the St. Clair River, Lake St. Clair and the Detroit River are under the jurisdiction of Sarnia Traffic and must radio their positions at predetermined locations. Call-in points (bold type on map) are not the same for upbound and downbound traffic. Average running times between call-in points are below. *

UPBOUND	Buoys 1&2	Black River	Stag Isl.	Salt Dock	X-32	Crib Light	Grassy Isl.
Detroit River Lt.	8:10	7:50	7:20	6:00	4:20	4:00	1:35
Grassy Island	6:45	6:25	5:55	4:35	2:55	2:35	
St. Clair Crib	4:10	3:50	3:20	2:00	0:25		
Light X-32	3:50	3:30	3:00	1:35			
Salt Dock	2:10	1:50	1:20				
Stag Isl. Upper	0:50	0:35					
Black River	0:20						

DOWNBOUND	Det. River	Grassy Isl.	Belle Isl.	Crib Light	Light 23	Salt Dock	Black River	7&8
30 min. above buoys 11 & 12	9:05	7:35	6:25	5:10	3:55	3:10	1:20	0:40
Buoys 7 & 8	8:15	6:55	5:45	4:30	3:15	2:30	0:40	
Black River	7:45	6:15	5:05	3:50	2:35	1:50		
Salt Dock	5:55	4:25	3:15	2:00	0:45			
Light 23	5:10	3:40	2:30	1:10				
St. Clair Crib	3:55	2:25	1:10					
USCG Belle Isle	2:40	1:10						
Grassy Isl.	1:30							

* Times can change if vessels stop for fuel or are delayed by other traffic.

BUOYS 11&12
DOWNBOUND ONLY

BUOYS 7&8
DOWNBOUND ONLY

BUOYS 1&2
UPBOUND ONLY

LAKE HURON

SARNIA

PORT HURON

BLACK RIVER

IMPERIAL FUEL DOCK

STAG ISLAND UPPER
UPBOUND ONLY

SHELL FUEL DOCK

ST. CLAIR

ST. CLAIR EDISON POWER PLANT
RECOR POINT

MARINE CITY

SALT DOCK

ALGONAC

HARSENS ISLAND

LIGHT 23
DOWNBOUND ONLY

X(RAY) 32
UPBOUND ONLY

ST. CLAIR CRIB LIGHT

LAKE ST. CLAIR

USCG BELLE ISLE
DOWNBOUND ONLY

J.W. WESTCOTT MAILBOAT

DETROIT

MISTERSKY FUEL

WINDSOR

ROUGE RIVER

STERLING FUEL

GRASSY ISLAND

FIGHTING ISLAND

GROSSE ILE

LIVINGSTONE CHANNEL

AMHERSTBURG CHANNEL

DETROIT RIVER LIGHT

N
W   E
S

POINT PELEE

PELEE PASSAGE

MONROE

LAKE ERIE

SOUTHEAST SHOAL

PELEE ISLAND

The St. Marys River flows out of the southeast corner of Lake Superior in a southeasterly direction to Lake Huron. Vessels transiting the St. Marys River system are under the jurisdiction of Soo Traffic, part of the U.S. Coast Guard at Sault Ste. Marie, Mich., and must radio their positions on VHF Ch. 12 (156.600 MHz) at predetermined locations. Vessels in the vicinity of the Soo Locks fall under the jurisdiction of the lockmaster, who must be contacted on VHF Ch. 14 (156.700 MHz) for lock assignments.

Call-in points (bold type on map) are not the same for upbound and downbound traffic. Approximate running times between call-in points are at left; times may vary due to other traffic and weather. Because of their size, 1,000-footers take more time to transit than smaller vessels.

Arrival times at the Soo Locks are available at the Information Center located in the locks park. Upbound vessels must make a pre-call to Soo Traffic one hour before entering the river at DeTour, and downbound traffic is required to make a one-hour pre-call above Ile Parisienne.

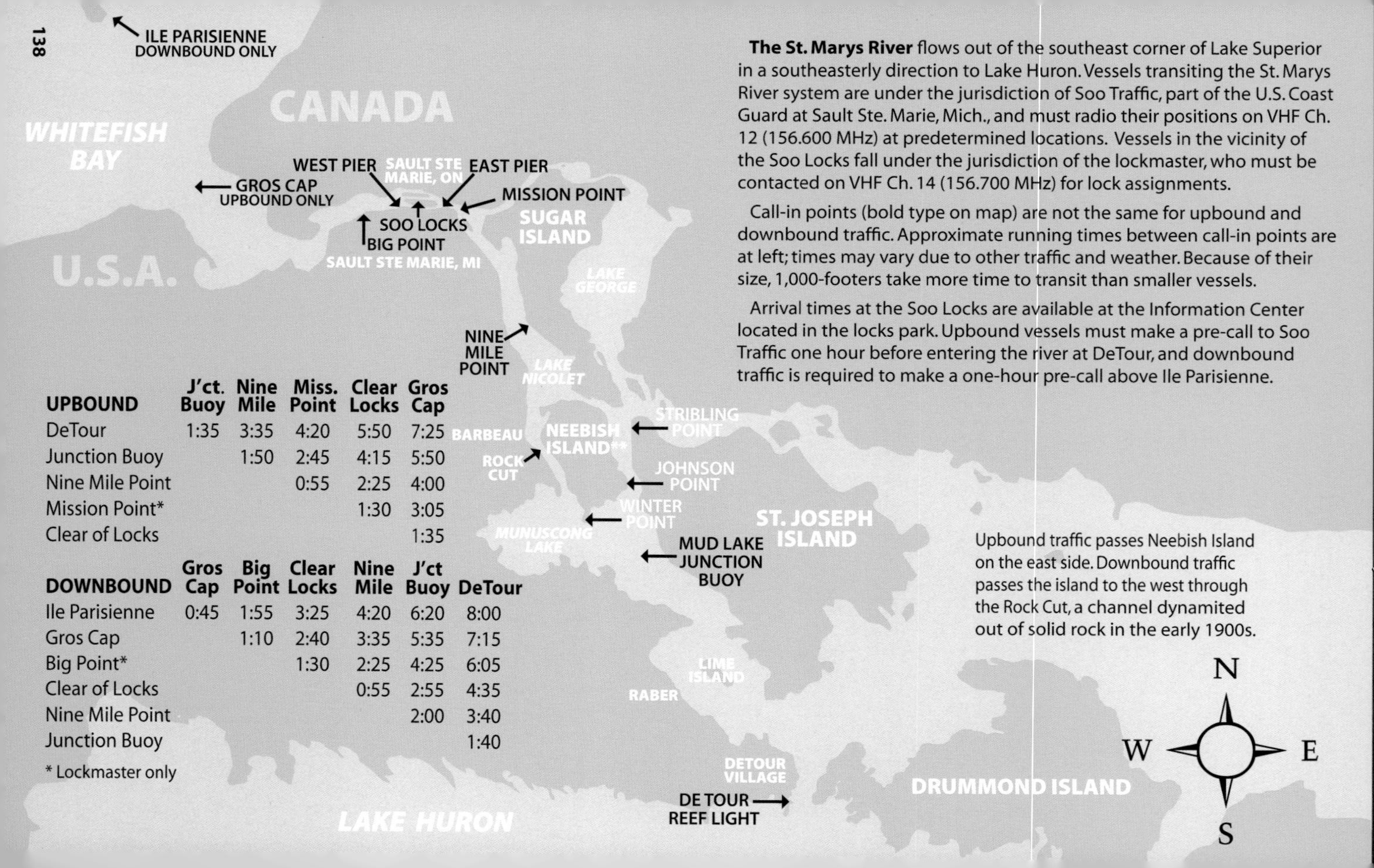

Upbound traffic passes Neebish Island on the east side. Downbound traffic passes the Rock Cut to the west through the Rock Cut, a channel dynamited out of solid rock in the early 1900s.

UPBOUND	J'ct. Buoy	Nine Mile	Miss. Point	Clear Locks	Gros Cap
DeTour	1:35	3:35	4:20	5:50	7:25
Junction Buoy		1:50	2:45	4:15	5:50
Nine Mile Point			0:55	2:25	4:00
Mission Point*				1:30	3:05
Clear of Locks					1:35

DOWNBOUND	Gros Cap	Big Point	Clear Locks	Nine Mile	J'ct Buoy	DeTour
Ile Parisienne	0:45	1:55	3:25	4:20	6:20	8:00
Gros Cap		1:10	2:40	3:35	5:35	7:15
Big Point*			1:30	2:25	4:25	6:05
Clear of Locks				0:55	2:55	4:35
Nine Mile Point					2:00	3:40
Junction Buoy						1:40

* Lockmaster only

Map labels: CANADA · U.S.A. · WHITEFISH BAY · ILE PARISIENNE DOWNBOUND ONLY · GROS CAP UPBOUND ONLY · WEST PIER · EAST PIER · SAULT STE. MARIE, ON · MISSION POINT · SOO LOCKS · BIG POINT · SAULT STE. MARIE, MI · SUGAR ISLAND · LAKE GEORGE · NINE MILE POINT · LAKE NICOLET · BARBEAU · STRIBLING POINT · NEEBISH ISLAND** · ROCK CUT · JOHNSON POINT · WINTER POINT · ST. JOSEPH ISLAND · MUNUSCONG LAKE · MUD LAKE JUNCTION BUOY · RABER · LIME ISLAND · DRUMMOND ISLAND · DETOUR VILLAGE · DETOUR REEF LIGHT · LAKE HURON

LOCKS & CANALS / *The Soo Locks*

The Soo Locks at Sault Ste. Marie, Mich., on the St. Marys River, overcome a 21-foot difference in water levels between Lake Superior and lakes Huron, Michigan and Erie. Under the jurisdiction of the U.S. Army Corps of Engineers, the locks operate on gravity, as do all locks in the St. Lawrence Seaway system. No pumps are used to empty or fill the lock chambers; valves are opened, and water is allowed to seek its own level. All traffic passes through the locks toll-free. Traffic is directed by radio to the appropriate lock according to size, other vessels in the locks area and the time the captain first calls in to the lockmaster. All vessels longer than 730 feet and /or wider than 76 feet are restricted by size to the **Poe**, or second, lock. Smaller vessels go to the **MacArthur Lock**, closest

to the viewing platform. Vessels are under engine and thruster control at all times, with crews ready to drop mooring lines over bollards on the lock wall to stop its movement. As soon as the vessel is in position, the engines are stopped and mooring lines are made fast. If the vessel is being lowered, valves at the lower end

Laker Kaye E. Barker heads upbound into the Poe Lock. The MacArthur Lock is at far left. (Dan Vaught)

of the lock chamber are opened to allow the water inside to flow out. If the vessel is being raised, valves at the upper end of the chamber are opened to allow water to enter. When the water reaches the desired level, the valves are closed, the protective boom is raised, the gates are opened, and the vessel leaves the lock.

The first canal on the American side was built from 1853-55. Several larger locks followed, spurred by the construction of even larger ships. Work began in 2009 to build a new Poe-sized lock, the only one that can handle the biggest vessels. At an estimated cost of more than $500 million, the project remains stalled due to lack of funding. The **Canadian Lock** at Sault Ste. Marie, Ont., has its origins in a canal constructed from 1887-95. The present lock, operated by Parks Canada, is used by pleasure craft, tugs and tour boats.

MORE ABOUT THE SYSTEM

The Empire State Building is 1,250 feet tall. The largest vessel using the Soo Locks, the American-flagged *Paul R. Tregurtha*, is 1,014 feet long.

There are about 125 major freighters, barges and tankers engaged almost exclusively in the Great Lakes and Seaway trade. That number is increased by a variety of saltwater vessels, or "salties," that enter the system during the season.

The Great Lakes shipping season runs from about March 25 to mid-January. In the spring and fall, icebreakers operated by the U.S. and Canadian coast guards, and commercial tugs help keep channels open.

A vessel traveling from the Atlantic Ocean to Lake Superior through the St. Lawrence Seaway and the Soo Locks rises nearly 600 feet. The first lift, a total of 224 feet, is provided by the seven St. Lawrence Seaway locks that begin at Montreal. The Welland Canal, connecting Lake Erie and Lake Ontario, and bypassing Niagara Falls, raises vessels an additional 326 feet. The Soo Locks complete the process.

One short toot on a vessel's horn while in a lock means "cast off lines."

A red-and-white flag flying from a vessel's mast indicates a pilot is on board. Saltwater vessels must pick up pilots at various points in their voyage.

No tolls are charged at the Soo Locks. Tolls are levied at St. Lawrence Seaway locks.

During 1953, 128 million tons of freight moved through the Soo Locks. This amazing record still stands.

BY BOAT, BARGE, TRAIN OR TRUCK			
To Transport 70,000 Net Tons Of Cargo It Would Take			
1 Vessel	47 Barges	700 Rail Cars	2,800 25-Ton Trucks

The **28-mile (44 km) Welland Canal** is the fourth version of a waterway link between Lake Ontario and Lake Erie, first built in 1829. The present canal was completed in 1932, deepened in the 1950s as part of the Seaway project and further straightened in 1973. Today its eight locks, all Canadian, lift ships 326 feet (100 meters) over the Niagara Escarpment.

Each of the seven Welland Canal locks has an average lift of 46.5 feet (14.2 meters). All locks (except Lock 8) are 859 feet (261.8 meters) long, 80 feet (24.4 meters) wide and 30 feet (9.1 meters) deep. Lock 8 measures 1,380 feet (420.6 m) long.

The largest vessel that may transit the canal is 740 feet (225.5 meters) long, 78 feet (23.8 meters) wide and 26.5 feet (8.08 meters) in draft. **Locks 1, 2** and **3** are at Port Weller and St. Catharines, Ont., on the Lake Ontario end of the waterway. At Lock 3, the Welland Canals Centre and St. Catharines Museum also houses an information desk (which posts a list of vessels expected at the lock), a gift shop and restaurant.

At Thorold, **Locks 4, 5** and **6**, twinned to help speed passage of vessels, are controlled with an elaborate interlocking system for safety. These locks (positioned end to end, they resemble a short flight of stairs) have an aggregate lift of 139.5 feet (42.5 meters). Just south of locks **4, 5** and **6** is **Lock 7. Lock 8**, 7 miles (11.2 km) upstream at Port Colborne,

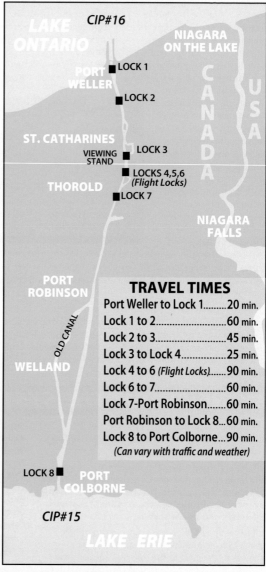

TRAVEL TIMES

Port Weller to Lock 1	20 min.
Lock 1 to 2	60 min.
Lock 2 to 3	45 min.
Lock 3 to Lock 4	25 min.
Lock 4 to 6 *(Flight Locks)*	90 min.
Lock 6 to 7	60 min.
Lock 7-Port Robinson	60 min.
Port Robinson to Lock 8	60 min.
Lock 8 to Port Colborne	90 min.

(Can vary with traffic and weather)

completes the process, making the final adjustment to Lake Erie's level.

In 1973, a new channel was constructed to replace the section of the old canal that bisected the city of Welland. The Welland Bypass eliminated long delays for canal navigation and for road and rail traffic. Two tunnels allow auto and train traffic to pass beneath the canal.

The average passage time for the canal is 8-11 hours, with the majority of the time spent transiting Locks 4-7. All vessel traffic though the Welland Canal is regulated by a control center, Seaway Welland, which also remotely operates the locks and the traffic bridges over the canal. Vessels passing through the Welland Canal and St. Lawrence Seaway must carry a qualified pilot at all times.

***Orsula* passes under the Allanburg Bridge on the Welland Canal in 2017.** *(Stephen Hause)*

***Baie Comeau* in the Welland Canal flight locks.** *(Alain Gindroz)*

Tanker Furuholmen in the Iroquois Lock, St. Lawrence Seaway. (Murray Blancher)

The St. Lawrence Seaway is a waterway extending some 2,038 miles (3,701.4 km) from the Atlantic Ocean to the head of the Great Lakes at Duluth, Minn., including Montreal harbor and the Welland Canal. More specifically, it is a system of locks and canals (U.S. and Canadian), built between 1954 and 1958 at a cost of $474 million and opened in 1959, that allows vessels to pass from Montreal to the Welland Canal at the western end of Lake Ontario. For the Montreal-Lake Ontario section, the average transit time is 24 hours upbound and 22 hours downbound. The difference is mainly due to the current in the St. Lawrence River. The vessel size limit within this system is 740 feet (225.6 meters) long, 78 feet (23.8 meters) wide and 26 feet (7.9 meters) draft. It takes 8-10 days for a ship to go from Lake Superior to the Atlantic Ocean.

LOCK DIMENSIONS

Length	766 feet (233.5 meters)
Width	80 feet (24 meters
Depth	30 feet (9.1 meters)

Closest to the ocean is the **St. Lambert Lock**, which lifts ships some 15 feet (4.6 meters) from Montreal harbor to the level of the Laprairie Basin, through which the channel sweeps in a great arc 8.5 miles (13.7 km) long to the second lock. The **Côte Ste. Catherine Lock**, like the other six St. Lawrence Seaway locks, is built to the dimensions shown in the table above. The Côte Ste. Catherine lifts ships from the level of the Laprairie Basin 30 feet (9.1 meters) to the level of Lake Saint-Louis, bypassing the Lachine Rapids. Beyond it, the channel runs 7.5 miles (12.1 km) before reaching Lake Saint-Louis.

The **Lower Beauharnois Lock**, bypassing the Beauharnois Power House, lifts ships 41 feet (12.5 meters) and sends them through a short canal to the **Upper Beauharnois Lock**, where they are lifted 41 feet (12.5 meters) to reach the Beauharnois Canal. After a 13-mile (20.9 km) trip in the canal and a 30-mile (48.3 km) passage through Lake Saint Francis, vessels reach the U.S. border and the **Snell Lock**, which has a lift of 45 feet (13.7 meters) and empties into the 10-mile (16.1 km) Wiley-Dondero Canal.

After passing through the Wiley-Dondero, ships are raised another 38 feet (11.6 meters) by the **Dwight D. Eisenhower Lock**, after which they enter Lake St. Lawrence, the pool upon which nearby power-generating stations draw for their turbines located a mile to the north.

At the western end of Lake St. Lawrence, the **Iroquois Lock** allows ships to bypass the Iroquois Control Dam. The lift here is only about 1 foot (0.3 meters). Once in the waters west of Iroquois, the channel meanders through the Thousand Islands to Lake Ontario, the Welland Canal and beyond.

Federal Bristol passes beneath the Seaway International Bridge at Massena, N.Y. *(Ronald Dole Jr.)*

ST LAMBERT

ST LAMBERT LOCK

MONTREAL

CÔTE STE CATHERINE LOCK

CÔTE STE CATHERINE LOCK

LAKE ST LOUIS

BEAUHARNOIS LOCKS

BEAUHARNOIS CANAL

CANADA

ST LAWRENCE RIVER

OTTAWA

SNELL LOCK

EISENHOWER LOCK

CORNWALL

LONG SAULT

INGLESIDE

MASSENA

MORRISBURG

IROQUOIS

IROQUOIS LOCK

OGDENSBURG

PRESCOTT

BROCKVILLE

U.S.A.

ALEXANDRIA BAY

CAPE VINCENT

KINGSTON

LAKE ONTARIO

SEAWAY – LOCK LIFTS

St. Lambert Lock	15 ft.
Côte Ste. Catherine Lock	30 ft.
Lower Beauharnois Lock	41 ft.
Upper Beauharnois Lock	41 ft.
Snell Lock	45 ft
Eisenhower Lock	38 ft.
Iroquois Lock	1 ft.

N E S W

FOLLOWING THE FLEET

With an inexpensive VHF scanner, boatwatchers can tune to ship-to-ship and ship-to-shore traffic using the following frequency guide.

Calling/distress only	Ch. 16 – 156.800 MHz	Calling/distress only
Commercial vessels only	Ch. 06 – 156.300 MHz	Working channel
Commercial vessels only	Ch. 08 – 156.400 MHz	Working channel
DeTour Reef – Lake St. Clair Light	Ch. 11 – 156.550 MHz	Sarnia Traffic - Sect. 1
Long Point Light – Lake St. Clair Light	Ch. 12 – 156.600 MHz	Sarnia Traffic - Sect. 2
Montreal – Mid-Lake St. Francis	Ch. 14 – 156.700 MHz	Seaway Beauharnois – Sect. 1
Mid-Lake St. Francis – Bradford Island	Ch. 12 – 156.600 MHz	Seaway Eisenhower – Sect. 2
Bradford Island – Crossover Island	Ch. 11 – 156.550 MHz	Seaway Iroquois – Sect. 3
Crossover Island-Cape Vincent	Ch. 13 – 156.650 MHz	Seaway Clayton – Sect. 4 St. Lawrence River portion
Cape Vincent – Mid-Lake Ontario	Ch. 12 – 156.600 MHz	Seaway Sodus – Sect. 4 Lake Ontario portion
Seaway Pilot Office – Cape Vincent	Ch. 14 – 156.700 MHz	Pilotage traffic
Mid-Lake Ontario – Welland Canal	Ch. 11 – 156.550 MHz	Seaway Newcastle – Sect. 5
Welland Canal	Ch. 14 – 156.700 MHz	Seaway Welland – Sect. 6
Welland Canal to Long Point Light	Ch. 11 – 156.550 MHz	Seaway Long Point – Sect. 7
Montreal traffic	Ch. 10 – 156.500 MHz	Vessel traffic
Soo Traffic	Ch. 12 – 156.600 MHz	Vessel control, Sault Ste. Marie
Lockmaster, Soo Locks	Ch. 14 – 156.700 MHz	Soo Lockmaster (WUE-21)
Coast Guard traffic	Ch. 21 – 157.050 MHz	United States Coast Guard
Coast Guard traffic	Ch. 22 – 157.100 MHz	United States Coast Guard
U.S. mailboat, Detroit, MI	Ch. 10 – 156.500 MHz	Mailboat *J. W. Westcott II*

The following prerecorded messages help track vessel arrivals and departures

Boatwatcher's Hotline	(218) 722-6489	Superior, Duluth, Two Harbors, Taconite Harbor and Silver Bay
CSX coal docks/Torco dock	(419) 697-2304	Toledo, Ohio, vessel information
Eisenhower Lock	(315) 769-2422	Eisenhower Lock vessel traffic
Michigan Limestone dock	(989) 734-2117	Calcite, Mich., vessel information
Michigan Limestone dock	(906) 484-2201	Press 1 – Cedarville, Mich., passages
Presque Isle Corp.	(989) 595-6611	Stoneport vessel information ext. 7
Seaway Vessel Locator	(450) 672-4115	
Soo Traffic	(906) 635-3224	Previous day – St. Marys River
Soo Traffic – Hotline	(906) 253-9290	Soo Locks traffic information
Superior Midwest Energy	(715) 395-3559	Superior, Wis., vessel information
Thunder Bay Port Authority	(807) 345-1256	Thunder Bay, Ont., vessel information
Welland Canal Traffic	(905) 688-6462	Welland Canal traffic

MEANINGS OF BOAT WHISTLES

1 SHORT: I intend to leave you on my port side (answered by same if agreed upon).

2 SHORT: I intend to leave you on my starboard side (answered by same if agreed upon). (Passing arrangements may be agreed upon by radio. If so, no whistle signal is required.)

1 PROLONGED: Vessel leaving dock.

3 SHORT: Operating astern propulsion.

1 PROLONGED, SOUNDED AT INTERVALS OF NOT MORE THAN 2 MINUTES: Vessel moving in restricted visibility.

1 SHORT, 1 PROLONGED, 1 SHORT: Vessel at anchor in restricted visibility (optional). May be accompanied by the ringing of a bell on the forward part of the ship and a gong on the aft end.

3 PROLONGED & 2 SHORT: Salute (formal)

1 PROLONGED & 2 SHORT: Salute (commonly used)

3 PROLONGED & 1 SHORT: International Shipmasters' Association member salute

5 OR MORE SHORT BLASTS SOUNDED RAPIDLY: Danger

Spotlight

- **Ships**
- **Sailors**
- **Adventures**

A Great Lakes pilot climbs from the Soo Pilot boat to the deck of the Algoscotia. (Joy Fett)

Captain George Haynes guides the Polish-flagged Drawsko. The red and white flag in the foreground means a pilot is on board.

In Good Hands

Pilots make sure salties steer a steady course

Climbing the pilot ladder is all in a day's work for a Great Lakes pilot.

STORY / PHOTOS By SAM HANKINSON

Salties are what folks on the Great Lakes call ocean freighters. Their element is the open sea, but no amount of studying can prepare an ocean captain for the Great Lakes. So when they're on the lakes, they need someone who knows the territory.

That's where Captain George Haynes and his colleagues come in. A 1986 graduate of SUNY Maritime College in New York, Haynes worked on Great Lakes freighters and ocean freighters before he found his calling in 1996.

A pilot on the bridge of a saltie is a key part of its navigation into the Great Lakes. "They may never have been here before, so they need a pilot to make sure their vessel gets through safely," says Haynes. In his 21-year tenure, Haynes estimates that he has averaged sailing on 85 ships each season.

A pilot's job is to guide the ships through the waterways. Pilots are not representatives of the companies for which the ships sail. "If we worked for the company, we might be inclined to take risks," says Haynes. "We work to ensure the ship gets safely through the waterways. Our job is to get the vessel from point A to point B safely."

In the Great Lakes/St. Lawrence Seaway system, American pilots are divided into three districts. District One starts at the Snell Lock in the St. Lawrence Seaway including all of Lake Ontario, and runs through the Welland Canal. District Two is the Welland Canal to Port Huron. District Three is everything on and between lakes Huron, Michigan and Superior. At any given time, there are more than 50 pilots working between Duluth, Minn., and the St. Lawrence Seaway, handing off ships to their colleagues like batons in a relay race.

A majority of the jobs the Port Huron-based Haynes does is taking salties either up or down the Detroit and St. Clair rivers, which is part of District Two. "If a ship's going to American port on Lake Erie or Detroit, it gets an American pilot. If it's going to a Canadian port, like Windsor, Nanticoke or Sarnia, then it gets a Canadian pilot," Haynes explains. "Most of the bulk carriers are going to American ports so we get a large number of those. Most tankers are going to Sarnia so they get Canadian pilots.

"During the 2017 shipping season, 215 salties making multiple trips required pilots. It typically costs a shipping company around $55,000 in pilotage fees to go from the Gulf of St. Lawrence (Escoumins, Que., is the first and last pilot station) to Duluth, Minn. It is 2,700 miles from Escoumins to Duluth.

To be a pilot you have to have at least two years of experience on vessels of 4,000 gross tons or more. "We only hire mariners who already have their first-class pilotage license with the Coast Guard, meaning they've already trained for these rivers, they already learned the courses, they already know the Great Lakes," Haynes says.

Stepping onto a ship where English might not be the first language presents a unique challenge. "The crew is interested in us because they may never have been to the United States before, or Canada, and they're interested in what it's like," he says. "We might be the first American they've ever seen."

Cultural barriers are often encountered, and while they're part of the job, they can sometimes be a problem. Haynes has had his share of such occasions. "Once I couldn't communicate with anybody on the ship very well. I was using my fingers, I had to repeat things two or three times, I had to listen two or three times," he said. "I couldn't trust the crew to understand me quick enough to handle an emergency, so I ordered two tugs for safety when we entered port."

A majority of pilot jobs are on salties, but there are other vessels that need pilots.

"Any oceangoing vessel on the Great Lakes or a vessel carrying foreign cargo has to take a pilot. It's by law," explains Haynes. Cruise ships and tall ships of foreign flag – even large yachts are required to take pilots. While Haynes is accustomed to the bridge of a saltie, different kinds of ships are a nice change of pace. "The neatest one I ever had was the Norwegian [tall ship] *Sørlandet*. She was a beautiful ship, a three-masted square rig. I had her up and down the river on her visit in 2013."

Perhaps the most daunting part of being a pilot is getting on and off the ships. A pilot boat takes

Continued on Page 148

Detroit's Renaissance Center looms to starboard.

the pilot out, and the way up to the deck is usually via a dauntingly frail-looking rope ladder. Haynes says he gives pilot ladders a careful look before he climbs. "I want to make sure I'm not going to get halfway up the ladder or down the ladder and something goes wrong," he explains. "I want to make sure the pilot boat is steady with the ship, and that's the pilot boat captain's job. He's responsible for getting me on and off safely," he says.

If lake conditions are poor, the saltie may create a windbreak so that the pilot is able to safely climb up or down the ladder more easily. "Sometimes these pilot ladders are pretty old," Haynes says. "The ropes are starting to fray, the wooden slats can be rotted, and I'm looking to make sure the guys up on the deck are watching.

"If I'm concerned that the pilot ladder is not secured well enough, I'll make a symbol with my arms crossed. I've had

Delicious dining on the Polish-flagged Drawsko.

issues where we're in heavy seas … where you might have 8-10 foot waves, where the ship is rolling, and the pilot boat is going up and down. That's usually off of Port Colborne, in a storm on Lake Erie, so then you go for a wild ride. You have to time your getting off the ladder while the boat is up high. You time it so that so when the boat is on the crest of the wave, you grab the ladder and scurry up."

Sailing on ships of different nationalities has allowed Haynes and his colleagues to try the foods of different countries. "Eating the foreign food, wherever the ship is from and whatever the cook is cooking, I kind of like that," he says. "I like the variety, I like the international-type cuisine, the variations." As a pilot, it's an added bonus to the trip, despite sometimes being served meals that are a little odd.

"Not all pilots are like that. Some pilots hate the food, some bring their own sandwiches, their own snacks, they eat very little of the ship's food. I think it's fun," he added. "Have I eaten some things that

Pilot boat Huron Maid.

Federal Kivalina passing the Maltese saltie Osogovo on the St. Clair River.

I wasn't sure what it was? Yes," Haynes readily admits.

Being a pilot means taking many short trips. As a result, Haynes is able to spend more time at home. "(When) I worked on the lakers, I was gone two or three months at a time, and now I'm home more frequently. If I have a river run, I'm home that day. I might be working every day, but I'm home a lot more."

Meeting the barge Great Lakes/ tug Michigan on Lake St. Clair.

The routine for each of Haynes' trips is pretty much the same. "Before I even leave home, I check the weather, number one," he says. "I want to know what the weather's going to be like when I'm getting on, when I'm getting off, and anything terrible in between."

Sun rises over industrial Sarnia, Ont.

"When I'm coming out on the pilot boat, I'm sizing up the ship before I even get on board. I'm looking at the drafts. I'm looking at the crane configuration. I'm getting information before I even climb aboard. As a pilot, you have to constantly look for information. If I don't know the ship, I'll look it up on marinetraffic.com and look it over. I'll see where it's going, where it's coming from."

Haynes doesn't have to take that much on board with him when he goes out for pilot jobs. "I have a day bag for the rivers, I have an overnight bag if I go across Lake Erie," he says. "My bag is never really unpacked, I just have to resupply it."

Most of the equipment Haynes brings with him on his runs is electronic, but there's one old-school item he makes sure he packs in his bag as well – a copy of *Know Your Ships* for the captain. "The captain and crew really like the book," " Haynes explained. "They sometimes see their own ship in the pictures. It's good information for them."

Captain Haynes navigates the St. Clair River.

A Brush with History

Above or below, artist Bob McGreevy knows his ships

STORY / PHOTOS By CHRIS WINTERS

Bob McGreevy is a master marine artist, widely known and respected by Great Lakes historians and vessel enthusiasts, and his watercolors and oils are eagerly sought by collectors all over the region. His works – nearly 400 on paper and canvas – occupy a place in the boatnerd firmament with Howard Sprague, Ken Marschall and Kinley Shogren.

It's well known that McGreevy has been hanging around the waterfront of Detroit and the Lake Huron shore since the early 1960s, that his grandfather worked as a ship's carpenter on the *Titanic*, and a pair of McGreevy uncles were recruited from the Old Sod to help build the *Edmund Fitzgerald* and Mackinac Bridge.

But here are some things you may not know about Bob McGreevy: He genuinely enjoyed his

30-year day job in Chrysler's design studio, where, among other notable feats of automotive styling, he sculpted the now-iconic hood ornament of the Dodge Ram pickup. His father-in-law was a percussionist in the *Tashmoo*'s house band (in a nice piece of cosmic symmetry, *Tashmoo* is his all-time favorite Frank Kirby-designed passenger liner). Also, his cat, Lewis, who he despises, is responsible for 90 percent of his artistic output over the years. The part about Lewis is, of course a fib. He dotes on Lewis.

McGreevy retired from Chrysler in 2000, and he and his wife Susanne moved their home and his studio from the Detroit area to a rambling 1920s farmhouse facing Lake Huron near Harbor Beach, Mich. He is free at last to indulge his avocation full-time, and proximity to the ever-changing

Detail work on whaleback Clifton.

Continued on Page 152

Bob McGreevy in his home studio near Lake Huron.

Tools of the artist's trade.

vista of Lake Huron "has really changed the way I paint the lake and the sky," he says.

Beyond its elegant composition and fine draftsmanship, McGreevy's work is prized for historical accuracy. In fact, he considers himself a historian first and an artist second. His commissions have encompassed all periods of Great Lakes vessel design and development, but pre-Civil War wooden vessels have always been his favorite challenge. With few photographs to record the appearance of these early Great Lakes ships, McGreevy rolls up his sleeves and drills down into contemporary newspaper accounts and tedious bundles of vessel enrollment papers, before deploying his technical training in drafting and perspective to reanimate the past.

McGreevy cites Howard Sprague as the peer he most admires. "He had a way of capturing water that really comes alive on the canvas. He was working before cameras, and I think he must have really internalized the way the water moves – that liquid quality shines through in his technique."

The liquid inspiration for McGreevy's own life's work came from the bottom up, as it turns out. He first put pencil to paper in an effort to illuminate Great Lakes maritime lore in 1982, after the discovery of the bow section of the *Daniel J. Morrell* by uber wreck hunter Dave Trotter.

"I cringe a little bit every time I look at those drawings," McGreevy chuckles. "In that era, divers got excited by eight or 10 feet of visibility. We did the best we could to piece the huge wreck site together 35mm frame by 35mm frame, 10 feet at a time. Initially, we weren't even sure we had the right shipwreck.

Bob McGreevy's beloved Tashmoo, painted on an interior panel salvaged from the vessel.

Sidewheel steamer Keystone State, lost on Lake Huron in 1861.

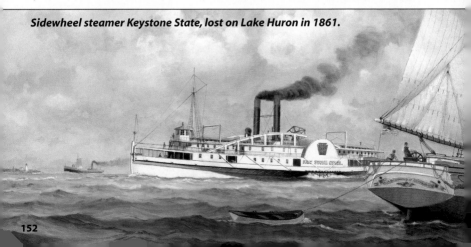

Frank H. Goodyear was lost in 1910 not far from McGreevy's Lake Huron shoreline studio.

We were comparing the slide images to blueprints, and nothing matched. Then we realized we were looking at the slides backwards."

McGreevy points out that divers now take for granted the Carribean-esque post-quagga mussel visibility and high performance, high-fidelity digital imaging gear available to virtually any serious enthusiast. McGreevy also remembers a time before online databases. "Research was much more hands-on when I began. Given the amount of detective work involved, by the end of a project, you really felt like you had contributed to the historical record."

McGreevy's connection with recent wreck discoveries – including the whaleback *Clifton* and Turkey Trail steamer *Jane Miller* in 2017 – has an additional benefit. His exhaustive research has shed light on the colorful livery of 19th century Great Lakes vessels. Color samples extracted from photo and video captures of freshwater sites–especially the 1850s-era sidewheel steamer *Detroit* in Lake Huron–confirm what splendid ships they must have been in an era before color film. Or film, period.

After 30-plus years at the easel, McGreevy has collected a mantle full of well-deserved honors and awards. He was named 2004 Great Lakes Historian of the Year by the Marine Historical Society of Detroit, and Alcona County Mich., named him its Historian of the Year in 2008. He's served as a board member of the Great Lakes Maritime Institute and was named a Shook Award recipient for his work with the Pointe aux Barques Lighthouse Society. He published his excellent chronicle of doomed lake vessels, *Lost Legends of the Lakes,* in 2009, and has been a contributing author to many publications, including a State History Award-winning book on the history of Huron County, Mich.

Visit **mcgreevy.com**, for details on the artist's upcoming speaking events how to purchase limited-edition prints, and his updated project blog.

Bob McGreevy and his feline muse Lewis.

Shipwatcher's Favorite for Over 20 Years!

DIAMOND JACK'S
RIVER TOURS

2 Hour Narrated Detroit River Tours
Detroit and Wyandotte

www.diamondjack.com

154

Choose a Cruise
Another vessel joins a growing market

No, you're not seeing double. Pleased with the success of the 202-passenger vessel *Victory 1*, which has offered warm-weather cruising on the Great Lakes since 2016, Miami, Fla.,-based Clipper Cruise Lines recently bought her sistership, renamed her *Victory II*, and has added her to their freshwater schedule for summer 2018. Built as *Cape Cod Light* in 2004, the vessel has been significantly upgraded and will begin her inaugural trips in late July.

The Great Lakes cruise market is currently experiencing significant growth, said Bruce Nierenberg, Victory Cruise Lines president and CEO. "Small-ship cruising is the fastest growing sector in the cruise industry. Many of the 47 new small ships that will be delivered to cruise operators in the next four years will be of a size that can use the Great Lakes for their vessels. This can only mean the increase in cruise travel to the Great Lakes will continue."

He said a number of circumstances are driving the increase in demand for quality cruises on the Great Lakes and St. Lawrence Seaway.

"The Great Lakes are a destination few cruisers have experienced. They have a special appeal to mature, experienced travelers 55-65 plus in age due to their historical depth of content, their convenience and a feeling of security in visiting the region. This demographic – well-traveled, affluent and in many cases, empty nesters – is the largest travel sector in the world and will dominate travel for the next 20 years," he explained.

Victory 1's upper deck and stateroom.

Continued on Page 156

Victory 1 off Port Colborne, Ont. She'll be joined by sister ship Victory II in 2018. (Nathan Leindecker)

Pearl Sea Cruises' Pearl Mist on the St. Marys River. (Roger LeLievre)

Another reason Great Lakes cruising is on the rise is because of terrorism and the uncertainty surrounding the safety of international travel. "There are no indications currently that a change in this situation is coming short term. If anything, it's going to increase as an issue," Nierenberg said.

In a major development, the Conference of Great Lakes Governors and Premiers has embraced cruising by creating a group to help the business grow. Additionally, mayors of many Canadian Great Lakes cities have decided to engage in research to better understand the infrastructure and capital needs of ports interested or involved in the cruise business.

In addition to Victory Cruise Lines, a number of other operators are returning to the Great Lakes. Pearl Sea Cruises, based in Connecticut, brings back the elegant *Pearl Mist* in 2018, with itineraries from Quebec to Lake Superior. St. Lawrence Cruise Lines' *Canadian Empress* continues to offer delightful and intimate small-ship cruises out of Kingston, Ont. to destinations along the St. Lawrence Seaway, including the beautiful Thousand Islands. The Quebec-based 68-passenger *Jacques-Cartier* expects to offer several cruises from Quebec City to Toronto. Blount Small Ship Adventures' *Grande Caribe* and *Grande Mariner* also return in 2018.

The ocean liner *Hamburg* – which some may recall from earlier visits to the lakes and seaway under her previous name, *c. Columbus* – also returns for more cruises catering mostly to Europeans who want to explore the North American heartland. And if that's not enough, France's Ponant fleet (remember the yacht-like *Le Levant* of a few years back?) plans to be inland in 2019 with the spanking new *Le Champlain*, while Hapag-Lloyd's new *Hanseatic Inspiration* is expected in 2020

Another industry veteran who views Great Lakes cruising with optimism is Stephen Burnett,

executive director of the Great Lakes Cruising Coalition, based in Kingston, Ont. In 2018, there will be 11,523 available berths, about a six percent increase over 2017, he said. Each cruise calls at a minimum of seven ports and, in some cases, nine ports, for a total of 720 scheduled in the region. If the ships sail full, they'll deliver nearly 100,000 passenger port visits.

Other reasons for the growth in business include the work ports have done to improve shore excursions and infrastructure, such as docks and terminals. "The product has become very sophisticated," Burnett explained, "with really good shore excursion packages. The providers have put a huge effort into product development in terms of quality and variety.

All in all, "It's an extremely pivotal time," Burnett said. 'It's quite dramatic to see the level of political interest.' And he said there's no reason why cruising's growth spurt should not continue.

"Overall, there's a huge amount happening at the moment," he said, adding that he's talking to several other cruise lines "that are looking for somewhere that doesn't have terrorists. There's

Continued on Page 158

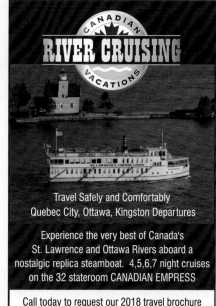

Le Champlain will be coming inland in 2019.

Canadian Empress on the Seaway. (Marc Piché)

Hamburg beneath the Seaway International Bridge in Massena, N.Y. (Ronald Dole Jr.)

a great discomfort with some of the exotic regions and the general world unrest."

If you're worried that small Great Lakes ports will be overwhelmed with passenger ships, like some popular cruise destinations around the world, Victory's Nierenberg doesn't see that happening on the Great Lakes. The waterways and locks restrict the size of ships that can enter the system.

"The Great Lakes will stay a small ship, affluent traveler market which will mean that a ship arrival in a port on the Great Lakes will never take over the community it is visiting and change the way the Great Lakes experience will be achieved," he observed.

Speaking of affluent, booking a trip on any of the cruise lines isn't cheap. Passengers can pay between $3,000-$5,000 (double occupancy and depending on the number of days) for a cruise. Judging from the way staterooms are selling, the price is no object for many passengers.

But if the bigger boats are not for you, there's no time for an extended adventure, or they are too expensive, there are plenty of shorter cruises available at pretty much every port on the Great Lakes and St. Lawrence Seaway that are well worth the time. And don't forget about the Lake Michigan carferry *Badger,* a National Historic Landmark that is always a fun trip back in time to the days of real steamboating.

See you on the Lido deck!

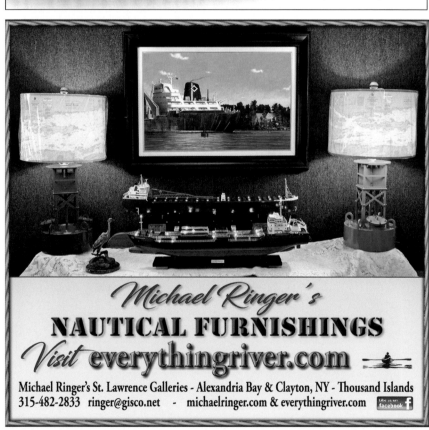

Historic Gallery

A crewman on the
steamer A. D. MacBeth
poses at Sandusky, Ohio,
in 1934. Rockcliffe Hall
is in the background.
(Robert Strauss Collection)

Christening of Red Wing for Upper Lakes Shipping in 1960.
(Skip Gillham Collection)

Frank E. Taplin of 1907 in the Welland Canal during October 1960.
The Taplin was scrapped in 1969. (Paul Sherlock photo, Jeff Cameron Collection)

Shenango II in the early 1960s. We know her now as Hon. James L. Oberstar. (Tom Manse)

FRANK E. TAPLIN

Diamond Alkali makes the turn at Mission Point in 1973. (Roger LeLievre)

Republic Steel's Silver Bay missed a turn in fog and ran aground at the Rock Cut in the St. Marys River on Nov. 7, 1970. (Tom Manse Photo)

Canadian Provider passing Brockville, Ont., in 2011. (Viktor Kaczkowski)

Saltie Prins Johan Willem Friso at Milwaukee on April 30, 1959.
(Press photo, Roger LeLievre Collection)

Carl D. Bradley from a postcard view.

60 Years: Remembering the Carl D. Bradley

Lake Michigan was in a mean mood the night of November 18, 1958, as the self-unloader *Carl D. Bradley* made her way north for one last load of the season.

The winds were 25-35 miles per hour at the start of her trip from Gary, Ind., to Calcite, Mich. The weather forecast was winds 50-65 mph from the south, changing to southwest. The *Bradley's* path would take it into a storm that was the result of two separate weather patterns merging.

At dinnertime, the onetime Queen of the Lakes seemed to be braving the storm in fine fashion. A few hours later, she would become another sad shipwreck legend, taking 33 of her 35-man crew to the bottom with her. Many of the crew were from the port town of Rogers City, Mich., and were friends, neighbors or even related to one another. Only two, Frank

Bradley opens the new MacArthur Lock July 11, 1943. (Both photos, Tom Manse Collection)

Mays and Elmer Fleming, survived their ordeal, plucked from a raft on the stormy lake by the German cargo vessel *Christian Sartori*.

Built in 1927 by the American Ship Building Co. in Lorain, Ohio, the *Bradley* was owned by the Michigan Limestone Division of U.S. Steel, and operated by the Bradley Transportation Line. When she sank, she was en route from Gary, Ind., to Calcite, Mich., for one more cargo, after which she was to lay up at the shipyard in Manitowoc, Wis., to have a new cargo hold fitted. The *Bradley* suffered some damage in the spring of 1958 but was not repaired. A board of inquiry eventually ruled the sinking was likely caused by undetected structural weakness or defect. They also wrote that Captain Roland Bryan exercised poor judgment when he decided to leave the shelter of the Wisconsin shore and sail into the open lake during the storm.

That decision mattered little to the 33 families that lost husbands and fathers that cold November night on an angry and unforgiving lake.

Cleveland Cliffs' steamer Cadillac at the Soo Locks. (Tom Manse)

Wilfred Sykes arrives at Indiana Harbor, Ind., on her first trip, 1949. (Press photo, Roger LeLievre Collection)

Coralia passses the Detroit skyline in 1948. (Press photo, Roger LeLievre Collection)

Willowdale on Sept. 26, 1962. The former tanker was scrapped in 1964. (Jeff Cameron Collection)

Living it up on the Milwaukee Clipper, 1951. *(Press photo, Roger LeLievre Collection)*

Belle River sails now as Walter J. McCarthy Jr. *(Tom Manse)*

Tug Roger assists B.F. Affleck at Milwaukee in 1961. (Press photo, Roger LeLievre Collection)

BELLE RIVER

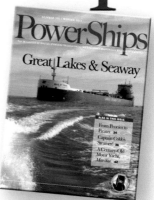

172

Steelcliffe Hall followed by John J. Boland above Port Huron in 1984. (Eric Treece)

Early steel steamer Ira H. Owen in the Soo Locks. The Owen was lost on Lake Superior in 1905.
(Tom Manse Collection)

Interlake Steamship Co.'s Pathfinder above the Soo Locks in the early 1960s. She later became Goderich for the Upper Lakes Fleet before being scrapped in 1984. (Tom Manse)

At 633 feet in length Canada Steamship Lines' Lemoyne was once the largest vessel on the Great Lakes. (Harry Stott)

William A. Irvin in the early 1960s. She is now a marine museum at Duluth, Minn. (Tom Manse)

Howard M. Hanna Jr. in the Davis Lock at the Soo circa the 1920s. Inset detail shows a portrait of fleet manager W.C. Richardson painted on the bulwark in front of the pilothouse. (A.E. Young, from the Peter B. Worden Collection)

HOWARD M. HANNA JR.

Whaleback tanker Meteor in 1956. *(Press photo, Roger LeLievre Collection)*

S.T. Crapo upbound with cement in the late 1970s. She now serves as a storage barge at Green Bay, Wis. *(Roger LeLievre)*

Samuel Mather upbound on the St. Marys River in 1971. (Roger LeLievre)

Leecliffe Hall loading her first grain cargo at Port Arthur, Ont., on Oct. 9, 1961. She would sink after a collision on the St. Lawrence Seaway on Sept. 5, 1964. (Press photo, Roger LeLievre Collection)

Myron C. Taylor in 1988. She was scrapped in 2008 as Calumet. *(Eric Treece)*

Cleveland Cliffs' Yosemite departs Marquette, Mich., on Sept. 29, 1954. *(Press photo, Roger LeLievre Collection)*

YOSEMITE

Gone But Not Forgotten

Canada Steamship Lines has long been known for its large fleet of cargo carriers. But from its inception in 1913 until 1965, CSL boasted a passenger fleet like no other, operating everything from day-excursion ships to elegantly appointed vessels making weeklong cruises. These steamers could be found in ports all the way from Duluth, Minnesota, to the lower St. Lawrence River in Quebec, where the company owned two fine hotels and even a shipyard that built some of its best passenger ships. With painstakingly chosen pictures and polished prose, *Great White Fleet* revisits a passenger fleet that had no peer.

GREAT LAKES GLOSSARY

AAA CLASS – Vessel design popular on the Great Lakes in the early 1950s. *Arthur M. Anderson* is one example.

AFT – Toward the back, or stern, of a ship.

AMIDSHIPS – The middle point of a vessel, referring to either length or width.

ARTICULATED TUG/BARGE (ATB) – Tug-barge combination. The two vessels are mechanically linked in one axis but with the tug free to move, or articulate, on another axis.

BACKHAUL – The practice of carrying a revenue-producing cargo (rather than ballast) on a return trip from hauling a primary cargo.

BARGE – Vessel with no engine, either pushed or pulled by a tug.

BEAM – The width of a vessel at it's widest point.

BILGE – Lowest part of a hold or compartment, generally where the rounded side of a ship curves from the keel to the vertical sides.

BOW THRUSTER – Propeller mounted transversely in a vessel's bow under the waterline to assist in moving sideways. A stern thruster may also be installed.

BRIDGE – The platform above the main deck from which a ship is steered/navigated. Also: PILOTHOUSE or WHEELHOUSE.

BULK CARGO – Goods, loose or in mass, that generally must be shoveled, pumped, blown or scooped out of a vessel.

BULKHEAD – Wall or partition that separates rooms, holds or tanks within a ship's hull.

BULWARK – The part of the ship that extends fore and aft above the main deck to form a rail.

DATUM – Level of water in a given area, determined by an average over time.

DEADWEIGHT TONNAGE – The actual carrying capacity of a vessel, equal to the difference between the light displacement tonnage and the heavy displacement tonnage, expressed in long tons (2,240 pounds or 1,016.1 kilograms).

DECK SPRINKLERS – The reason for water spraying on a vessel's deck is to help cool the upper part of a boat and prevent hogging (bending due to temperature differences above and below the waterline). With decks exposed to the sun all day, the surface can get very hot. The hull of the boat underwater stays cooler. Hogging can affect cargo capacity and the depth to which a boat can load.

DISPLACEMENT TONNAGE – The actual weight of the vessel and everything aboard her, measured in long tons. The displacement is equal to the weight of the water displaced by the vessel. Displacement tonnage may be qualified as light – indicating the weight of the vessel without cargo, fuel and stores – or heavy, indicating the weight of the vessel loaded with cargo, fuel and stores.

DRAFT – The depth of water a ship needs to float. Also, the distance from keel to waterline.

FIT OUT – The process of preparing a vessel for service after a period of inactivity.

FIVE-YEAR INSPECTION – U.S. Coast Guard survey, conducted in a drydock every five years, of a vessel's hull, machinery and other components.

FLATBACK – Lakes slang for a non-self-unloader.

FOOTER – Lakes slang for 1,000-foot vessel.

FOREPEAK – The space below the forecastle.

FREEBOARD – The distance from the waterline to the main deck.

GEARLESS VESSEL – One that is not a self-unloader.

GROSS TONNAGE – The internal space of a vessel, measured in units of 100 cubic feet (2.83 cubic meters) = a gross ton.

HATCH – An opening in the deck through which cargo is lowered or raised. A hatch is closed by securing a hatch cover over it.

IMO # – Unique number issued by International Maritime Organization, or IMO, to ships for identification. Not all vessels have an IMO number.

INTEGRATED TUG/BARGE (ITB) – Tug-barge combination in which the tug is rigidly mated to the barge. *Presque Isle* is one example.

IRON DECKHAND – Mechanical device that runs on rails on a vessel's main deck and is used to remove and replace hatch covers.

JONES ACT – A U.S. law that mandates that cargoes moved between American ports be carried by U.S.-flagged, U.S.-built and U.S.-crewed vessels.

KEEL – A ship's steel backbone. It runs along the lowest part of the hull.

LAID UP or **LAY-UP** – Out of service.

MARITIME CLASS – Style of lake vessel built during World War II as part of the nation's war effort. *Mississagi* is one example.

NET REGISTERED TONNAGE – The internal capacity of a vessel available for carrying cargo. It does not include the space occupied by boilers, engines, shaft alleys, chain lockers or officers' and crew's quarters. Net registered tonnage is usually referred to as registered tonnage or net tonnage and is used to calculate taxes, tolls and port charges.

PLIMSOLL LINE – A reference mark located on a ship's hull that indicates the maximum depth to which the vessel may be safely immersed when loaded with cargo.

RIVER CLASS – Group of vessels built in the 1970s to service smaller ports and negotiate narrow rivers.

SELF-UNLOADER – Vessel able to discharge its own cargo using a system of conveyor belts and a movable boom.

STEM – The extreme forward end of the bow.

STEMWINDER – Vessel with all cabins aft.

STERN – The back of the ship.

STRAIGHT-DECKER – Non-self-unloading vessel.

STEM – The extreme forward end of the bow.

TACONITE – Processed, pelletized iron ore. Easy to load and unload, this is the primary type of ore shipped on the Great Lakes and St. Lawrence Seaway. Also known as pellets.

TOLL – Fee charged against a ship, cargo and passengers for a complete or partial transit of a waterway covering a single trip in one direction.

TURKEY TRAIL – Route from North Channel (above Manitoulin Island) into the St. Marys River, named for the many courses which zigzag through the area's islands, shoals and ports.

VESSEL LOG / Record your own ship spottings

Date	Vessel Name	Location

Algolake approaching the Ambassador Bridge spanning the Detroit River. (Matt Miner)

ADVERTISER INDEX *Thank you!*

The information in this book was obtained from the U.S. Army Corps of Engineers, the U.S. Coast Guard, the Lake Carriers' Association, Lloyd's Register, NOAA, Transport Canada, The St. Lawrence Seaway Authority, Great Lakes Tugs & Workboats, Shipfax, Tugfax, BoatNerd.com and vessel owners / operators.

MORE KYS PHOTOS ONLINE

Every year, *Know Your Ships* gets nearly 1,000 great photo submissions. Unfortunately, there isn't room in the book for them all, so we've created galleries of some of these images at **knowyourships.com**. Please stop by and take a look.

Baie Comeau gets an avian escort near Point Edward, Ont. (Marc Dease)

Michigan's Maritime College

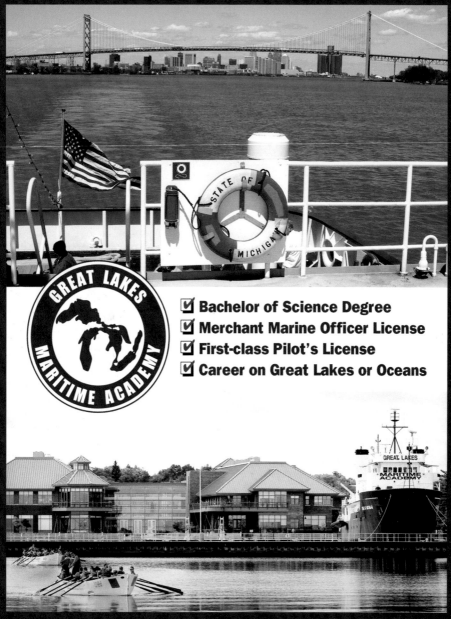

- Bachelor of Science Degree
- Merchant Marine Officer License
- First-class Pilot's License
- Career on Great Lakes or Oceans

nmc.edu/maritime • 877-824-7447